MATHEMATICS
The Basic Skills

From the same publishers:

Smith: A NEW GENERAL ARITHMETIC – Part A
– Part B

Smith: EXAMPLES IN ARITHMETIC

Smith: EXAMPLES IN MATHEMATICS – Book 1
– Book 2

Greer: A COMPLETE O-LEVEL MATHEMATICS

and many others. A full list is available free on request.

MATHEMATICS
The Basic Skills

WITH ANSWERS

S. Llewellyn

A. Greer

SECOND EDITION

Stanley Thornes (Publishers) Ltd

First edition 1983

Second edition 1983 with new Chapters on
Similarity and Further Topics

Reprinted 1984

Published by

Stanley Thornes (Publishers) Ltd
Old Station Drive
Leckhampton
CHELTENHAM GL53 0DN

British Library Cataloguing in Publication Data

Llewellyn, S.
    Mathematics—2nd Ed.
    with answers
    1. Mathematics—1961–
    I. Title   II. Greer, A.
    510   QA39.2

ISBN 0-85950-147-7

Typeset by Tech-Set, Gateshead.
Printed and bound in Great Britain by Bell & Bain Ltd, Glasgow.

Contents

Introduction

Mathematics is used in:

<u>construction</u> – building houses, towers, monuments, etc.;

<u>surveying</u> – making maps, finding the heights of mountains, etc.;

<u>commerce</u> – trading in shops and business;

<u>navigation</u> – finding the way at sea and in the air;

<u>the home and the community</u> – home decorating, shopping, income tax, rates, VAT, mortgages, insurance, etc.

We can only make guesses *why* mathematics evolved. Some think that people wanted to keep a record of their property in case it was stolen!

As mathematics developed so mathematical *tools* developed too.

The abacus is an early counting aid which is still in use in some parts of the world such as China and Malaysia. Some of them are made in beautiful hardwoods and sold as souvenirs to tourists.

Clay tablets were used to *record* numbers using a stone or stick to scratch the surface. When the clay was soft it was easy to make marks and then the clay was baked hard. The marks used were not the same as the symbols used today. It took many years for people to find the best way of writing numbers.

As people began to trade, different *money* systems grew up. Goods were *weighed* and *measured*.

Tally sticks with notches on them were used to *compare* records.

The modern tools are pen, paper, ink, calculators, computers and many other scientific and engineering instruments.

1

Number

THE NUMBER SYSTEM

We use the symbols, 0, 1, 2, 3, 4, 5, 6, 7, 8 and 9 (arabic numbers), and the *positions* of the figures gives the value of the number:

		1
100		1
100	10	1
100	10	1
HUNDREDS	TENS	UNITS
3	2	4

324 is three hundred and twenty-four
324 is 3 hundreds 2 tens and 4 units

One hundred is ten times ten. Ten is ten times one.

The word *unit* means one.

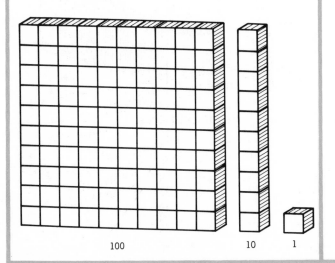

100   10   1

The Romans found it much more difficult to work with roman numbers because they did not use *place value* in the same way that we do. (Place value is the idea of a number having a different value when it is in a different place.)

In 614 the 4 means 4 *units*
In 146 the 4 means 4 *tens*
In 461 the 4 means 4 *hundreds*

In these three numbers the 4 stands for a different value when it is in a different place.

It is important to remember that the *smallest* numbers, the *units*, are always on the *right hand side* of the whole number.

Arabic numbers in

Words	Figures
one	1
two	2
three	3
four	4
five	5
six	6
seven	7
eight	8
nine	9
ten	10
eleven	11
twelve	12
thirteen	13
fourteen	14
fifteen	15
sixteen	16

seventeen	17
eighteen	18
nineteen	19
twenty	20
twenty-one	21
twenty-two	22
twenty-three	23
twenty-four	24
twenty-five	25
twenty-six	26
twenty-seven, etc.	27

These examples show how important 0 is in our number system:

205 is 2 hundreds 0 tens and 5 units
250 is 2 hundreds 5 tens and 0 units

In 205 the zero keeps the place for the missing *tens*
In 250 the zero keeps the place for the missing *units*

Counting in tens:

10	ten
20	twenty
30	thirty
40	forty
50	fifty
60	sixty
70	seventy
80	eighty
90	ninety
100	one hundred

In words:

205 is two hundred and five
250 is two hundred and fifty

The Romans found it quite hard to do arithmetic with roman numbers. They did not have a symbol for 0.

Roman numbers	Values
I	1
II	2
III	3
IIII (later IV)	4
V	5
VI	6
VII	7
VIII	8
VIIII (later IX)	9
X	10
L	50
C	100
D	500
M	1000

Roman numbers are written by putting the letters side by side:

MMCCCV	2305
MDCLVI	1656
CCCLXIII	363

Dates (on cinema films and TV programmes) and numbers on clocks are often written using roman numbers.

--- **EXERCISE 1** ---

Write the following numbers (i) in figures, (ii) in roman numbers

1) (a) thirty-five
   (b) three hundred and five
   (c) three hundred and fifty

2) (a) seventy-nine
   (b) seven hundred and nine
   (c) seven hundred and ninety

3) (a) sixty-five
   (b) six hundred and five
   (c) six hundred and fifty.

Write the following in words

4)	(a) 980	(b) 98	(c) 908
5)	(a) 800	(b) 80	(c) 8
6)	(a) 89	(b) 890	(c) 809
7)	(a) 110	(b) 101	(c) 11
8)	(a) 78	(b) 708	(c) 780
9)	(a) 130	(b) 103	(c) 13
10)	(a) 14	(b) 140	(c) 104.

Write the following in figures

11) (a) twenty-six
    (b) two hundred and six
    (c) two hundred and sixty

12) (a) fifty-five
    (b) five hundred and fifty
    (c) five hundred and five

13) (a) twelve
    (b) one hundred and twenty
    (c) one hundred and two

14) (a) twenty-one
    (b) two hundred and ten
    (c) two hundred and one

15) (a) seven hundred
    (b) seventy
    (c) seven.

16) Copy the table below and fill in the missing numbers and words.

| Number in words | Figures | | |
	H	T	U
twenty-four			
nineteen			
seventy-six			
eight			
one hundred and sixty-four			
seven hundred and eight			
three			
		6	1
	2	5	4
		5	8

Fill in the missing numbers

17) 542 is ___ hundreds ___ tens ___ units

18) 902 is ___ hundreds ___ tens ___ units.

19) What does the number 5 mean in
    (a) 580   (b) 56   (c) 35   (d) 159?

20) What does the number 3 mean in
    (a) 113   (b) 300   (c) 35   (d) 13?

21) What does the number 9 mean in
    (a) 98   (b) 897   (c) 689   (d) 902?

22) For which of these numbers does the number 7 mean 7 units?
    (a) 709   (b) 79   (c) 867   (d) 17

23) For which of these numbers does the number 3 mean 3 tens?
    (a) 173   (b) 832   (c) 113   (d) 31

24) For which of these numbers does the number 8 mean 8 hundreds?
    (a) 678   (b) 890   (c) 834   (d) 508

25) Put these numbers in order of size with the smallest first
    (a) 123   (b) 321   (c) 132

26) Put these numbers in order of size with the smallest first
    (a) 305   (b) 35   (c) 350   (d) 530
    (e) 503   (f) 53

27) Put these numbers in order of size with the smallest first
    (a) 103   (b) 301   (c) 130   (d) 31
    (e) 13   (f) 310

28) Put these numbers in order of size with the largest first
    (a) 51   (b) 15   (c) 510   (d) 150
    (e) 105   (f) 501

29) Put these numbers in order of size with the largest first
    (a) 123   (b) 132   (c) 321   (d) 312
    (e) 231   (f) 213.

999 is the largest whole number using hundreds, tens and units. For larger numbers we use *thousands*:

1000 is *one thousand*
10 000 is *ten thousand*
100 000 is *one hundred thousand*

5

For large numbers a gap is left between each group of three numbers counting from the right. Care must be taken when there are noughts in the middle of the number:

5008 is five thousand and eight
16 012 is sixteen thousand and twelve
505 040 is five hundred and five thousand and forty

———————— EXERCISE 2 ————————

Write the following in figures

1) two thousand, four hundred and fifty-one
2) five thousand, three hundred and eleven
3) six thousand, one hundred and twelve
4) one thousand and fourteen
5) six thousand and nine
6) five thousand three hundred
7) fourteen thousand
8) twenty-four thousand
9) seventy thousand
10) sixteen thousand, two hundred and eight
11) seventy-five thousand, one hundred and forty-two
12) forty thousand and sixty-four
13) three hundred thousand
14) one hundred and ninety-five thousand, five hundred and eighty
15) one hundred and fourteen thousand, six hundred and thirteen
16) three hundred and fifty-one thousand, six hundred and forty-five
17) seven hundred and twelve thousand, two hundred and one.

Write the following in words

18) 5763
19) 6721
20) 9884
21) 16 000
22) 65 000
23) 809 000
24) 72 050
25) 7009
26) 8002
27) 7080
28) 8090
29) 6050
30) 8900
31) 7800
32) 65 332
33) 14 500
34) 163 404
35) 900 009
36) 452 986
37) 304 021.

38) Copy the table below and fill in the missing numbers

Number in words	Hundred thousands	Ten thousands	Thousands	Hundreds	Tens	Units
five thousand						
sixty-two thousand						
three hundred thousand						
seventy-four thousand and nine						
six hundred thousand two hundred						
seventy thousand and fifty						
ninety-nine thousand						
six thousand						

Numbers larger than 999 999 are counted in *millions*:

1 000 000 is *one million*
10 000 000 is *ten million*
100 000 000 is *one hundred million*

6 789 435 is six million, seven hundred and eighty-nine thousand, four hundred and thirty-five

16 987 853 is sixteen million, nine hundred and eighty-seven thousand, eight hundred and fifty-three

235 634 798 is two hundred and thirty-five million, six hundred and thirty-four thousand, seven hundred and ninety-eight

Again care must be taken when there are noughts in the middle of the number:

5 082 406 is five million, eighty-two thousand, four hundred and six

14 405 600 is fourteen million, four hundred and five thousand, six hundred

300 012 015 is three hundred million, twelve thousand and fifteen

After 999 999 999 numbers are counted in billions:

1 000 000 000 is *one billion*.

EXERCISE 3

Write the following in figures

1) eight million
2) nineteen million
3) six hundred million
4) three hundred and twenty-four million, five hundred and sixty-seven
5) three million, seven hundred thousand and thirty
6) four million and forty
7) sixty-four million, three hundred thousand, six hundred and sixty-six
8) nine hundred and ninety-nine million
9) four hundred and sixty-four million, three hundred and thirty thousand, two hundred and six.

Write the following in words

10) 7 000 000
11) 57 000 000
12) 189 000 000
13) 7 012 506
14) 5 869 014
15) 167 189 112
16) 900 003 040.

17) Copy the table below and fill in the missing numbers.

Number in words	Billions	Hundred millions	Ten millions	Millions	Hundred thousands	Ten thousands	Thousands	Hundreds	Tens	Units
one billion, six hundred and ten million										
eight million, thirty thousand and fifty										
seven hundred and six million										

FACTORS

One of the most basic ideas about numbers is how they break down into "factors":

6 is a *factor* of 36 because it divides into 36 without leaving a remainder.

You can easily see this either by using a dot pattern:

or by looking at tins stacked in layers of six tins:

$6 \times 6 = 36$

$\times$ is the *"times"* sign (it means *"lots of"*)

Chess boards have $8 \times 8 = 64$ squares:

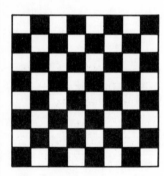

$=$ is the *"equals"* sign (it means *"is the same as"*)

8 is a factor of 64 because it goes into 64 without leaving a remainder.

However, 7 *is not* a factor of 15 because there will be a remainder of 1 if we divide 7 into 15:

$$\begin{array}{r} 2 \text{ rem } 1 \\ 7\overline{)15} \end{array}$$

A number is a factor of another number if it goes into that number without leaving a remainder.

Here are some more examples:

    5 is a factor of 20
    3 is a factor of 12
    7 is not a factor of 17
    2 is not a factor of 11
    6 is not a factor of 19.

1) Is 6 a factor of
   (a) 12   (b) 18   (c) 21   (d) 27
   (e) 36   (f) 42   (g) 54   (h) 56?

2) Is 5 a factor of
   (a) 3   (b) 10   (c) 15   (d) 17
   (e) 20   (f) 22   (g) 27   (h) 30?

3) Is 8 a factor of
   (a) 16   (b) 20   (c) 27   (d) 36
   (e) 32   (f) 40   (g) 56   (h) 58?

4) Is 9 a factor of
   (a) 18   (b) 20   (c) 27   (d) 36
   (e) 44   (f) 45   (g) 54   (h) 56?

5) Is 10 a factor of
   (a) 15   (b) 20   (c) 25   (d) 30
   (e) 45   (f) 50   (g) 99   (h) 100?

6) Which of the following numbers are factors of 15?
   (a) 2   (b) 3   (c) 5   (d) 10

7) Which of the following numbers are factors of 18?
   (a) 2   (b) 3   (c) 4   (d) 5
   (e) 6   (f) 7   (g) 8   (h) 9
   (i) 10   (j) 12

8) Which of the following numbers are factors of 50?
   (a) 2   (b) 3   (c) 5   (d) 10
   (e) 25

9) Which of the following numbers are factors of 56?
   (a) 7   (b) 8   (c) 9   (d) 10

Reminder: *A number is a factor of another number if it goes into that number without leaving a remainder.*

    3 *is a factor of 12*
    5 *is not a factor of 11*

8

The factors of 60 are:

1, 2, 3, 4, 5, 6, 10, 12, 15, 20, 30 and 60

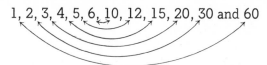

Notice that 1 and 60 are counted as factors. They "pair off" from each end if the factors are arranged in order of size:

$1 \times 60 = 60$
$2 \times 30 = 60$
$3 \times 20 = 60$
$4 \times 15 = 60$, etc.

The factors of 12 are:

1, 2, 3, 4, 6 and 12

You can check you have all the factors by pairing them off from each end.

──────────── EXERCISE 5 ────────────

1) Write down all the factors of these numbers. Arrange them in order of size and check that you have all the factors by pairing them off from each end.
   (a) 10   (b) 14   (c) 15   (d) 16
   (e) 20   (f) 25   (g) 36   (h) 42

For more difficult numbers it is helpful to know about the rules which will be described next.

This work is important because it helps you to become "at ease" with numbers (and often makes the working of problems easier too).

You almost certainly know this rule already:

If a number ends in 0, 2, 4, 6 or 8 then it is an even number and 2 will divide into it without leaving a remainder.

EXAMPLE

The numbers

   4, 16, 12, 18, 22 and 28

are all even numbers.

If 2 will divide into a number without leaving a remainder we say that the number *"is divisible by 2"*.

──────────── EXERCISE 6 ────────────

1) Which of the following numbers are divisible by 2?
   (a) 6   (b) 8   (c) 9   (d) 11
   (e) 26   (f) 35   (g) 41   (h) 72
   (i) 190   (j) 789   (k) 1764   (l) 3156
   (m) 6583   (n) 2018   (o) 4102   (p) 6155

The rule for 3 is not so well known. It sounds quite difficult but is really quite easy as the examples will show. First we explain the meaning of the words "digit sum".

The *digits* of a number are the single figures in that number, for example the digits of 612 are 6, 1 and 2.

The *digit sum* of a number is found by adding the digits together so the digit sum of 612 is $6 + 1 + 2$ which is 9. (+ is the "plus" sign; it means "add".)

Sometimes the digit sum is not a single figure so we keep adding the digits together until we have a single figure.

EXAMPLE

Find the digit sum of 1768.

Add the digits $1 + 7 + 6 + 8$ to get 22.

Add the digits again $2 + 2$ to get 4.

The digit sum of 1768 is 4.

EXAMPLE

Find the digit sum of 667.

Add the digits $6 + 6 + 7$ to get 19.

Add the digits again $1 + 9$ to get 10.

Add the digits again $1 + 0$ to get 1.

The digit sum of 667 is 1.

─────────── **EXERCISE 7** ───────────

Write down the digit sums of these numbers

1) (a) 611   (b) 502   (c) 304   (d) 321
2) (a) 506   (b) 410   (c) 175   (d) 56
3) (a) 28   (b) 912   (c) 108   (d) 820
4) (a) 1653   (b) 1998   (c) 2346   (d) 7653.

3 will go into a number without leaving a remainder if it goes exactly into the digit sum of the number.

EXAMPLE

Does 3 go into 411 without leaving a remainder?

The digit sum of 411 is $4 + 1 + 1$ which is 6.

3 goes into 6 exactly so it also goes into 411 without leaving a remainder.

EXAMPLE

Does 3 go into 5734 without leaving a remainder?

Adding the digits of 5734:

   $5 + 7 + 3 + 4 = 19$
   $1 + 9 = 10$
   $1 + 0 = 1$

So the digit sum of 5734 is 1.

3 does not go into 1 exactly so 3 will not go into 5734 without leaving a remainder.

If 3 goes into a number without leaving a remainder we say that the number is *"divisible"* by 3.

─────────── **EXERCISE 8** ───────────

By using the digit sum rule discover which of these numbers are divisible by 3

1) (a) 314   (b) 405   (c) 512   (d) 891
2) (a) 689   (b) 321   (c) 613   (d) 144
3) (a) 172   (b) 540   (c) 153   (d) 181
4) (a) 108   (b) 72   (c) 85   (d) 192
5) (a) 1886 (b) 2665 (c) 5184
6) (a) 7101 (b) 1200 (c) 5103
7) (a) 5004 (b) 1823 (c) 6102.

Numbers that are divisible by 3 are called *"multiples"* of 3.

─────────── **EXERCISE 9** ───────────

Which of the following numbers are multiples of 3 and are also even numbers?

1) (a) 651   (b) 288   (c) 512
2) (a) 504   (b) 36   (c) 1002
3) (a) 109   (b) 901   (c) 108
4) (a) 864   (b) 5121 (c) 4122

The divisibility rule for 5:

   5 will go into a number without leaving a remainder if the number ends in 0 or 5 and will not do so otherwise.

EXAMPLE

15, 25, 35, 40, 65 and 100 are divisible by 5 (they all end in 0 or 5).

16, 27, 141 and 269 are *not* divisible by 5.

Which of the following numbers are divisible by 5?

1) (a) 10   (b) 30   (c) 45   (d) 31
   (e) 66
2) (a) 125   (b) 150   (c) 175   (d) 109
3) (a) 105   (b) 501   (c) 615   (d) 803
4) (a) 10 000   (b) 65 655   (c) 555 551
5) (a) 561 100   (b) 13 455   (c) 5 000 000

Numbers which are not even are called "*odd numbers*". Odd numbers end in 1, 3, 5, 7 or 9.

——————— EXERCISE 11 ———————

1) Copy these numbers and underline the odd numbers
   (a) 33   (b) 61   (c) 40   (d) 53
   (e) 62   (f) 77   (g) 95   (h) 88
   (i) 99   (j) 612   (k) 303   (l) 450
   (m) 1567   (n) 88 993.

2) Using the divisibility rules or otherwise find which of the following numbers are divisible by (i) 2 and 5, (ii) 2, 3 and 5?
   (a) 15   (b) 30   (c) 45   (d) 36
   (e) 42   (f) 40   (g) 56   (h) 60
   (i) 48   (j) 90   (k) 100   (l) 70
   (m) 54   (n) 75   (o) 120

3) All of the following numbers are (i) divisible by 2 or (ii) divisible by 3 or (iii) divisible by 5 or (iv) not divisible by 2, 3 or 5.
   Draw up a chart with four columns headed (i), (ii), (iii) and (iv) and put the numbers in the correct columns.
   (a) 8   (b) 9   (c) 4   (d) 7
   (e) 25   (f) 16   (g) 35   (h) 33
   (i) 34   (j) 104   (k) 19   (l) 206
   (m) 215   (n) 321

Numbers which end in 0 are divisible by 10.

EXAMPLE

60, 100, 500 and 70 000 are all divisible by 10.

71, 609 and 3598 are *not* divisible by 10.

——————— EXERCISE 12 ———————

1) Which of the following numbers are divisible by 10?
   (a) 98   (b) 755   (c) 400   (d) 1000
   (e) 35   (f) 670   (g) 1001   (h) 80

2) Which of the following numbers *are not* divisible by 10?
   (a) 72   (b) 80   (c) 85   (d) 900
   (e) 1857

6 will go exactly into a number only if both 2 and 3 also go exactly into the number.

——————— EXERCISE 13 ———————

Using the divisibility rules find which of these numbers are divisible by 6.

1) (a) 14   (b) 24   (c) 30   (d) 36
   (e) 42
2) (a) 45   (b) 54   (c) 60   (d) 66
   (e) 72
3) (a) 285   (b) 336   (c) 405   (d) 512

——————— TYPES OF NUMBERS ———————

Positive numbers have a value greater than zero.

They either have no sign at all in front of them or a + sign.

Some examples of *positive whole numbers* are:

   3   8   +7   +11   +190   +345

Negative numbers have a value less than zero. They have a − sign in front of them. Negative numbers are used on thermometers to show centigrade temperatures below freezing point.

Negative numbers are also used on graphs:

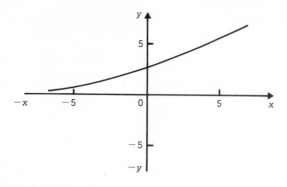

Some examples of *negative whole numbers* are:

$$-6 \quad -11 \quad -45 \quad -100$$

Positive and negative numbers do not have to be whole numbers. *Parts of a whole number are shown by using either "fractions" or "decimals".*

Some examples of *positive fractions* are:

$$\frac{1}{2} \quad \frac{3}{4} \quad \frac{7}{8}$$

We might use $\frac{1}{2}$ p or talk about $\frac{1}{4}$ hour.

Some examples of *positive decimals* are:

$$0.10 \quad 0.5 \quad 0.75 \quad 0.9$$

Decimal is short for "decimal fraction". Decimals are just another way of writing fractions.

10 p written as part of a pound is £0.10 and a very small weight might be measured as 0.75 grams. Decimals are used in everyday life especially when using money, weighing or measuring.

Some examples of *negative fractions* are:

$$-\frac{1}{2} \quad -\frac{3}{4} \quad -\frac{5}{8}$$

and some *negative decimals* are:

$$-0.6 \quad -0.03 \quad -0.028$$

EXERCISE 14

Describe the following in words (for example negative whole number, positive fraction, etc.)

1) -6
2) $\frac{1}{2}$
3) 0.10
4) $+7$
5) $-\frac{3}{4}$
6) -0.03
7) 51
8) -0.1
9) $\frac{7}{8}$

When writing a whole number and a fraction or a whole number and a decimal then the *whole number is always written before the fraction or decimal point.*

In these numbers the whole number has been underlined:

$$\underline{3}\tfrac{1}{2} \quad \underline{14}\tfrac{1}{2} \quad \underline{3}.5 \quad \underline{45}.1 \quad \underline{450}.01$$

EXERCISE 15

Copy these numbers and underline the whole numbers.

1) (a) $6\frac{1}{2}$ (b) $13\frac{1}{2}$ (c) $509\frac{1}{2}$
2) (a) 4.1 (b) 45.2 (c) 390.12

1) Write two hundred and forty in figures.
2) Write 605 in words.
3) In 6008 what does the figure 6 mean?
4) Does 7 mean 7 units in 7512?
5) Write forty thousand and eighteen in figures.
6) Write 50 020 in words.
7) Is 8 a factor of 72?
8) Is 6521 an even number?
9) Is 301 an odd number?
10) Is 5 a factor of 35?
11) Is 381 divisible by 3? (Use the digit sum rule.)
12) Is 49 a multiple of 7?
13) Does 5 go into 1000 without leaving a remainder?
14) Write down all the factors of
(a) 9   (b) 21.
15) Is -16 a positive whole number?
16) Is $+8\frac{1}{2}$ negative?
17) Is 0.5 a positive decimal?
18) Is 60 a multiple of 5?
19) Does 7 go into 42 without leaving a remainder?

20) Is 199 an odd number?
21) Write down all the even numbers between 11 and 21.
22) Write down all the multiples of three between 5 and 25.
23) Does 8 go into 96 without leaving a remainder?
24) Is 56 a multiple of 7?
25) Is -0.6 a negative decimal?
26) Is $+800$ a positive whole number?
27) Underline the whole numbers in
(a) $2\frac{1}{2}$ (b) 12.5.
28) Are 6 and 5 both factors of 30?
29) Are 3 and 8 both factors of 24?
30) Write 60 050 in words.
31) Fill in the missing numbers
312 is ___ hundreds ___ tens ___ units.
32) Fill in the missing words
3002 is 3 _____ 2 _____.
33) Write down the digit sum of
(a) 512   (b) 604.
34) Which of these numbers are divisible by both 2 and 5?
(a) 560   (b) 650   (c) 905.

2

The Four Rules for Number

SIGNS

The arithmetic *signs* are:

+   plus
−   minus
×   times
÷   divided by

It is very important to have the ideas associated with these signs clearly understood.

ADDITION

Addition is concerned with putting things together.

For example putting discs together on a table:

2 + 3   =   **5**

two plus three   equals   five

or putting distances together on a map:

Birmingham   18   Coventry   24   Leicester   Distances in miles

It is $18 + 24 = 42$ miles from Birmingham to Leicester via Coventry.

When adding it is important to make sure that the *units* are underneath each other by lining up the figures on the *right hand sides* of the whole numbers. (Otherwise your answers will be wrong.)

EXAMPLE

Add $785 + 43 + 1889$.

```
  785
   43
 1889 +
 ─────
 2717
 1 2 1
```

The *units* figures 5, 3 and 9 have been lined up underneath each other.

Start adding at the *right hand* column.

You can either begin at the *top* of the units column and add *downwards* (5 and 3 is 8, 8 and 9 is 17 which is 1 *ten* and 7 *units* so 1 is carried forward into the tens column and 7 is put down in the units column, etc.), or begin at the *bottom* and add *upwards* (9 and 3 is 12, etc.).

When you get to the tens column *do not forget* to add the 1 that has been carried. It can be put underneath the line to remind you or it can be put above the line by the 8.

The answer is called the *sum*. The sum of 785, 43 and 1889 is 2717.

EXERCISE 1

These addition sums have already been lined up correctly. Copy the numbers (writing the figures clearly) and add the numbers together.

1) 12
   124
   ———

2) 78
   131
   ———

3) 72
   291
   ———

4) 125
   35
   ———

5) 419
   3 558
   ———

6) 798
   7 903
   ———

7) 1 891
   121
   ———

8) 980
   8 976
   ———

9) 9 087
   26
   ———

10) 10 877
    15 099
    ———

11) 23
    198
    ———

12) 6 789
    1 009
    ———

13) 45 672
    1 097
    8 003
    ———

14) 88 007
    982
    54
    ———

15) 91 900
    7
    2 065
    ———

16) 31 111
    202
    55
    ———

17) 111 902
    23 034
    3 167
    ———

18) 900 876
    54
    1 098
    ———

19) 89
    564
    17 885
    ———

20) 9 008
    1 076
    888
    ———

21) 345 001
    308 577
    456 098
    ———

22) 981 176
    897 101
    22 439
    ———

23) 892
    8 345
    1 540
    ———

24) 448
    21
    ———

25) 253 261
    303 511
    109 907
    ———

26) 1 019
    76
    8 004
    ———

27) 976 309
    707 521
    ———

28) 17 156
    81 043
    ———

29) 109 824
    340 198
    98 008
    33 557
    ———

30) 119 987
    219 998
    976 695
    808 009
    ———

31) 8 999
    45 101
    11 933
    67 003
    ———

32) 389 197
    202 070
    54 562
    717 122
    ———

33) 188 709
    335 007
    4
    25
    ———

34) 1 008
    50 901
    6 121
    300
    ———

35) 112 091
    56 083
    7 071
    21 890
    ———

36) 7 933
    55
    7
    908 002
    ———

Line these figures up correctly and add the numbers

37) 145 + 2035
38) 4381 + 117
39) 156 + 142
40) 92 + 305
41) 1089 + 745
42) 2704 + 8009
43) 3865 + 198 + 1008
44) 270 + 303 + 57
45) 505 + 72 + 4881

46) $109 + 7 + 36$
47) $11 + 8 + 940$
48) $3 + 8 + 137$
49) $5 + 7 + 21 + 52$
50) $11 + 24 + 56 + 78$
51) $613 + 5008 + 8 + 27$
52) $5008 + 4978 + 303 + 6921$
53) $117\,908 + 897\,113$
54) $56\,707 + 3008 + 45\,098$
55) $24\,687 + 56 + 3008$
56) $1\,233\,405 + 2\,876\,881$
57) $245\,640\,707 + 33\,998\,707$
58) $11\,987 + 1988 + 27 + 6$
59) $16 + 5 + 303 + 23\,998 + 7665$
60) $91\,187 + 34\,998 + 98\,666.$

SUBTRACTION

Subtraction means taking away.

$$3 - 1 = 2$$

We read $3 - 1 = 2$ as "three minus one equals two" or "the *difference* between 3 and 1 is 2". If I buy some goods costing £2.80 and pay with a £5 note then I *take £2.80 away from* £5.00 to find the change I should have:

```
 £
 5.00
 2.80 —
 2.20
```

There should be £2.20 change.

When subtracting it is again important to make sure that the *units* are underneath each other by lining up the figures on the *right hand sides of the whole numbers.*

EXAMPLE

Subtract 56 from 845.

```
845
 56 —
789
```
The *units* figures (5 and 6) have been lined up underneath each other. Start at the *right hand* end.

We say "6 from 5 won't go, so we *borrow from the next column*. We borrow a ten. Adding this to the 5 we get 15; 6 from 15 is 9 so we put the figure 9 down underneath the 6 in the units column".

There are two methods in general use for "paying back" the ten that has been borrowed.

In the first method the ten is "paid back at the bottom":

```
845
 56 —
   1 1
789
```
We say "5 and 1 is 6, 6 from 4 won't go so we borrow again from the next column; 6 from 14 is 8; put 8 down and pay back again at the bottom; 0 and 1 is 1; 1 from 8 is 7; put 7 down".

In the second method the figures are crossed off at the top:

```
 7 3
8̸4̸5
 56 —
789
```
We say "cross the 4 off and put 3 in its place; 5 from 3 won't go so we borrow again from the next column; 5 from 13 is 8; put 8 down, cross off the 8 and put 7; 0 from 7 is 7; put 7 down".

You should use the method you know.

Difficulty sometimes arises in the second method when there is a 0 in the next column.

EXAMPLE

Subtract 61 from 5000.

```
 4 9 9
  1 1 1
5̸0̸0̸0̸
   61 —
4939
```
We say "1 from 0 won't go so borrow from the next column, but this is a nought so we go across the columns until we come to the 5; cross off the 5 and put 4 and put 1 by the 0 in the
```
```

next column. Now we can borrow from this since it has become a 10, so cross off the 10 and put 9 with a 1 by the 0 in the tens column. Again we can borrow from it so cross off the 10 and put 9 with a 1 by the units column. Now we can take 1 from 10 which is 9; put 9 down and go to the tens column; 6 from 9 is 3; put 3 down; nothing from 9 is 9; put 9 down; nothing from 4 is 4; put 4 down''.

This sounds very complicated but becomes automatic after some practice. Notice the effect is to cross off 500 and put 499 in its place with a 1 by the 0 in the units column.

─────────── **EXERCISE 2** ───────────

Subtract the following numbers.

1) 47
    15 —
    ──

2) 29
    16 —
    ──

3) 56
    23 —
    ──

4) 69
    36 —
    ──

5) 78
    45 —
    ──

6) 82
    39 —
    ──

7) 56
    38 —
    ──

8) 94
    28 —
    ──

9) 63
    37 —
    ──

10) 82
    36 —
    ──

11) 156
     42 —
    ───

12) 459
    308 —
    ───

13) 672
    439 —
    ───

14) 567
    396 —
    ───

15) 165
     97 —
    ───

16) 785 — 314
17) 987 — 238
18) 7000 — 82
19) 5000 — 57
20) 3000 — 61
21) 8000 — 89
22) 5000 — 63
23) 7652 — 6187
24) 5109 — 1089
25) 6003 — 4552
26) 5090 — 4113
27) 6080 — 123
28) 9971 — 325
29) 3050 — 441
30) 5581 — 303
31) 4561 — 224
32) 6670 — 119
33) 1000 — 507

17

34) 8713−511
35) 9981−119
36) 2000−402
37) 3000−517
38) 90 000−87 111
39) 14 090−13 020
40) 54 131−506
41) 11 103−7009
42) 38 561−29 140
43) 95 613−20 517
44) 11 012−9091
45) 92 945−51 014
46) 11 011−11 009
47) 30 000−5008
48) 55 000−4098

A subtraction can be checked by adding the bottom two numbers. Their sum should equal the top number.

EXAMPLE

```
4281        Check:
2113−       2113
2168        2168+
            4281
```

───────── **EXERCISE 3** ─────────

Subtract these numbers and check each answer.
 1) 356−121
 2) 502−319
 3) 559−381
 4) 691−312
 5) 5567−1009
 6) 3398−2897
 7) 567−94
 8) 192−17
 9) 8132−6109
10) 5101−321
11) 6000−3081
12) 4000−292

COMBINED ADDITION AND ─── SUBTRACTION ───

To find the value of
$$24+5-7+6-18$$

first pick out all the *positive* numbers (the ones with no sign or a + sign in front of them) and add these together:

```
24
 5
 6+
35
 1
```

and then pick out all the *negative* numbers (the ones with a − sign in front of them)

and add these together:

```
 7
18+
25
 1
```

and take the sum of the negative numbers away from the sum of the positive numbers:

```
35
25−
10
```

so that:
$$24+5-7+6-18 = 10$$

───────── **EXERCISE 4** ─────────

1) 6+5−2−1
2) 8+4−3−2
3) 8−4+3−1
4) 17−5+11
5) 8−6+2
6) 18+11−17

7) $21 + 18 - 20 - 10$
8) $17 - 5 + 4 - 3$
9) $25 - 6 + 8 - 11$
10) $13 + 8 - 9 - 4 - 2$
11) $6 + 3 - 1 + 4 - 7$
12) $17 + 1 + 8 - 2 - 6 - 5$
13) $10 + 3 + 6 - 2 - 9$
14) $5 - 6 + 4 - 2 + 3$
15) $28 + 42 - 56 - 3$

—— MULTIPLICATION ——

Multiplication is a quick way of adding equal numbers.

$$\begin{array}{r} 6 \\ 6 \\ 6 \\ 6\,+ \\ \hline 24 \\ \hline \end{array}$$

$4 \times 6 = 24$ (four times six equals twenty-four)

24 is called the *product* of 4 and 6.

You do not have to count the number of pills in this packet in order to tell there are 24. From the picture you can see that $6 \times 4 = 4 \times 6 = 24.$

There are six bricks on each layer of this tower and there are four layers altogether. There are 24 bricks. On the bottom layer there are two rows of three bricks or $2 \times 3 = 6$ bricks in each layer. It would be possible to write 24 as the product of three factors:

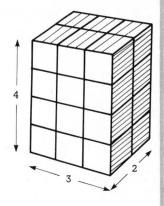

$24 = 2 \times 3 \times 4$

The order in which the factors are written down does not matter:

$24 = 3 \times 2 \times 4$
or $\quad 4 \times 3 \times 2$
or $\quad 4 \times 2 \times 3$

(Check for yourself that this is so.)

The important things to remember about multiplication are:
1) it is repeated addition,
2) the order in which the numbers are multiplied does not matter (this is called the *commutative law*).

—— TABLES ——

The multiplication table

1	2	3	4	5	6	7	8	9	10
2	4	6	8	10	12	14	16	18	20
3	6	9	12	15	18	21	24	27	30
4	8	12	16	20	24	28	32	36	40
5	10	15	20	25	30	35	40	45	50
6	12	18	24	30	36	42	48	54	60
7	14	21	28	35	42	49	56	63	70
8	16	24	32	40	48	56	64	72	80
9	18	27	36	45	54	63	72	81	90
10	20	30	40	50	60	70	80	90	100

B

To find 6×8 look along the *sixth* row and down the *eighth* column.

There you find the product of 6 and 8 which is 48

$6 \times 8 = 48$

This table is useful for revising your tables.

You should try to make sure that you know up to 10×10 without looking at the table.

— **EXERCISE 5** —

1) 7×8
2) 5×6
3) 3×7
4) 9×7
5) 8×4
6) 6×8
7) 7×6
8) 9×5
9) 3×8
10) 4×9
11) 5×8
12) 6×5
13) 8×2
14) 9×9
15) 7×7
16) Multiply these numbers by (i) 2 (ii) 3 (iii) 4 (iv) 6
    (a) 2 (b) 3 (c) 4 (d) 5.
17) Multiply these numbers by (i) 5 (ii) 6 (iii) 9
    (a) 6 (b) 7 (c) 8 (d) 9.

— SHORT MULTIPLICATION —

EXAMPLE

Multiply 67 by 5. This means "how many is 5 lots of 67?"

```
H T U
  6 7
    5 ×
3 3 5
    3
```

H stands for hundreds, T for tens and U for units. We say 5 times 7 which is 35 (from tables). We put the *units* figure down (which is 5) and carry the *tens* figure (which is 3) and usually put it down under the line to remind ourselves to add it in next time. We then multiply 5 by 6 to get 30 and add in the carried 3 to make 33 and put this down with one 3 in the tens column and the other in the hundreds column.

This is the pattern of working:

You should always make sure that your figures are lined up very carefully.

— **EXERCISE 6** —

1) 35
     2 ×
   ——

2) 23
     3 ×
   ——

3) 48
     3 ×
   ——

4) 52
     5 ×
   ——

5) 64
     7 ×
   ——

6) 81
     9 ×
   ——

7) 37
     8 ×
   ——

8) 83
     5 ×
   ——

9) 54
     6 ×
   ——

10) 56
      7 ×
    ——

EXAMPLE

Multiply 214 by 8.

```
  214
    8 ×
1712
 1 3
```

20

We say "8 times 4 is 32 (from tables); put 2 down and carry 3; then 8 times 1 is 8 and the carried 3 makes 11; put 1 down and carry 1; then 8 times 2 is 16 and the carried 1 makes 17 so put 17 down".

$$5 \times 10 = 50$$
$$24 \times 10 = 240$$
$$356 \times 10 = 3560$$

To multiply by 100 add two noughts

$$6 \times 100 = 600$$
$$34 \times 100 = 3400$$
$$456 \times 100 = 45\,600$$

--------- **EXERCISE 7** ---------

1) 567×8
2) 405×3
3) 319×7
4) 562×6
5) 680×5
6) 452×3
7) 198×4
8) 926×9
9) 307×7
10) 456×6
11) 135×5
12) 758×7
13) 672×8
14) 903×6
15) 877×8
16) 241×9
17) 526×8
18) 753×4
19) 697×6
20) 584×8

--------- **EXERCISE 8** ---------

Multiply these numbers by (i) 10 (ii) 100.

1) 8   5) 151
2) 65   6) 4000
3) 17   7) 4990
4) 331   8) 51 199

To multiply a whole number by a number such as 50, 60, 70, etc., multiply by the single figure and then add a nought.

32×40.

$$32 \times 4 = 128$$
$$32 \times 40 = 128\underline{0}$$

To multiply a whole number by 10 add a nought (this has the effect of moving the figures along one place to the left in the columns).

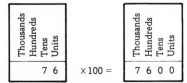

--------- **EXERCISE 9** ---------

Multiply the following numbers by (i) 20 (ii) 30 (iii) 50 (iv) 80.

1) 34   7) 301
2) 72   8) 6553
3) 151   9) 56
4) 789   10) 31
5) 45   11) 681
6) 60   12) 2008

LONG MULTIPLICATION

EXAMPLE

Multiply 173 by 35.

The pattern is

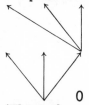

```
        173
         35 ×
        865
       5190
    0  6055
```

We say 5 times 173 (as for short multiplication) and put 865.

Next we multiply by 30: put a nought and multiply by 3: 3 times 173 is 519. Add the two rows to get 6055.

(This is the pattern the eye follows.)

Some people multiply by 30 first and then 5:

```
     173
      35 ×
    5190
     865
    6055
```

and some people leave a blank instead of putting a nought:

```
     173
      35 ×
     865
     519
    6055
```

You should use whichever method you are used to.

EXERCISE 10

1) 473
   24 ×
   ——

2) 568
   31 ×
   ——

3) 481
   28 ×
   ——

4) 512
   16 ×
   ——

5) 721
   78 ×
   ——

6) 789
   14 ×
   ——

7) 582
   15 ×
   ——

8) 285
   35 ×
   ——

9) 605
   33 ×
   ——

10) 293
    75 ×
    ——

11) Multiply 105 by 26
12) Multiply 314 by 23
13) Multiply 634 by 36
14) Multiply 718 by 25
15) Multiply 346 by 45
16) Multiply 316 by 82

17) 628 × 56
18) 378 × 75
19) 306 × 35
20) 513 × 56

EXAMPLE

A harder problem: multiply 143 by 276.

```
      143
      276 ×
      858
    10 010
    28 600
    39 468
```

First multiply by 6. Next by 70 (put a nought and multiply by 7). Then by 200 (put two noughts and multiply by 2). Add the three rows to get 39 468.

Multiplying by a number like 520 or 406 results in a row of noughts which can be left out if desired.

EXERCISE 11

1) 162
   284 ×
   ——

2) 314
   406 ×
   ——

3) 3010
   123 ×
   ——

4) Multiply 1050 by 301
5) Multiply 512 by 251
6) 304 × 520
7) 709 × 319
8) 1020 × 708
9) 987 × 410
10) 126 × 218

DIVISION

Division is concerned with sharing into equal parts.

EXAMPLE

Share £6 equally between three people.

$6 \div 3 = 2$ dot pattern

· · ·
· · ·

(six divided by three equals two)

Each person will get £2 each.

EXAMPLE

Cut a piece of string, 15 cm long, into three equal pieces. How long will each piece be?

$15 \div 3 = 5$ dot pattern

· · ·
· · ·
· · ·
· · ·
· · ·

Each piece will be 5 cm long:

| 5 cm | 5 cm | 5 cm |

There are many ways of writing division sums:

15 divided by 3 may be written $15 \div 3$ or $3\overline{)15}$ or $\frac{15}{3}$.

$24 \div 8$ is the same as $8\overline{)24}$ or $\frac{24}{8}$
$36 \div 3$ is the same as $3\overline{)36}$ or $\frac{36}{3}$
$81 \div 9$ is the same as $9\overline{)81}$ or $\frac{81}{9}$
$110 \div 11$ is the same as $11\overline{)110}$ or $\frac{110}{11}$
$56 \div 8$ is the same as $8\overline{)56}$ or $\frac{56}{8}$

SHORT DIVISION

EXAMPLE

Divide 432 by 8.

This says "how many 8s are in 432?"

The numbers have special names:

8 is called the *divisor*
432 is called the *dividend*
the answer is called the *quotient*.

$$\begin{array}{r} 54 \\ 8\overline{)432} \end{array}$$

8s into 4 won't go; 8s into 43 go 5 (from tables). Put 5 above the 3; 5 times 8 is 40; take 40 away from 43 leaving 3; put 3 by the 2 to make 32; 8s into 32 go 4; put 4 above the 2, so that:

$432 \div 8 = 54$.

EXAMPLE

Divide 4205 by 3.

$$\begin{array}{r} 1401 \text{ rem } 2 \\ 3\overline{)4205} \end{array}$$

In this example there is a remainder. When 3 is divided into 4205 there will be 2 left over.

EXERCISE 12

1) $2\overline{)7128}$
2) $2\overline{)316}$
3) $4\overline{)512}$
4) $6\overline{)368}$
5) $5\overline{)653}$
6) $7\overline{)343}$
7) $8\overline{)344}$
8) $5\overline{)509}$
9) $5\overline{)625}$
10) $7\overline{)245}$
11) $9\overline{)819}$
12) $11\overline{)671}$
13) $203 \div 7$
14) $200 \div 8$
15) $281 \div 3$
16) $451 \div 4$
17) $3418 \div 8$
18) $8190 \div 6$
19) $4187 \div 6$
20) $5008 \div 7$
21) $9087 \div 8$
22) $6151 \div 3$
23) $5091 \div 9$
24) $3050 \div 5$
25) $\dfrac{506}{5}$
26) $\dfrac{4517}{4}$
27) $\dfrac{2880}{9}$
28) $\dfrac{7343}{7}$
29) $\dfrac{2345}{5}$
30) $\dfrac{3456}{8}$
31) $\dfrac{2319}{9}$
32) $\dfrac{1451}{6}$

LONG DIVISION

Divide 1032 by 24.

This says "how many 24s in 1032?"

$$24\overline{)1032} \quad \frac{43}{}$$
$$\frac{96}{72}$$

We say "24s into 1 won't go; try 24s into 10; 24s into 10 won't go; try 24s into 103; 24s into 103 go 4" (you work this out by working out the 24 times table:

$$1 \times 24 = 24$$
$$2 \times 24 = 48$$
$$3 \times 24 = 72$$
$$\underline{4 \times 24 = 96}$$
$$5 \times 24 = 120$$

you can see that 5 times 24 would be too big.)

Put the 4 above the 3 and take 96 away from 103. This leaves 7. In short division the 7 would go up by the 2 but in long division to make the working easier we bring down the 2 and put it by the 7 to make 72. The next step is to say "how many 24s in 72?" By looking at the 24 times table you can see that the answer is 3; put 3 next to the 4 above the line so that:

$$1032 \div 24 = 43.$$

Long division can always be checked by multiplying back:

$$\begin{array}{r} 43 \\ 24 \times \\ \hline 172 \\ 860 \\ \hline 1032 \\ \hline \end{array}$$

Also a rough check can be made:

24 is roughly 25
1032 is roughly 1000

there are 40 times 25 in 1000 so the answer is not *obviously* wrong.

EXAMPLE

Divide 350 000 by 50.

$$50\overline{)350\,000} \quad \frac{7\,000}{}$$
$$350$$

$$350\,000 \div 50 = 7000.$$

50 will not divide into 3 or 35 so we try 50 into 350. This goes 7 exactly leaving no remainder. The remaining three zeros are written above the line.

EXAMPLE

Divide 92 579 by 44.

$$44\overline{)92\,579} \quad \frac{2\,104}{} \text{ rem } 3$$
$$\frac{88}{45}$$
$$\frac{44}{179}$$
$$\frac{176}{3}$$

44s into 92 go 2 remainder 4. Bring down the 5. 44s into 45 go 1 remainder 1. Bring down the 7. 44s into 17 won't go. Put a 0. Bring down the 9. 44s into 179 go 4 remainder 3.

EXERCISE 13

1) $21\overline{)567}$

2) $32\overline{)512}$

3) $54\overline{)1242}$

4) $37\overline{)505}$

5) $56\overline{)616}$

6) $71\overline{)3410}$

7) $25\overline{)825}$

8) $61\overline{)1159}$

9) Divide 75 000 by 50

10) Divide 46 800 by 18

11) Divide 16 500 by 22

12) Divide 3253 by 25

13) Divide 90 343 by 43

14) Divide 16 695 by 45

— SEQUENCE OF OPERATIONS —

In working out problems of the following types:

$$2 \times (3 + 2)$$
$$\text{or } 4(7 + 11)$$
$$\text{or } 16 - (5 - 1)$$
$$\text{or } 3 \times 5 + 2$$
$$\text{or } 3 + 8 \div 4$$

a certain sequence must be observed.

Brackets must be worked out first.

EXAMPLES

$2 \times (3 + 2) = 2 \times 5 = 10$
   (3 is added to 2 first)

$4(7 + 11)$ means $4 \times (7 + 11)$
$4 \times (7 + 11) = 4 \times 18 = 72$

We get the same answer (and sometimes make the working easier) if we *expand the bracket* and say

$4(7 + 11) = 4 \times 7 + 4 \times 11$
$\qquad\quad\, = 28 + 44 = 72$

$16 - (5 - 1) = 16 - 4 = 12$
   (1 is taken from 5 first)

Multiplication and division must be done before addition and subtraction.

EXAMPLES

$3 \times 5 + 2 = 15 + 2 = 17$
   (3 times 5 is done first)
$4 + 2 \times 3 = 4 + 6 = 10$
   (2 times 3 is done first)
$8 \div 4 + 3 = 2 + 3 = 5$
   (8 divided by 4 is done first)
$6 + 12 \div 3 = 6 + 4 = 10$
   (12 divided by 3 is done first)

1) $4 \times (5 + 3)$
2) $5 \times (6 + 2)$
3) $9 \times (1 + 3)$
4) $7 \times (3 + 4)$
5) $6 \times (5 + 2)$
6) $9 \times (3 + 4)$
7) $8 \times (6 + 3)$
8) $5 \times (5 + 4)$
9) $3(2 + 7)$
10) $4(3 + 5)$
11) $11(3 + 5)$
12) $8(9 + 3)$
13) $15 - (3 - 1)$
14) $17 - (4 - 3)$
15) $24 - (6 - 2)$
16) $35 - (16 - 12)$
17) $22 - (15 - 3)$
18) $33 - (10 - 8)$
19) $45 - (17 - 12)$
20) $20 - (9 - 6)$
21) $15 - (8 - 4)$
22) $13 - (9 - 6)$
23) $20 - (15 - 5)$
24) $14 - (6 - 4)$
25) $5 + 2 \times 6$
26) $7 + 4 \times 3$
27) $9 + 3 \times 2$
28) $8 + 7 \times 4$
29) $3 + 8 \times 3$
30) $5 + 8 \times 9$
31) $4 + 7 \times 7$
32) $3 + 6 \times 7$
33) $2 + 3 \times 7$
34) $8 + 7 \times 5$
35) $7 + 9 \times 6$
36) $9 + 7 \times 9$
37) $5 + 20 \div 4$
38) $3 + 24 \div 8$
39) $5 + 36 \div 6$
40) $9 + 54 \div 9$
41) $5 + 32 \div 4$
42) $8 + 45 \div 5$
43) $6 + 15 \div 3$
44) $5 + 63 \div 7$

45) $8 + 72 \div 8$	57) $(7 + 8) - (3 - 2)$
46) $5 + 60 \div 12$	58) $6 \times 7 + 2 \times 5$
47) $4 + 16 \div 2$	59) $(24 + 36) \div 12$
48) $8 + 40 \div 8$	60) $(19 + 14) - (27 - 16)$
49) $7 \times 9 + 6 \times 3$	61) $22 \div 11 + 44 \div 4$
50) $11 - (5 - 3)$	62) $6 \times (7 + 2) - 9$
51) $5 + 81 \div 9 - 6$	63) $5 + 4 \times 3 + 1$
52) $6 \times 4 + 64 \div 8$	64) $2 + 4 \times 8 - 2$
53) $6 + 2 \times 3 - 5$	65) $3 \times 5 - 2 + 1$
54) $(7 + 5) \div 2 + 1$	66) $27 \div 3 + 27 \div 9$
55) $(3 + 4) \times 5$	67) $25 - (30 - 10)$
56) $(8 + 2) \div (2 + 3)$	68) $4 + 2 \times 7 + 6$

CHECKING THE ACCURACY OF A CALCULATION

Always make sure your answers are sensible! You can often see if there is a mistake by looking at the *size* of the answer. (If you invest £100 for 2 years at $12\frac{1}{2}\%$ interest you would not expect to end up with twenty-five million pounds!)

If you round your numbers to the nearest ten (or to the nearest hundred or thousand if they are large) then you can make a quick estimate to see if your answer is likely to be right.

EXAMPLE

Make a rough check to see if this bill is correct:

	£		
Fittings	199	this is roughly	200
Pipes	389	this is roughly	400
Plaster	201	this is roughly	200
Tiles	590	this is roughly	600 +
TOTAL	1779		1400

The bill is incorrect.

Make a rough check and say if these sums are correct.

1)	5 099	5)	689
	3 999		372
	1 001 +		110 +
	90 099		11 171
2)	35	6)	20
	15		19
	45 +		31 +
	95		80
3)	6001	7)	5002
	300		3001
	999 +		1001 +
	7300		94
4)	20 000	8)	4 001
	5 989		2 002
	1 303 +		2 999 +
	19 392		90 002

Long multiplication can be checked by using digit sums.

Reminder: to find the *digit sum* of a number such as 698 add the digits together:

$$6 + 9 + 8 = 23$$

and add again to get a single figure:

$$2 + 3 = 5$$

So the digit sum of 698 is 5.

EXAMPLE

Multiply 503 by 65 and check the answer.

```
    503
     65 ×
   2 515
  30 180
  32 695
```

26

If you multiply the digit sums of 503 and 65 and reduce this to a single figure then this should equal the digit sum of the answer.

Check: the digit sum of 503 is 8. The digit sum of 65 is 2.

$$8 \times 2 = 16$$

Reducing this to a single figure:

$$1 + 6 = 7$$

so the digit sum of the answer *should* be 7.

Now we check:

$$3 + 2 + 6 + 9 + 5 = 25$$

Reducing this to a single figure:

$$2 + 5 = 7$$

The long multiplication is likely to be correct.

––––––––––– EXERCISE 16 –––––––––––

Multiply the following and check each answer using the digit sum check.

1) 651×17
2) 282×13
3) 312×15
4) 519×23
5) 204×17
6) 328×34
7) 561×12
8) 708×29
9) 526×34
10) 386×17
11) 6128×43
12) 5298×75

––––––––––– EXERCISE 17 –––––––––––

1) Add 5, 7, 3 and 4.
2) Add 2, 4, 9, 6 and 5.
3) Add 35 and 47.
4) Add 46, 17 and 39.
5) Subtract 13 from 46.
6) Subtract 72 from 100.
7) Subtract 151 from 160.
8) Multiply 15 by 4.
9) Multiply 72 by 6.
10) Divide 45 by 9.
11) Divide 72 by 8.
12) Multiply 45 by 12.
13) Divide 372 by 12.
14) Increase 300 by 100.
15) Take 19 away from 50.
16) What is 6 times 7?
17) Does $6 \times 7 = 7 \times 6$?
18) Add $8 + 8 + 8 + 8$.
19) How many 12s in 48?
20) Increase 1400 by 20.

––––––––––– EXERCISE 18 –––––––––––

1) Add these sets of figures

6078	3263	613
234	4609	534
19	3579	234
3009 +	4007 +	609 +

2) Subtract the following
   (a) $400 - 56$ (b) $356 - 79$
   (c) $6005 - 227$ (d) $4651 - 303$
   (e) $12\,301 - 11\,809$ (f) $11\,601 - 9876$

3) Multiply
   (a) 654×7 (b) 128×9
   (c) 516×8 (d) 803×3
   (e) 889×6

4) Divide
   (a) 343 by 7
   (b) 819 by 9
   (c) 216 by 6
   (d) 850 by 5

5) Multiply these numbers and check your answers (i) with a rough check and (ii) by using digit sums
   (a) 512×5 (b) 708×25
   (c) 314×97 (d) 105×73
   (e) 4132×91

6) Work out these answers by using long division
   (a) $330 \div 15$ (b) $187 \div 17$
   (c) $234 \div 13$ (d) $2400 \div 25$
   (e) $782 \div 34$

7) $7 + 5 \times 3$
8) $15 - 2 \times 4$
9) $3 \times 4 - 2 \times 3$
10) $20 \div 4 + 5$
11) $5 + 20 \div 5$
12) $56 - 13 + 12 - 15$
13) $13 + 11 - 14 + 25 - 9$
14) $10 + 13 - 9 - 5 - 2 + 3$

EXERCISE 19

The questions in this exercise are all of a practical nature. They all depend on the four rules for their solution.

1) The following diagram shows a shaft for a lathe. Find its overall length.

2) Five resistors in an electrical system are connected in series. Their values are 898, 763, 1175, 72 and 196 ohms. Their total resistance is found by adding these five values — what is it?

3) Two holes are drilled in a steel plate as shown in the diagram below. Find the dimension marked A.

4) A small tank holds 798 litres of oil when full. If 39 litres are run off, how much oil remains in the tank?

5) A housewife went shopping and bought 500 grams of tomatoes, 250 grams of butter, 3000 grams of potatoes and 1200 grams of bacon. What was the total weight of her purchases?

6) A metal casting has a weight of 138 kilograms. A piece having a weight of 9 kilograms is removed. What is the weight of the casting remaining?

7) The diagram shows a shaft intended for a diesel engine. Calculate the dimension marked X.

8) A screw has a weight of 12 grams. What is the total weight of 1250 such screws?

9) A bale of cloth contains 189 metres. Lengths of 15 metres, 36 metres and 29 metres are cut from the bale. How much cloth remains on it?

10) 19 hole centres are to be marked off 34 millimetres apart. What is the distance between the first and last hole centres?

11) A plank of wood 918 millimetres long is to be divided into 51 equal parts. What is the length of each part?

12) A shop buys 27 similar dresses for £351. How much does each dress cost?

13) The recipe for a small cake uses 85 grams of butter, 114 grams of sugar, 142 grams of plain flour and 14 grams of baking powder. What is the total weight of these ingredients?

14) 98 steel forgings have a total weight of 8134 kilograms. How much does each forging weigh?

15) A furniture shop on one day sells a dining room suite for £532, two easy chairs for £183 each, a settee for £348 and a divan bed for £93. How much are the total sales for the day?

28

16) A steel bar is 936 millimetres long. How many lengths, each 32 millimetres long, can be cut from the bar and what length remains?

17) A woman in a clothing factory cuts three patterns in 15 minutes. How many patterns can she cut in an 8 hour shift allowing 20 minutes for starting and 10 minutes for finishing the shift and 1 hour for her lunch break?

18) In the first 2 hours of a shift an operator makes 32 soldered joints per hour. In the next 3 hours the operator makes 29 joints per hour. In the final 2 hours 26 joints are made per hour. How many joints are made altogether in the 7 hour shift?

19) A farmer digs 23 210 kilograms of potatoes which are then placed in bags, each bag containing 55 kilograms. How many bags of potatoes does the farmer obtain?

20) 15 hole centres are to be marked off 39 millimetres apart. If 18 millimetres are to be allowed between the centres of the end holes and the edges of the plate, find the total length of plate required.

21) A woman is on a diet and is allowed 850 calories per day. Below is given a list of foods, their weights and the number of calories they contain.

Food	Weight (grams)	Calories
Cabbage, boiled	113	8
Carrots, boiled	113	8
Cauliflower, boiled	113	10
Chicken, roast	113	167
Coffee with milk	cup	25
Cucumber	57	6
Egg, poached	57	86
Grapefruit	113	25
Ham, lean	113	136
Lettuce	57	7
Orange	one	44
Plaice, steamed	113	105
Tea with milk	cup	20
Tomatoes	113	16
Toast with butter	slice	136

For breakfast she has: 1 grapefruit, a poached egg, a slice of toast with butter and 1 cup of tea with milk. For lunch she has: 113 g of boiled carrots, 113 g of cauliflower, 113 g of steamed plaice and 1 cup of coffee with milk.
(a) Calculate the number of calories in the breakfast.
(b) Calculate the number of calories in the lunch.
(c) Find the number of calories she can consume for dinner.

22) A typist can type 80 words per minute. She has to type a manuscript consisting of 48 000 words. How long will it take her to type the manuscript?

23) A typist finds that she can get 14 words on one line and 28 lines per page of typing. If she types out a manuscript consisting of 39 200 words, how many pages will she type?

24) A car travels 9 kilometres on 1 litre of petrol. How many litres will be needed for a journey of 324 kilometres?

25) A wall is 342 bricks long. If it has 23 courses of bricks, how many bricks have been used in building the wall?

3

The Four Rules for Fractions

We talk about $\frac{1}{2}$ lb of butter or $\frac{1}{4}$ hour. These are examples of fractional amounts.

A fraction is a fragment or a small piece.

SKETCHING FRACTIONS

The number on the bottom (the denominator) tells you into how many equal pieces to divide the whole:

$\frac{1}{6}$ means divide the whole into six equal pieces.

The number on the top (the numerator) tells you how many parts to take:

$\frac{5}{6}$ means take five parts.

EXERCISE 1

1) Here are some drawings of fractions of a disc:

$\frac{1}{2}$ $\frac{1}{5}$

$\frac{3}{4}$ $\frac{3}{5}$

This is what three of those discs would look like from the top:

Which one has been left out?

2) Here is a sketch of a disc with $\frac{1}{4}$ shaded (i) side view (ii) from the top:

(i)   (ii)

In a similar way sketch these portions of a disc

(a) $\dfrac{3}{8}$ (b) $\dfrac{1}{5}$ (c) $\dfrac{1}{12}$ (d) $\dfrac{4}{5}$

(e) $\dfrac{5}{12}$ (f) $\dfrac{5}{8}$

3) Draw three sketches of a circle and shade
(a) $\dfrac{1}{3}$ (b) $\dfrac{2}{3}$ (c) $\dfrac{5}{6}$

CHANGING TO EQUIVALENT FRACTIONS

In these diagrams $\frac{1}{2}$ a circle and $\frac{3}{6}$ of a circle have been shaded:

You can see that the amount of shaded area is the same in both diagrams. So:

$$\frac{1}{2} = \frac{3}{6}$$

To change $\frac{1}{2}$ into $\frac{3}{6}$ we have multiplied top and bottom by 3.

If you drew more sketches of fractions you would find that *if you multiply top and bottom of a fraction by the same number you do not alter its value.*

EXAMPLES

$$\frac{1}{2} = \frac{5}{10} \qquad \frac{3}{4} = \frac{6}{8}$$

EXERCISE 2

Draw suitable sketches to show that

1) $\frac{4}{5} = \frac{8}{10}$ 5) $\frac{3}{4} = \frac{9}{12}$

2) $\frac{1}{3} = \frac{3}{9}$ 6) $\frac{1}{3} = \frac{4}{12}$

3) $\frac{2}{3} = \frac{4}{6}$ 7) $\frac{3}{5} = \frac{6}{10}$

4) $\frac{1}{5} = \frac{2}{10}$ 8) $\frac{1}{3} = \frac{2}{6}$

---

9) $\frac{2}{3} = \frac{8}{12}$

10) Say what fraction of each circle has been shaded

    (a)   (b)   (c)   (d)

There is a definite pattern when changing fractions:

$$\frac{3}{7} \quad \overset{5 \times 3 = 15}{\underset{7\text{s into }35\text{ go }5}{\xrightarrow{\quad 5 \quad}}} \quad \frac{15}{35} \qquad \frac{3}{7} = \frac{15}{35}$$

$$\frac{4}{9} \quad \overset{4 \times 4 = 16}{\underset{9\text{s into }36\text{ go }4}{\xrightarrow{\quad 4 \quad}}} \quad \frac{16}{36} \qquad \frac{4}{9} = \frac{16}{36}$$

$$\frac{2}{3} \quad \overset{4 \times 2 = 8}{\underset{3\text{s into }12\text{ go }4}{\xrightarrow{\quad 4 \quad}}} \quad \frac{8}{12} \qquad \frac{2}{3} = \frac{8}{12}$$

EXERCISE 3

Copy these fractions and fill in the missing numbers.

1) (a) $\frac{1}{4} = \frac{}{20}$ (b) $\frac{2}{3} = \frac{}{6}$

  (c) $\frac{5}{6} = \frac{}{12}$ (d) $\frac{4}{5} = \frac{}{20}$

2) (a) $\frac{3}{4} = \frac{}{16}$ (b) $\frac{1}{2} = \frac{}{10}$

  (c) $\frac{3}{8} = \frac{}{24}$ (d) $\frac{3}{5} = \frac{}{10}$

3) (a) $\frac{5}{6} = \frac{}{18}$ (b) $\frac{1}{4} = \frac{}{24}$

  (c) $\frac{6}{7} = \frac{}{42}$ (d) $\frac{9}{11} = \frac{}{88}$

4) (a) $\dfrac{4}{9} = \dfrac{}{27}$ (b) $\dfrac{6}{11} = \dfrac{}{22}$

(c) $\dfrac{5}{8} = \dfrac{}{56}$ (d) $\dfrac{3}{4} = \dfrac{}{20}$

5) (a) $\dfrac{5}{6} = \dfrac{}{36}$ (b) $\dfrac{6}{7} = \dfrac{}{21}$

(c) $\dfrac{3}{5} = \dfrac{}{25}$ (d) $\dfrac{7}{8} = \dfrac{}{32}$

6) (a) $\dfrac{3}{8} = \dfrac{}{40}$ (b) $\dfrac{2}{3} = \dfrac{}{18}$

(c) $\dfrac{5}{9} = \dfrac{}{45}$ (d) $\dfrac{3}{5} = \dfrac{}{30}$

7) (a) $\dfrac{5}{11} = \dfrac{}{33}$ (b) $\dfrac{3}{8} = \dfrac{}{64}$

(c) $\dfrac{1}{2} = \dfrac{}{40}$ (d) $\dfrac{2}{3} = \dfrac{}{27}$

8) (a) $\dfrac{4}{5} = \dfrac{}{25}$ (b) $\dfrac{7}{8} = \dfrac{}{56}$

(c) $\dfrac{3}{7} = \dfrac{}{49}$ (d) $\dfrac{5}{12} = \dfrac{}{60}$

REDUCING A FRACTION TO ITS
LOWEST TERMS

By drawing you can see

$$\dfrac{4}{6} = \dfrac{2}{3} \qquad \text{and} \qquad \dfrac{3}{12} = \dfrac{1}{4}$$

We can divide the top and the bottom of a fraction by the same number without altering the value of the fraction.

(Drawing does not provide a proof of the rule but it shows you, perhaps, why it works.)

Fractions like $\frac{2}{3}$ and $\frac{1}{3}$ are said to be in their *lowest terms* (there is no number which will divide into top and bottom).

EXAMPLE

Reduce   (a) $\frac{4}{6}$ (b) $\frac{3}{12}$ to their lowest terms.

(a) $\dfrac{4}{6} = \dfrac{2}{3}$ (dividing top and bottom by 2)

(b) $\dfrac{3}{12} = \dfrac{1}{4}$ (dividing top and bottom by 3)

Sometimes top and bottom can be divided more than once:

EXAMPLE

Reduce $\frac{42}{56}$ to its lowest terms.

$$\dfrac{42}{56} = \dfrac{6}{8} \quad \text{(dividing top and bottom by 7)}$$

$$= \dfrac{3}{4} \quad \text{(dividing top and bottom by 2)}$$

EXERCISE 4
---

1) By drawing show that

(a) $\dfrac{6}{9} = \dfrac{2}{3}$ (b) $\dfrac{6}{8} = \dfrac{3}{4}$

(c) $\dfrac{4}{12} = \dfrac{1}{3}$.

Reduce the following to their lowest terms

2) $\dfrac{3}{9}$ 4) $\dfrac{15}{25}$

3) $\dfrac{5}{20}$ 5) $\dfrac{5}{15}$

6) $\dfrac{6}{12}$ 17) $\dfrac{14}{21}$

7) $\dfrac{10}{30}$ 18) $\dfrac{18}{24}$

8) $\dfrac{36}{42}$ 19) $\dfrac{12}{20}$

9) $\dfrac{42}{49}$ 20) $\dfrac{6}{10}$

10) $\dfrac{12}{16}$ 21) $\dfrac{5}{30}$

11) $\dfrac{56}{64}$ 22) $\dfrac{7}{49}$

12) $\dfrac{21}{35}$ 23) $\dfrac{11}{33}$

13) $\dfrac{10}{40}$ 24) $\dfrac{15}{30}$

14) $\dfrac{16}{20}$ 25) $\dfrac{16}{24}$

15) $\dfrac{12}{24}$ 26) $\dfrac{9}{18}$

16) $\dfrac{15}{20}$

TYPES OF FRACTIONS

$\frac{8}{5}$ is known as a *top-heavy* fraction. The number on top is larger than the number underneath. (Sometimes top-heavy fractions are known as "improper fractions".)

$1\frac{3}{5}$ is known as a *mixed fraction*. It is a whole number and a fraction:

$$\frac{8}{5} = \frac{5}{5} + \frac{3}{5} = 1\frac{3}{5}$$

$$\frac{5}{5} = 1$$

We have a rule for making top-heavy fractions into mixed fractions:

Divide by the number underneath. The answer goes as the whole number. The remainder goes on top of the fraction and the number underneath stays the same.

EXAMPLE

Turn $\frac{17}{5}$ into a mixed fraction.

5s into 17 go 3 remainder 2:

$$\frac{17}{5} = 3\frac{2}{5}$$

--- **EXERCISE 5** ---

Turn the following top-heavy fractions into mixed fractions

1) $\dfrac{9}{4}$ 9) $\dfrac{11}{4}$

2) $\dfrac{11}{3}$ 10) $\dfrac{17}{6}$

3) $\dfrac{15}{7}$ 11) $\dfrac{32}{5}$

4) $\dfrac{17}{8}$ 12) $\dfrac{25}{4}$

5) $\dfrac{20}{7}$ 13) $\dfrac{19}{9}$

6) $\dfrac{51}{8}$ 14) $\dfrac{35}{6}$

7) $\dfrac{5}{2}$ 15) $\dfrac{27}{4}$

8) $\dfrac{7}{3}$ 16) $\dfrac{43}{8}$

17) $\dfrac{29}{11}$ 27) $\dfrac{43}{5}$

18) $\dfrac{57}{8}$ 28) $\dfrac{23}{7}$

19) $\dfrac{13}{4}$ 29) $\dfrac{21}{4}$

20) $\dfrac{18}{5}$ 30) $\dfrac{17}{4}$

21) $\dfrac{82}{9}$ 31) $\dfrac{26}{5}$

22) $\dfrac{57}{5}$ 32) $\dfrac{35}{4}$

23) $\dfrac{37}{4}$ 33) $\dfrac{13}{2}$

24) $\dfrac{53}{12}$ 34) $\dfrac{24}{5}$

25) $\dfrac{15}{8}$ 35) $\dfrac{3}{2}$

26) $\dfrac{11}{5}$ 36) $\dfrac{33}{8}$

To make mixed fractions top-heavy, multiply the whole number by the number underneath the fraction and add the number on top of the fraction. This goes on top. The number underneath stays the same.

EXAMPLE

$2\dfrac{3}{4} = \dfrac{11}{4}$ (2 times 4 plus 3 is 11)

pictorially:

Make the following mixed fractions top-heavy

1) $3\dfrac{1}{2}$ 19) $3\dfrac{2}{9}$

2) $5\dfrac{3}{4}$ 20) $11\dfrac{3}{5}$

3) $6\dfrac{1}{3}$ 21) $2\dfrac{5}{7}$

4) $4\dfrac{2}{3}$ 22) $3\dfrac{7}{8}$

5) $7\dfrac{1}{2}$ 23) $5\dfrac{3}{5}$

6) $2\dfrac{1}{2}$ 24) $8\dfrac{9}{10}$

7) $3\dfrac{2}{3}$ 25) $4\dfrac{3}{7}$

8) $4\dfrac{2}{5}$ 26) $9\dfrac{5}{7}$

9) $5\dfrac{1}{3}$ 27) $3\dfrac{1}{3}$

10) $8\dfrac{5}{6}$ 28) $8\dfrac{6}{7}$

11) $9\dfrac{5}{5}$ 29) $9\dfrac{3}{8}$

12) $6\dfrac{7}{8}$ 30) $15\dfrac{1}{2}$

13) $6\dfrac{2}{7}$ 31) $2\dfrac{3}{5}$

14) $3\dfrac{1}{5}$ 32) $9\dfrac{1}{4}$

15) $9\dfrac{5}{6}$ 33) $7\dfrac{4}{5}$

16) $8\dfrac{4}{7}$ 34) $5\dfrac{4}{5}$

17) $2\dfrac{1}{7}$ 35) $6\dfrac{2}{3}$

18) $3\dfrac{5}{9}$

LOWEST COMMON MULTIPLE (LCM)

The LCM of a set of numbers is the smallest number into which all of the numbers will divide exactly.

EXAMPLES

The LCM of 2, 3 and 4 is 12
The LCM of 5 and 15 is 15
The LCM of 4, 5 and 6 is 60.

EXERCISE 7

Find the LCM of the following numbers

1) 2 and 3
2) 3 and 5
3) 4 and 8
4) 2 and 6
5) 5 and 10
6) 4 and 5
7) 6 and 9
8) 2 and 5
9) 3 and 4
10) 7 and 14
11) 2, 3 and 5
12) 3, 5 and 10
13) 4, 8 and 16
14) 5, 10 and 15
15) 8 and 9
16) 6 and 7
17) 5, 10 and 20
18) 9, 18 and 2
19) 6 and 12
20) 6 and 8
21) 5 and 6
22) 2, 4 and 8
23) 2, 3, 4 and 6
24) 9 and 10

When putting fractions in order of size, make them of the same type first.

EXAMPLE

Put the following fractions in order of size with the smallest first.

(a) $\dfrac{7}{8}$ (b) $\dfrac{3}{4}$ (c) $\dfrac{1}{4}$ (d) $\dfrac{1}{2}$ (e) $\dfrac{3}{8}$

Look at the numbers underneath the fractions. The LCM of 8, 4 and 2 is 8. Change the fractions into eighths:

$\dfrac{7}{8} \rightarrow \dfrac{7}{8}$ $\dfrac{3}{4} \rightarrow \dfrac{6}{8}$ $\dfrac{1}{4} \rightarrow \dfrac{2}{8}$

$\dfrac{1}{2} \rightarrow \dfrac{4}{8}$ $\dfrac{3}{8} \rightarrow \dfrac{3}{8}$

Now putting them in order of size we have:

$$\frac{2}{8}, \ \frac{3}{8}, \ \frac{4}{8}, \ \frac{6}{8}, \ \frac{7}{8}$$

and putting the fractions back into their original form:

$$\frac{1}{4}, \ \frac{3}{8}, \ \frac{1}{2}, \ \frac{3}{4}, \ \frac{7}{8}$$

EXERCISE 8

Put the following fractions in order of size, smallest first

1) (a) $\dfrac{1}{3}$ (b) $\dfrac{1}{2}$ (c) $\dfrac{5}{6}$ (d) $\dfrac{3}{4}$

2) (a) $\dfrac{3}{5}$ (b) $\dfrac{1}{2}$ (c) $\dfrac{7}{10}$ (d) $\dfrac{4}{5}$

3) (a) $\dfrac{5}{12}$ (b) $\dfrac{3}{4}$ (c) $\dfrac{1}{6}$ (d) $\dfrac{1}{4}$

4) (a) $\dfrac{1}{2}$ (b) $\dfrac{1}{8}$ (c) $\dfrac{1}{4}$ (d) $\dfrac{3}{4}$

   (e) $\dfrac{7}{8}$

— ADDITION OF FRACTIONS —

Sometimes we need to add fractions together.

EXAMPLE

I have $\frac{2}{3}$ bag of ready-mix cement left and I am given $\frac{1}{2}$ bag by my neighbour. How much do I have altogether?

We must add $\frac{2}{3} + \frac{1}{2}$.

We must change them into fractions of the *same type* before they can be added.

We do this by looking at the denominators (the numbers underneath the fractions) and finding their LCM (the smallest number that they will both go into without leaving a remainder).

The LCM of 3 and 2 is 6 so change the fractions into sixths:

$$\frac{2}{3} \rightarrow \frac{4}{6} \quad \text{and} \quad \frac{1}{2} \rightarrow \frac{3}{6}$$

So

$$\frac{2}{3} + \frac{1}{2} = \frac{4}{6} + \frac{3}{6}$$

$\left(\text{sometimes written with a with a long line like this: } \dfrac{4+3}{6}\right)$

$$= \frac{7}{6}$$

$$= 1\frac{1}{6}$$

In picture form:

$$\frac{2}{3} + \frac{1}{2} = \frac{4}{6} + \frac{3}{6} = \frac{7}{6} = 1\frac{1}{6}$$

Notice that $\frac{7}{6}$ was top-heavy so it was changed to a whole number and a fraction.

ADDITION OF FRACTIONS WITH
— WHOLE NUMBERS —

If whole numbers are present we add them first.

EXAMPLE

$$5\frac{3}{4} + 6\frac{1}{2} = 11\frac{3}{4} + \frac{1}{2}$$

The smallest number that 4 and 2 go into is 4, so change the fractions to quarters.

$$= 11\frac{3}{4} + \frac{2}{4}$$

$$= 11\frac{5}{4}$$

But $\frac{5}{4}$ is top-heavy, so we turn it into a whole number and a fraction.

$$= 11 + 1\frac{1}{4}$$

$$= 12\frac{1}{4}$$

EXAMPLE

$$7\frac{1}{3} + 1\frac{1}{6} = 8\frac{1}{3} + \frac{1}{6}$$

The smallest number that 3 and 6 both go into is 6, so change the fractions to sixths.

$$= 8\frac{2}{6} + \frac{1}{6}$$

$$= 8\frac{3}{6}$$

But $\frac{3}{6}$ is not in its lowest terms.

$$= 8\frac{1}{2}$$

— **EXERCISE 9** —

1) $\dfrac{3}{4} + \dfrac{1}{2}$

2) $\dfrac{1}{3} + \dfrac{1}{2}$

3) $\dfrac{3}{4} + \dfrac{1}{8}$

4) $\dfrac{2}{5} + \dfrac{3}{10}$

5) $\frac{3}{4} + \frac{1}{3}$

6) $\frac{5}{6} + \frac{2}{3}$

7) $\frac{5}{8} + \frac{1}{4}$

8) $\frac{4}{5} + \frac{2}{3}$

9) $\frac{1}{7} + \frac{2}{3}$

10) $\frac{1}{3} + \frac{1}{4}$

11) $\frac{5}{6} + \frac{1}{12}$

12) $\frac{2}{3} + \frac{5}{12}$

13) $\frac{3}{4} + \frac{5}{8}$

14) $\frac{7}{8} + \frac{3}{16}$

15) $\frac{3}{5} + \frac{2}{15}$

16) $\frac{3}{8} + \frac{3}{4}$

17) $\frac{1}{3} + \frac{1}{5}$

18) $\frac{3}{7} + \frac{1}{3}$

19) $\frac{1}{2} + \frac{2}{3}$

20) $\frac{2}{5} + \frac{3}{4}$

21) $\frac{1}{8} + \frac{1}{2}$

22) $\frac{3}{4} + \frac{4}{5}$

23) $\frac{5}{6} + \frac{1}{5}$

24) $\frac{7}{9} + \frac{1}{3}$

25) $5\frac{1}{2} + 2\frac{3}{4}$

26) $3\frac{3}{4} + 4\frac{1}{8}$

27) $1\frac{1}{5} + 2\frac{1}{4}$

28) $5\frac{3}{8} + 4\frac{1}{4}$

29) $6\frac{3}{5} + 2\frac{1}{10}$

30) $4\frac{1}{3} + 2\frac{3}{5}$

31) $3\frac{1}{4} + 2\frac{3}{8}$

32) $4\frac{3}{5} + 1\frac{1}{4}$

33) $5\frac{3}{7} + \frac{1}{14}$

34) $3\frac{1}{2} + 1\frac{1}{2}$

35) $4\frac{1}{3} + \frac{2}{3}$

36) $12\frac{1}{4} + 1\frac{1}{2}$

37) $4\frac{1}{3} + 1\frac{5}{6}$

38) $7\frac{1}{3} + \frac{1}{12}$

39) $2\frac{2}{3} + 3\frac{4}{9}$

40) $\frac{1}{7} + \frac{1}{8}$

41) $\frac{5}{9} + \frac{4}{7}$

42) $2\frac{3}{7} + 3\frac{1}{14}$

43) $3\frac{1}{7} + 2\frac{5}{7}$

44) $5\frac{3}{4} + 2\frac{1}{8}$

45) $3\frac{1}{3} + 1\frac{1}{6}$

46) $3\frac{4}{5} + \frac{2}{3}$

47) $\frac{4}{11} + \frac{3}{22}$

48) $3\frac{3}{10} + \frac{4}{5}$

– SUBTRACTION OF FRACTIONS –

If a pane of glass has to be replaced in a window then some space allowance has to be made. If the pane of glass was bought to fit the window exactly it would be under too much strain and might break. About 6 mm ($\frac{1}{8}$ inch) is subtracted from the measurements of the window.

To be able to take fractions away from each other they have to be made into fractions of the same type. (In the same way as for adding fractions.)

EXAMPLE

$\frac{2}{3} - \frac{1}{2}$ We cannot say $\frac{2-1}{3-2}$.

This is quite *wrong*!

The smallest number that 3 and 2 goes into without leaving a remainder is 6 so we turn the fractions into sixths.

$$\frac{2}{3} \diagdown \frac{4}{6}$$

and

$$\frac{1}{2} \diagdown \frac{3}{6}$$

so that

$$\frac{2}{3} - \frac{1}{2} = \frac{4}{6} - \frac{3}{6} = \frac{1}{6}$$

EXERCISE 10

1) $\dfrac{1}{5} - \dfrac{1}{10}$ 6) $\dfrac{3}{11} - \dfrac{1}{22}$

2) $\dfrac{2}{7} - \dfrac{1}{14}$ 7) $\dfrac{5}{6} - \dfrac{1}{3}$

3) $\dfrac{1}{2} - \dfrac{3}{8}$ 8) $\dfrac{7}{12} - \dfrac{1}{2}$

4) $\dfrac{4}{5} - \dfrac{3}{10}$ 9) $\dfrac{2}{5} - \dfrac{1}{10}$

5) $\dfrac{3}{8} - \dfrac{1}{4}$ 10) $\dfrac{3}{4} - \dfrac{2}{3}$

SUBTRACTION OF FRACTIONS — WITH WHOLE NUMBERS —

When there are whole numbers, we take them away first and then subtract the fractions (sometimes we have to "borrow" from the whole number).

EXAMPLE

Subtract $11\frac{5}{7}$ from $13\frac{3}{7}$.

$$13\frac{3}{7} - 11\frac{5}{7} = 2 + \frac{3}{7} - \frac{5}{7}$$

We cannot take $\dfrac{5}{7}$ from $\dfrac{3}{7}$ so "borrow" from the 2 and say

$$2 = 1 + \frac{7}{7}$$

$$= 1 + \frac{7}{7} + \frac{3}{7} - \frac{5}{7}$$

$$= 1\frac{5}{7}$$

For small numbers "borrowing" can be avoided by making the fractions top-heavy first:

EXAMPLE

$$1\frac{1}{2} - \frac{7}{8} = \frac{3}{2} - \frac{7}{8} \quad \text{but} \quad \frac{3}{2} \diagdown \frac{12}{8}$$

$$= \frac{12}{8} - \frac{7}{8}$$

$$= \frac{5}{8}$$

EXERCISE 11

1) $1\dfrac{3}{4} - \dfrac{1}{4}$ 7) $2\dfrac{5}{12} - 1\dfrac{7}{12}$

2) $2\dfrac{5}{6} - \dfrac{1}{3}$ 8) $1\dfrac{1}{3} - \dfrac{3}{4}$

3) $1\dfrac{1}{2} - \dfrac{2}{3}$ 9) $1\dfrac{1}{4} - \dfrac{7}{8}$

4) $3\dfrac{1}{3} - \dfrac{1}{12}$ 10) $2\dfrac{1}{3} - 1\dfrac{11}{12}$

5) $2\dfrac{1}{12} - \dfrac{1}{6}$ 11) $2\dfrac{1}{5} - 1\dfrac{7}{10}$

6) $3\dfrac{3}{4} - 2\dfrac{7}{8}$ 12) $3\dfrac{1}{3} - \dfrac{5}{6}$

COMBINED ADDITION AND SUBTRACTION OF FRACTIONS

EXAMPLE

$$1\frac{1}{2} - 1\frac{1}{8} + 2\frac{1}{4} = \frac{3}{2} - \frac{9}{8} + \frac{9}{4}$$

$$= \frac{12 - 9 + 18}{8}$$

$$= \frac{21}{8}$$

$$= 2\frac{5}{8}$$

──────── **EXERCISE 12** ────────

1) $2\frac{1}{4} - 1\frac{1}{8} + 1\frac{1}{2}$

2) $3\frac{1}{12} - 2\frac{11}{12} + \frac{5}{6}$

3) $\frac{1}{5} - \frac{1}{10} + \frac{1}{20}$

4) $1\frac{1}{3} - \frac{5}{6} + \frac{5}{12}$

5) $1\frac{1}{4} + 1\frac{1}{8} - 1\frac{1}{2}$

6) $2\frac{1}{3} - 1\frac{5}{6} + \frac{7}{12}$

7) $\frac{5}{12} - \frac{1}{6} + \frac{1}{3}$

8) $1\frac{1}{3} + 1\frac{1}{6} - 2\frac{1}{12}$

9) $1\frac{3}{4} + \frac{1}{2} - \frac{5}{8}$

MULTIPLICATION OF FRACTIONS

If there are whole numbers make them top-heavy first. Then multiply the numbers on top together and multiply the numbers on the bottom together.

EXAMPLE

$$1\frac{2}{3} \times 2\frac{1}{2} = \frac{5}{3} \times \frac{5}{2} = \frac{5 \times 5}{3 \times 2} = \frac{25}{6}$$

$$= 4\frac{1}{6}$$

Sometimes you can make the working easier by *cancelling*. You may cancel any number on top with any number underneath.

EXAMPLE

$$1\frac{1}{2} \times 3\frac{1}{3} = \frac{\overset{1}{\cancel{3}}}{\underset{1}{\cancel{2}}} \times \frac{\overset{5}{\cancel{10}}}{\underset{1}{\cancel{3}}} = \frac{1 \times 5}{1 \times 1} = 5$$

The 3s have been *cancelled*. Also 2 and 10 are divided by 2 leaving 1 and 5. If there are whole numbers, do not cancel until the fractions have been made top-heavy.

──────── **EXERCISE 13** ────────

1) $\frac{2}{3} \times \frac{3}{4}$ 7) $3\frac{1}{2} \times 4\frac{1}{7}$

2) $\frac{3}{5} \times \frac{4}{7}$ 8) $1\frac{1}{2} \times \frac{2}{3}$

3) $\frac{3}{4} \times \frac{1}{5}$ 9) $4\frac{1}{2} \times \frac{1}{9}$

4) $\frac{3}{5} \times \frac{5}{9}$ 10) $5\frac{2}{5} \times \frac{5}{9}$

5) $2\frac{1}{2} \times \frac{4}{5}$ 11) $\frac{7}{9} \times \frac{3}{14}$

6) $\frac{3}{5} \times 1\frac{1}{3}$ 12) $\frac{4}{15} \times \frac{5}{8}$

13) $1\frac{1}{5} \times \frac{2}{3}$

14) $1\frac{1}{4} \times \frac{1}{5}$

15) $3\frac{1}{2} \times \frac{4}{7}$

16) $\frac{4}{5} \times \frac{25}{32}$

17) $\frac{1}{3} \times \frac{2}{5}$

18) $1\frac{1}{4} \times \frac{3}{5}$

19) $1\frac{1}{2} \times \frac{1}{2}$

20) $\frac{1}{4} \times \frac{1}{8}$

21) $3\frac{1}{2} \times \frac{8}{21}$

22) $\frac{7}{8} \times \frac{32}{63}$

23) $\frac{6}{7} \times \frac{7}{12}$

24) $\frac{5}{11} \times \frac{33}{50}$

25) $2\frac{1}{2} \times \frac{2}{5}$

26) $7\frac{1}{7} \times \frac{21}{25}$

27) $1\frac{1}{2} \times 1\frac{1}{3}$

28) $\frac{5}{7} \times \frac{14}{15}$

— DIVISION OF FRACTIONS —

$\frac{2}{3} \div \frac{1}{2}$ is a division sum which asks the question: "how many halves in two-thirds?"

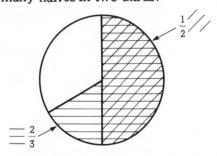

If we draw a picture you can see that there is more than *one* half in two-thirds but less than *two* halves. In fact there are $1\frac{1}{3}$ halves in two-thirds.

The rule for division of fractions is:

If there are mixed fractions make them top-heavy first. Then turn the second fraction upside down and multiply.

EXAMPLES

$$\frac{2}{3} \div \frac{1}{2} = \frac{2}{3} \times \frac{2}{1} = \frac{2 \times 2}{3 \times 1} = \frac{4}{3} = 1\frac{1}{3}$$

$$1\frac{3}{4} \div 1\frac{2}{3} = \frac{7}{4} \div \frac{5}{3} = \frac{7}{4} \times \frac{3}{5} = \frac{7 \times 3}{4 \times 5} = \frac{21}{20}$$

$$= 1\frac{1}{20}$$

$$1\frac{1}{2} \div 2\frac{1}{2} = \frac{3}{2} \div \frac{5}{2} = \frac{3}{2} \times \frac{2}{5}$$

it is not a good idea to try to squash these two steps into one

$$= \frac{3 \times \overset{1}{2}}{\underset{1}{2} \times 5} = \frac{3 \times 1}{1 \times 5} = \frac{3}{5}$$

You can cancel any number on the top with any number on the bottom if they have a common factor at the multiplication stage. *Do not cancel across a division sign.*

————————— **EXERCISE 14** —————————

1) $\frac{3}{4} \div \frac{1}{2}$

2) $\frac{5}{6} \div \frac{2}{3}$

3) $\frac{4}{5} \div \frac{2}{7}$

4) $\frac{2}{5} \div \frac{3}{5}$

5) $2\frac{1}{2} \div 1\frac{1}{4}$

6) $3\frac{3}{4} \div \frac{5}{16}$

7) $5\frac{1}{3} \div \frac{4}{9}$

8) $3\frac{1}{3} \div 1\frac{2}{3}$

9) $\frac{5}{9} \div \frac{2}{3}$

10) $\frac{6}{11} \div \frac{3}{22}$

11) $\frac{5}{12} \div 2\frac{1}{2}$

12) $\frac{7}{8} \div 1\frac{5}{16}$

13) $6\frac{1}{2} \div 4\frac{1}{3}$

14) $3\frac{1}{4} \div 4\frac{1}{3}$

15) $2\frac{1}{3} \div \frac{7}{8}$

16) $1\frac{1}{2} \div \frac{3}{7}$

17) $2\frac{1}{2} \div \frac{1}{2}$

18) $1\frac{3}{4} \div \frac{1}{8}$

19) $\dfrac{2}{3} \div 1\dfrac{1}{3}$

22) $1\dfrac{1}{6} \div 4\dfrac{2}{3}$

20) $\dfrac{3}{5} \div \dfrac{9}{20}$

23) $3\dfrac{1}{3} \div \dfrac{5}{9}$

21) $1\dfrac{1}{4} \div 1\dfrac{1}{2}$

24) $1\dfrac{7}{8} \div 1\dfrac{1}{4}$

To make a whole number top-heavy divide by 1.

For example:

$$6 = \dfrac{6}{1} \qquad 9 = \dfrac{9}{1} \qquad 20 = \dfrac{20}{1} \quad \text{etc.}$$

EXAMPLE

Find $5 \div 1\frac{1}{3}$.

$$5 \div 1\dfrac{1}{3} = \dfrac{5}{1} \div \dfrac{4}{3}$$

$$= \dfrac{5}{1} \times \dfrac{3}{4}$$

$$= \dfrac{5 \times 3}{1 \times 4}$$

$$= \dfrac{15}{4}$$

$$= 3\dfrac{3}{4}$$

CALCULATING FRACTIONS OF A WHOLE NUMBER

EXAMPLE

Find $\frac{3}{4}$ of 360.

Method 1

$$\dfrac{3}{4} \text{ of } 360 = \dfrac{3}{4} \times 360$$

$$= \dfrac{3}{\cancel{4}_{1}} \times \dfrac{\cancel{360}^{90}}{1}$$

$$= \dfrac{3 \times 90}{1 \times 1}$$

$$= 270$$

Method 2

To find $\frac{3}{4}$ of 360 *divide by 4 and multiply by 3.*

$$\begin{array}{r} 90 \\ 4\overline{)360} \end{array}$$

$$\begin{array}{r} 90 \\ 3\times \\ \hline 270 \end{array} \qquad \text{so that } \dfrac{3}{4} \text{ of } 360 = 270$$

EXERCISE 15

1) $4 \div \dfrac{3}{4}$

5) $2\dfrac{1}{2} \div 10$

2) $3 \div 1\dfrac{1}{2}$

6) $3\dfrac{3}{4} \div 5$

3) $7 \div \dfrac{7}{9}$

7) $3\dfrac{1}{3} \div 15$

4) $11 \div 2\dfrac{3}{4}$

8) $3\dfrac{1}{5} \div 8$

EXERCISE 16

1) $\dfrac{3}{4}$ of 16

5) $\dfrac{5}{7}$ of 84

2) $\dfrac{4}{5}$ of 15

6) $\dfrac{3}{4}$ of 240

3) $\dfrac{5}{8}$ of 24

7) $\dfrac{1}{7}$ of 630

4) $\dfrac{3}{8}$ of 56

8) $\dfrac{3}{5}$ of 200

1) Here are some drawings of fractions of a disc. What fractions have been shaded?

(a)   (b)

(c)   (d)

2) Draw three sketches of a circle and shade in

(a) $\dfrac{1}{4}$ (b) $\dfrac{7}{12}$ (c) $\dfrac{3}{8}$

3) Draw a sketch to show that
$$\frac{5}{6} = \frac{10}{12}$$

4) What fraction of this circle is shaded?

5) Fill in the missing numbers

(a) $\dfrac{3}{4} = \dfrac{}{8}$ (b) $\dfrac{1}{2} = \dfrac{}{20}$

(c) $\dfrac{1}{6} = \dfrac{}{12}$ (d) $\dfrac{3}{5} = \dfrac{}{15}$

6) Reduce these fractions to their lowest terms

(a) $\dfrac{5}{10}$ (b) $\dfrac{3}{15}$ (c) $\dfrac{9}{12}$ (d) $\dfrac{7}{56}$

7) Turn these top-heavy fractions into mixed fractions

(a) $\dfrac{27}{5}$ (b) $\dfrac{29}{8}$ (c) $\dfrac{31}{6}$ (d) $\dfrac{43}{6}$

8) Make these mixed fractions top-heavy

(a) $1\dfrac{2}{3}$ (b) $6\dfrac{2}{3}$ (c) $7\dfrac{3}{8}$ (d) $11\dfrac{1}{2}$

9) Find the LCM of 2, 4, 5 and 8.

10) Put these fractions in order of size with the smallest first
$$\frac{3}{4}, \frac{5}{8}, \frac{1}{2}, \frac{3}{5}.$$

11) (a) $3\dfrac{1}{2} + 2\dfrac{1}{4}$

(b) $\dfrac{4}{5} + \dfrac{3}{10}$

(c) $3\dfrac{1}{3} + 1\dfrac{1}{6} + 2\dfrac{5}{12}$

12) (a) $2\dfrac{1}{5} - 1\dfrac{3}{10}$

(b) $3\dfrac{1}{12} - 1\dfrac{1}{6}$

(c) $\dfrac{5}{8} - \dfrac{3}{16}$

(d) $\dfrac{7}{20} - \dfrac{1}{5}$

13) $1\dfrac{3}{4} + 2\dfrac{1}{2} - 3\dfrac{1}{8}$

14) $3\dfrac{1}{2} - 1\dfrac{1}{4} + 1\dfrac{1}{8} - \dfrac{5}{8}$

15) (a) $\dfrac{3}{5} \times \dfrac{5}{6}$

(b) $\dfrac{4}{7} \times \dfrac{7}{8}$

(c) $1\dfrac{1}{2} \times 1\dfrac{1}{3}$

(d) $1\dfrac{1}{4} \times 1\dfrac{1}{5}$

16) (a) $\dfrac{4}{5} \div \dfrac{5}{6}$

(b) $1\dfrac{1}{3} \div 2\dfrac{1}{2}$

17) Work out the following, remembering that brackets must be worked out first and that multiplication and division must be done before addition and subtraction.

(a) $\left(1\dfrac{1}{4}+\dfrac{5}{8}\right)\div 2\dfrac{1}{2}$

(b) $1\dfrac{1}{7}\times\left(2\dfrac{1}{3}-1\dfrac{1}{6}\right)$

(c) $\dfrac{5}{8}+\dfrac{3}{4}\times\dfrac{2}{3}$

(d) $\dfrac{5}{6}-\dfrac{1}{3}\div\dfrac{1}{2}$

18) Find (a) $\dfrac{3}{4}$ of 560 (b) $\dfrac{4}{5}$ of 350.

EXERCISE 18

The questions in this exercise are all of a practical nature. They all depend on fractions for their solution.

1) A girl spends $\frac{3}{4}$ of her pocket money and has 45 pence left. How much did she have to start with?

2) What is $\frac{7}{8}$ of £1600?

3) A reel of ribbon contains $31\frac{1}{2}$ yards. Lengths of $3\frac{1}{4}$, $5\frac{3}{8}$ and $8\frac{7}{8}$ yards are cut from it. How much ribbon remains on the reel?

4) A brand of tea is sold in packs containing $\frac{1}{8}$ kilogram. How many packs can be obtained from a box containing $51\frac{1}{2}$ kilograms?

5) A cask of lemonade contains 32 litres. It is poured into glasses each containing $\frac{1}{5}$ of a litre. How many glasses can be obtained?

6) A plank of wood is $31\frac{1}{2}$ metres long. It is cut into 6 equal lengths. What is the length of each piece?

7) A snail crawls 1 metre in $1\frac{1}{2}$ minutes. How long will it take to crawl $29\frac{1}{4}$ metres?

8) A man is paid $182\frac{1}{2}$ pence per hour. What is his weekly wage if he works 38 hours per week?

9) A watering can holds $11\frac{1}{2}$ litres. It is filled 9 times from a tank containing 250 litres. How much is left in the tank?

10) A school has 800 pupils, $\frac{1}{5}$ are in the upper school, $\frac{3}{8}$ are in the middle school and the remainder are in the lower school. How many pupils are there in the lower school?

11) An alloy consists of $\frac{7}{10}$ of copper, $\frac{9}{50}$ of tin and $\frac{3}{25}$ of zinc. How much of each metal is there in 900 grams of the alloy?

12) Calculate the total weight of coal carried by a train of 38 trucks if 20 carry $19\frac{1}{2}$ tonnes and the remainder carry $18\frac{3}{4}$ tonnes.

13) A motorcyclist covers $484\frac{1}{2}$ metres in $12\frac{3}{4}$ seconds. How far does he travel in 1 second?

14) A factory produces 660 engines per week. It increases its output by $\frac{5}{12}$. How many engines per week does it then produce each week?

15) The profits of a business are £14 500. It is shared between two partners A and B. If A receives $\frac{2}{5}$, how much does B receive?

43

c

4

—————— The Four Rules for Decimals ——————

We are familiar with "addition" (adding on) and "subtraction" (taking away) of whole numbers.

We need to be able to do *decimal* addition and subtraction in order to be able to add up money or to work out change.

All money can be written in decimal form, for example

£20 can be written as £20.00

with a *decimal point* separating the pounds and the pence.

The decimal point always goes *after* the whole number.

Figures *before* the decimal point are the *whole number*	Figures *after* the decimal point are a *fraction* (part) of a *whole number*
56	24

56.24 is a number between 56 and 57.

£56.24 is an amount of money between £56 and £57. The 24 p is *part* of a whole pound

£6.01 is six pounds and one penny. Since there are one hundred pence in a pound then one penny is *one hundredth* of a pound.

Pounds	Pence
£6	01

Units			Hundredths
6	.	0	1

The second column after the point in decimals means hundredths and the number in the column tells you how many hundredths to take.

£6.10 is six pounds ten pence. Since there are ten 10 ps in one pound then 10 p is *one tenth* of a pound.

Pounds	Pence
£6	10

Units		Tenths	Hundredths
6	.	1	0

The first column after the decimal point means tenths and the number in the column tells you how many tenths to take.

The *first* place after the decimal point represents *tenths*

The *second* place after the decimal point represents *hundredths*

This can be extended:

The *third* place after the decimal point represents *thousandths*

The *fourth* place after the decimal point represents *ten thousandths*

The *fifth* place after the decimal point represents *hundred thousandths*

The *sixth* place after the decimal point represents *millionths*

etc.

Each column represents a number ten times smaller than the one before it.

Units		Tenths	Hundredths	Thousandths	Ten thousandths	Hundred thousandths
4	.	2	5	4	1	6

↑ ↑ ↑

These figures represent *very small* quantities compared to the others.

6.2 means 6 units 2 tenths

0.04 means 4 hundredths

13.01 means 1 ten 3 units 0 tenths 1 hundredth

3.12 means 3 units 1 tenth 2 hundredths

0.728 means 7 tenths 2 hundredths 8 thousandths

EXERCISE 1

What do these decimal numbers mean?

1) 0.2
2) 3.4
3) 10.04
4) 16.02
5) 8.24

6) 15.16
7) 3.817
8) 0.082
9) 50.207
10) 0.304

11) What does the 6 in 10.63 mean?
12) What does the 2 in 1.02 mean?
13) What does the 7 in 71.3 mean?
14) What does the 5 in 12.135 mean?

MARKING DECIMALS ON A SCALE

EXERCISE 2

Make a copy of the scale below.

Draw arrows and label these points. The first one has been done for you.

1) 6.3
2) 5.8
3) 2.5
4) 4.4
5) 0.7
6) 5.3
7) 7.0
8) 6.8
9) 2.1
10) 1.4
11) 0.2
12) 5.2

Say which is larger

13) 0.2 or 0.7
14) 5.3 or 5.8
15) 6.8 or 7.0
16) 0.7 or 7.0
17) 2.5 or 5.2
18) 2.5 or 2.1
19) 6.3 or 6.8
20) 4.4 or 1.4
21) 0.2 or 2.1
22) 5.3 or 5.2

THE DECIMAL POINT AND FOLLOWING ZEROS

Notice that:

7 means 7 units

7.0 means 7 units 0 tenths

7.00 means 7 units 0 tenths 0 hundredths

7.000 means 7 units 0 tenths 0 hundredths 0 thousandths

so that

7 = 7.0 = 7.00 = 7.000, etc.

To make a whole number into a decimal, put a decimal point after the whole number and add as many zeros as required.

EXERCISE 3

1) Write (a) 5 (b) 8 (c) 9 as a decimal with (i) one zero (ii) two zeros (iii) three zeros after the decimal point.

2) Does 4 equal (a) 4.00 (b) 4.000 (c) 4.0 (d) 40?

3) Does 15 equal (a) 15.000 (b) 15.0 (c) 15.00 (d) 150?

4) Write the following numbers as whole numbers without zeros and without a decimal point
(a) 2.000   (b) 56.0   (c) 342.000
(d) 15.00

UNNECESSARY ZEROS

One source of confusion is which noughts are needed and which are not.

1) You do not need noughts in front of whole numbers (though they may be put in when dividing to make sure the numbers are lined up correctly), for example:

$$\begin{array}{r} 05.2 \\ \hline 3)\overline{15.6} \end{array} \quad \text{and} \quad 05.2 = 5.2$$

2) Noughts are not needed if they come after the decimal point at the end of the figures (but they are sometimes put in to show how accurate a measurement is) e.g. 0.700 m would mean that the measurement has been taken correct to one millimetre.

6.300 = 6.3

4.70 = 4.7

3.00 = 3

3) The noughts *are* needed in these numbers:

70 .203 500 .3005

Notice that in 70 the nought is put in to keep the place for the missing tens, in .203 the noughts keeps the place for the missing hundredths, etc.

.203 is *not* equal to .23

4) One zero is generally left *before* the point for tidiness but it is not essential.

.827 is generally written 0.827

.5 is generally written 0.5 etc.

00.5 would be the same as 0.5 but it is unusual to write more than one nought before the decimal point.

EXAMPLES

0067.50 is the same as 67.5

3.000 is the same as 3

004.0 is the same as 4

46

0.700   is the same as 0.7 or .7

00.023   is the same as 0.023 or .023
         (but *not* .23)

60.0   is the same as 60 (but *not* 6)

EXERCISE 4

Copy these numbers and then write them without the unnecessary zeros. Leave one zero before the decimal point for tidiness.

1) 0048.80
2) 4.0000
3) 006.00
4) 08
5) 0.8000
6) .70
7) 00.045
8) 1.1030
9) 5070.00
10) 300.000
11) 0000.2720
12) 11.000 000 0
13) 002.0200
14) 00.055
15) 6.0
16) Does 6.05 equal 6.50?
17) Does 6.5 equal 6.50?
18) Does £6.50 equal £6.05?
19) On a calculator would £6.50 appear as 6.05 or 6.5?

EXAMPLE

Write the following fractions as decimals

(a) $\dfrac{4}{10}$ (b) $\dfrac{5}{100}$ (c) $\dfrac{12}{100}$ (d) $\dfrac{2}{1000}$

(e) $\dfrac{145}{1000}$ (f) $\dfrac{12}{1000}$.

	Units	Tenths $\dfrac{1}{10}$	Hundredths $\dfrac{1}{100}$	Thousands $\dfrac{1}{1000}$
(a) $\dfrac{4}{10} =$	0 .	4		
(b) $\dfrac{5}{100} =$	0 .	0	5	
(c) $\dfrac{12}{100} =$	0 .	1	2	
(d) $\dfrac{2}{1000} =$	0 .	0	0	2
(e) $\dfrac{145}{1000} =$	0 .	1	4	5
(f) $\dfrac{12}{1000} =$	0 .	0	1	2

Look closely at example (c).

The 2 goes in the hundredths column and the 1 spills over into the tenths column.

For example (f) the 2 goes into the thousandths column and the 1 spills over into the hundredths column.

EXERCISE 5

Write the following as decimals

1) $\dfrac{6}{10}$ 7) $\dfrac{8}{100}$

2) $\dfrac{3}{100}$ 8) $\dfrac{9}{1000}$

3) $\dfrac{4}{1000}$ 9) $\dfrac{14}{100}$

4) $\dfrac{25}{100}$ 10) $\dfrac{628}{1000}$

5) $\dfrac{127}{1000}$ 11) $\dfrac{5}{10}$

6) $\dfrac{3}{10}$ 12) $\dfrac{7}{100}$

13) $\dfrac{6}{1000}$ 19) $\dfrac{15}{100}$

14) $\dfrac{75}{100}$ 20) $\dfrac{205}{1000}$

15) $\dfrac{954}{1000}$ 21) $\dfrac{11}{1000}$

16) $\dfrac{2}{10}$ 22) $\dfrac{15}{1000}$

17) $\dfrac{6}{100}$ 23) $\dfrac{62}{1000}$

18) $\dfrac{3}{1000}$ 24) $\dfrac{58}{1000}$.

DECIMAL ADDITION

The important thing to remember when doing decimal addition is to *line up the decimal points*. If whole numbers are present then put a decimal point at the *end* of the whole number and add zeros as required.

EXAMPLE

Add $62.1 + 0.53 + 215$.

215 is the same as 215.00.

```
  62.1
   0.53
 215.00 +
 277.63
```

The decimal point in the answer goes underneath the other decimal points.

EXERCISE 6

1) $62.34 + 41.11$
2) $1.3 + 4.2 + 3.1$
3) $12.11 + 8.71 + 29.11$
4) $89.71 + 49.1 + 98$

5) $761.3 + 291.1 + 497.4$
6) $12.3 + 0.56 + 1.12$
7) $0.3 + 7 + 6.25$
8) $17 + 11 + 29.4$
9) $18 + 16.23 + 0.25$
10) $141 + 20 + 17.1$
11) $9.125 + 0.726$
12) $17.63 + 0.129 + 11$
13) $18.251 + 11.257$
14) $6.28 + 12 + 18.19$
15) $17.1 + 3.05 + 25.1$
16) $7.12 + 0.67 + 0.2$
17) $11.6 + 12.8 + 1.9$
18) $14.52 + 0.05 + 6.1$
19) $17.56 + 2.14 + 0.006$
20) $32.4 + 14 + 16.5$
21) $67.104 + 18.029 + 7.315$
22) $17.51 + 1.105 + 0.069 + 0.37$

23)
```
 191.103
 206.040
  15.900 +
 _____
```

24)
```
 21.09
  2.56
  0.18
 25.07 +
 _____
```

25)
```
 671.32
  19.41
 151.5  +
 _____
```

26)
```
 726.13
  13.5
   0.462 +
 _____
```

27)
```
 175.68
  13.5
   0.462 +
 _____
```

28)
```
 39.76
 21.95
  0.275 +
 _____
```

29) 165.4
     1.98
    17.2 +
  ─────

30) 318.1
    0.12
   67.9 +
  ─────

31) Add together 53.124, 0.761 and 24.128.
32) Add together 72.1, 11.81 and 14.29.
33) Add together 26.03, 0.15 and 2.91.
34) Add together 7.21, 3.48 and 11.57.

DECIMAL SUBTRACTION

The decimal points must be lined up underneath each other.

The answer can be *checked* by adding the bottom two lines which should give the top line. The actual subtraction is carried out in the same manner as for whole number subtraction.

EXAMPLE

$7.2 - 3.4$

The first number goes on top. Start at the right hand end.

  7.2
  3.4 −
  ───
  3.8

Check by adding 3.4 and 3.8 to get 7.2.

EXAMPLE

$500 - 0.14$

Remember that 500 is the same as 500.00.

  500.00
    0.14 −
  ──────
  499.86

1) $15.38 - 11.06$
2) $2.75 - 1.36$
3) $14.2 - 9.1$
4) $70.08 - 13.59$
5) $315.75 - 0.93$
6) $17.2 - 15.8$
7) $1.42 - 1.38$
8) $11.5 - 7.7$
9) $142.8 - 29.7$
10) $12.5 - 7$
11) $13 - 0.12$
12) $800 - 0.16$
13) $49.5 - 13.8$
14) $7000 - 52.5$
15) $6003.5 - 729.9$
16) $218.6 - 204.1$
17) $198.3 - 4.27$
18) $502 - 34.508$
19) $62.46 - 50$
20) $157.2 - 3.898$

21) 17.58
   11.24 −
  ─────

22) 77.51
   36.90 −
  ─────

23) 159.87
    27.16 −
  ──────

24) 103.12
    27.06 −
  ──────

25) 61.19
   51.07 −
  ─────

26) 300.0
    1.5 −
  ─────

27) 418.26
    29.38 —
    ———

28) 51.123
    38.762 —
    ———

29) 0.0152
    0.0098 —
    ———

30) 0.607
    0.509 —
    ———

31) Subtract 17.38 from 29.72.
32) Subtract 15.1 from 207.5.
33) Subtract 0.82 from 0.97.
34) Subtract 7.285 from 15.34.
35) Subtract 65.2 from 158.3.
36) Subtract 218.6 from 527.5.

COMBINED ADDITION AND — SUBTRACTION OF DECIMALS —

When working out the answer to a question such as:

$$62.5 + 33.14 - 0.67 + 11.5 - 19.81 - 8.21$$

first add the numbers with a plus sign (or no sign, such as the first one), then add the numbers with a minus sign and take away the second sum from the first:

62.5	0.67
33.14	19.81
11.5 +	8.21 +
107.14	28.69

```
107.14
 28.69 —
 78.45
```

─────── **EXERCISE 8** ───────

1) $14.3 + 25.8 - 0.51 - 2.42$
2) $6.54 + 0.29 + 3.12 - 0.67$
3) $14.21 - 0.28 + 5.32 - 7.11$
4) $152.6 + 104.12 - 0.253 - 0.45$
5) $53.125 + 120.61 - 72.188 - 27.1 + 3.1$
6) $57.6 + 106.1 - 15 - 11.3$
7) $23.4 - 34.5 + 67.91 - 3.1 - 6.2$
8) $0.92 - 0.64 + 2.1 - 4.1 + 11.4$
9) $23.45 + 34.89 - 14.5 - 13.8$
10) $13.5 + 98.1 - 12.1 - 0.3 - 5.09$

MULTIPLICATION OF DECIMALS ─── BY POWERS OF 10 ───

Decimals may easily be multiplied by 10, 100 1000, etc.

EXAMPLE

Find (a) 6.2×10 (b) 6.2×100 (c) 6.2×1000.

(a) $6.2 \times 10 = 62$ since

$$6.2 = 6\frac{2}{10} \text{ and } 6\frac{2}{10} \times 10 = \frac{62}{10} \times \frac{10}{1} = 62$$

(b) $6.2 \times 100 = 620$ since

$$6.2 = 6\frac{2}{10} \text{ and } 6\frac{2}{10} \times 100 = \frac{62}{10} \times \frac{100^{10}}{1}$$
$$= 620$$

(c) $6.2 \times 1000 = 6200$ since

$$6.2 = 6\frac{2}{10} \text{ and } 6\frac{2}{10} \times 1000 = \frac{62}{10} \times \frac{1000^{100}}{1}$$
$$= 6200$$

Notice *the effect of multiplying by 10 is to move the decimal point one place to the right.*

The effect of multiplying by 100 is to move the decimal point two places to the right.

The effect of multiplying by 1000 is to move the decimal point three places to the right.

EXAMPLE

Multiply these numbers by (i) 10 (ii) 100 (iii) 1000:

(a) 0.53   (b) 62.73   (c) 0.6.

(a) (i) 5.3 (ii) 53 (iii) 530
(b) (i) 627.3 (ii) 6273 (iii) 62 730
(c) (i) 6 (ii) 60 (iii) 600

In some of these cases zero has to be put in to make up the missing places.

—————————— EXERCISE 9 ——————————

Multiply these numbers by (i) 10 (ii) 100 (iii) 1000.

1) 5.7
2) 6.21
3) 0.023
4) 0.46
5) 0.2178
6) 0.002 854
7) 0.5823
8) 0.007
9) 160.07
10) 0.147 29

MULTIPLICATION OF DECIMALS

First multiply the numbers as if there were no decimal point. Then add the number of decimal places in the first number to the number of decimal places in the second number, and count back this number of places from the *right* to find where to put the decimal point.

EXAMPLE

$$\begin{array}{r} 6.2 \\ 3\times \\ \hline 18.6 \\ \hline \end{array}$$
one decimal place
no decimal place
one decimal place in the answer

$$\begin{array}{r} 4.41 \\ 3\times \\ \hline 13.23 \\ \hline \end{array}$$
two decimal places
no decimal place
two decimal places in the answer

$$\begin{array}{r} 0.087 \\ 1.1\times \\ \hline 870 \\ 87 \\ \hline 0.0957 \\ \hline \end{array}$$
three decimal places
one decimal place
four decimal places in the answer

—————————— EXERCISE 10 ——————————

1) 6.7×4
2) 3.5×3
3) 4.8×7
4) 12.2×6
5) 17.8×7
6) 35.4×9
7) 1.25×6
8) 3.41×7
9) 5.83×8
10) 30.5×15
11) 25.6×24
12) 3.05×17
13) 0.052×1.1
14) 0.02×0.4
15) 0.357×0.9
16) 10.07×0.2
17) 43.5×0.4
18) 59.6×0.7
19) 0.72×0.8
20) 6.781×0.12
21) 9.32×2.5
22) 10.6×3.8
23) 3.21×5.1
24) 4.03×2.7
25) 83.6×4.8
26) 7.25×2.1
27) 0.06×1.2
28) 35.8×2.3
29) 4.25×2.7
30) 2.06×1.9
31) Multiply 2.251 by 9.
32) Multiply 3.02 by 0.08.

33) Multiply 0.013 by 1.8.
34) Multiply 34.2 by 7.
35) Multiply 8.7 by 0.003.
36) Multiply 6.1 by 0.12.
37) Multiply 7.2 by 1.2.
38) Multiply 8.4 by 9.5.
39) Multiply 7.3 by 0.87.
40) Multiply 0.56 by 0.27.

DIVISION OF DECIMALS BY POWERS OF 10

EXAMPLE

Divide 2.5 by (a) 10 (b) 100 (c) 1000.

(a) $2.5 \div 10 = 0.25$

since

$$2.5 = 2\frac{5}{10} \text{ and } 2\frac{5}{10} \div 10 = \frac{25}{10} \div \frac{10}{1}$$
$$= \frac{25}{10} \times \frac{1}{10}$$
$$= \frac{25}{100}$$
$$= 0.25$$

Similarly

(b) $2.5 \div 100 = 0.025$

and

(c) $2.5 \div 1000 = 0.0025$

The effect of dividing by 10 is to move the decimal point one place to the left.

The effect of dividing by 100 is to move the decimal point two places to the left.

The effect of dividing by 1000 is to move the decimal point three places to the left.

EXAMPLE

Divide these numbers by (i) 10 (ii) 100
(iii) 1000:
(a) 0.6   (b) 5.78   (c) 5671.2

(a) (i) 0.06 (ii) 0.006 (iii) 0.0006
(b) (i) 0.578 (ii) 0.0578 (iii) 0.005 78
(c) (i) 567.12 (ii) 56.712 (iii) 5.6712

EXERCISE 11

Divide these numbers by (i) 10 (ii) 100
(iii) 1000

1) 6.1	6) 1.28
2) 72.5	7) 0.0026
3) 0.05	8) 325.5
4) 260.05	9) 4628.9
5) 0.469	10) 713.598

DIVISION OF DECIMALS BY WHOLE NUMBERS

EXAMPLE

$72.12 \div 6$

$$\begin{array}{r} 12.02 \\ 6\overline{)72.12} \end{array}$$

6s into 7 go 1 remainder 1. Put 1 above the 7 and the remainder 1 by the 2 to make 12.

6s into 12 go 2. Put 2 above the 2.

Put a decimal point above the other decimal point. 6s into 1 won't go so put a nought above the 1. Carry the 1 by the 2 to make 12. 6s into 12 go 2 so put 2 above the line above the other 2.

Make sure you line up your figures carefully and also line up the decimal points. This is very important.

1) $52.5 \div 3$	16) $2.2 \div 11$
2) $48.5 \div 5$	17) $4.632 \div 3$
3) $8.12 \div 4$	18) $8.664 \div 4$
4) $0.552 \div 3$	19) $9.333 \div 9$
5) $2.55 \div 5$	20) $4.284 \div 12$
6) $45.32 \div 4$	21) $8.565 \div 5$
7) $16.32 \div 2$	22) $0.352 \div 2$
8) $1.561 \div 7$	23) $1.89 \div 9$
9) $2.16 \div 6$	24) $32.45 \div 5$
10) $8.127 \div 9$	25) $62.10 \div 6$
11) $216.3 \div 3$	26) $5.532 \div 3$
12) $804.4 \div 4$	27) $72.36 \div 9$
13) $715.6 \div 4$	28) $15.4 \div 7$
14) $3.824 \div 8$	29) $5.232 \div 3$
15) $0.819 \div 9$	30) $4.824 \div 4$

DIVISION OF A DECIMAL BY A DECIMAL

EXAMPLE

$0.255 \div 0.5$

Move the decimal point the *same number of places to the right* in both numbers until the second number is a whole number. Then divide as before:

$$0.255 \div 0.5 = 2.55 \div 5$$

$$\begin{array}{r} 0.51 \\ 5\overline{)2.55} \end{array} \text{ so } 0.255 \div 0.5 = 0.51$$

EXAMPLE

Divide 87.64 by 0.07.

$$87.64 \div 0.07 = 8764 \div 7$$

$$\begin{array}{r} 1252 \\ 7\overline{)8764} \end{array} \text{ so } 87.64 \div 0.07 = 1252$$

EXAMPLE

Divide 3 by 0.06.

$$3 \div 0.06 = 300 \div 6 \quad \text{\textit{two zeros must be written after the 3}}$$

$$\begin{array}{r} 50 \\ 6\overline{)300} \end{array} \text{ so } 3 \div 0.06 = 50$$

EXAMPLE

Divide 336.6 by 16.5

$$336.6 \div 16.5 = 3366 \div 165$$

$$\begin{array}{r} 20.4 \\ 165\overline{)3366.0} \\ 330 \\ \hline 66\,0 \\ 66\,0 \end{array}$$

Use long division. We can put in a decimal point and zero since $3366 = 3366.0$

1) $4.24 \div 0.4$	16) $51.63 \div 0.3$
2) $5.25 \div 0.5$	17) $78.8 \div 0.04$
3) $62.1 \div 0.9$	18) $9.216 \div 0.9$
4) $34.5 \div 0.005$	19) $8.8 \div 0.11$
5) $5.6 \div 0.07$	20) $45.09 \div 0.09$
6) $64.8 \div 0.008$	21) $515.5 \div 0.5$
7) $0.231 \div 1.1$	22) $0.3372 \div 0.003$
8) $0.42 \div 0.7$	23) $0.1561 \div 0.7$
9) $0.65 \div 0.05$	24) $14.4 \div 0.2$
10) $205.5 \div 0.003$	25) $9.612 \div 0.09$
11) $4.9 \div 0.07$	26) $12.12 \div 0.6$
12) $0.032 \div 0.08$	27) $36.54 \div 0.9$
13) $4.25 \div 0.5$	28) $0.72 \div 0.8$
14) $7.21 \div 0.7$	29) $0.2414 \div 0.02$
15) $62.82 \div 0.0002$	30) $7.35 \div 0.5$

31) Divide 1.428 by 0.35.
32) Divide 0.007 263 by 0.807.
33) Divide 0.0196 by 0.14.
34) Divide 0.002 55 by 0.015.
35) Divide 10.8 by 1.25.

DECIMAL PLACES

Sometimes the numbers do not divide exactly. In this case the division is usually only carried out to two or three decimal places.

Decimal places (often shortened to "d.p.") means the *number of figures after the decimal point*:

    6.253   has three decimal places
    0.25   has two decimal places
    15.6142 has four decimal places

EXAMPLES

4.82 = 4.8 correct to one decimal place

4.89 = 4.9 correct to one decimal place

3.71 = 3.7 correct to one decimal place

3.76 = 3.8 correct to one decimal place

By convention, if the last figure is a 5 (or more) we go up to the next figure so that 6.85 = 6.9 correct to one decimal place.

EXERCISE 14

How many decimal places do these numbers have?

1) 6.23
2) 7.1298
3) 6.414
4) 4.155
5) 0.000 562 03
6) 0.5
7) 3.128 62
8) 25.554
9) 109.1
10) 19 087.1651

EXERCISE 15

Put these numbers correct to one decimal place

1) 2.21
2) 5.79
3) 9.35
4) 8.12
5) 1.23
6) 2.28
7) 5.71
8) 9.32
9) 8.19
10) 1.26

The number 6.22 is marked on the ruler below. It is nearer to 6.2 than 6.3:

We would say that 6.22 = 6.2 correct to one decimal place.

The number 6.28 is marked on the ruler below. It is nearer to 6.3 than 6.2:

We would say that 6.28 = 6.3 correct to one decimal place.

We said that 6.22 = 6.2 correct to one decimal place and 6.28 = 6.3 correct to one decimal place (because 6.28 is nearer to 6.3 than 6.2).

We could carry this accuracy further by giving a number correct to two, three or four decimal places. (Remember decimal places are the number of figures after the decimal point.)

EXAMPLE

Put (a) 5.291 (b) 5.297 correct to two decimal places.

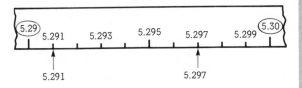

5.291   5.297

From the diagram 5.291 is nearer to 5.29 and 5.297 is nearer to 5.30:

    5.291 = 5.29 correct to two decimal places

    5.297 = 5.30 correct to two decimal places

————————— EXERCISE 16 —————————

Put these numbers correct to two decimal places

1) 0.251	7) 0.799
2) 0.357	8) 0.791
3) 0.683	9) 5.231
4) 0.786	10) 5.237
5) 0.112	11) 7.216
6) 0.119	12) 7.218

Here are some more difficult examples:

      0.955 = 0.96   correct to 2 d.p. ←

→ 0.683 71 = 0.68 correct to 2 d.p.

      2.995 = 3.00   correct to 2 d.p.

      5.179 82 = 5.18 correct to 2 d.p.

    107.198 = 107.20 correct to 2 d.p.

0.683 <u>71</u>

we ignore figures in the fourth or later decimal places

0.955 is halfway between 0.95 and 0.96 but for a 5 or over in the third decimal place we increase the previous figure by one

——————————— EXERCISE 17 ———————————

Put these numbers correct to two decimal places

1) 0.855	9) 3.695
2) 0.755	10) 4.595
3) 0.555	11) 8.295
4) 5.655	12) 11.195
5) 0.2487	13) 102.183
6) 0.1925	14) 84.1932
7) 0.3856	15) 15.7811
8) 0.4889	16) 14.285 67

For *three decimal places* we count three figures after the decimal point and look at the figure in the fourth decimal place. If it is a 5 or more we increase the previous figure by 1.

EXAMPLE

Put 0.7786 correct to three decimal places. ←

                There is a 6 in the fourth place so we increase 8 by 1

0.7786 = 0.779 correct to 3 d.p.

EXAMPLE

Put 2.4195 correct to three decimal places. ←

   2.419

     1 +

   2.420

There is a 5 in the fourth place, increasing 9 by 1 causes a difficulty so we increase 19 by 1 to make 20

2.4195 = 2.420 correct to 3 d.p.

EXAMPLE

Put 3.9997 correct to three decimal places. ↰

This is a difficult one because the numbers change so completely. However since 7 is more than 5 we have to add 1

$$3.999$$
$$1\ +$$
$$\overline{4.000}$$

3.9997 = 4.000 correct to 3 d.p.

EXAMPLE

Put 0.8812 correct to three decimal places. ↰

This is much more straight forward. We do not need to increase the previous figure because 2 is less than 5

0.8812 = 0.881 correct to 3 d.p.

————————— EXERCISE 18 —————————

Put these numbers correct to three decimal places

1) 0.6528	11) 0.7799
2) 0.6522	12) 0.7791
3) 0.6529	13) 0.7795
4) 0.6525	14) 2.9995
5) 0.6521	15) 2.9999
6) 5.5123	16) 2.9991
7) 5.5129	17) 2.9993
8) 5.5120	18) 2.9998
9) 5.5127	19) 2.9997
10) 5.5125	20) 2.9993

EXAMPLE

Work out 2.51 ÷ 0.3 correct to three decimal places.

$$2.51 \div 0.3 = 25.1 \div 3$$ (make the second number a *whole* number by moving the decimal point in *both* numbers)

$$\frac{8.3666}{3)\overline{25.1000}}$$ work to four decimal places and correct to three:

$$2.51 \div 0.3 = 8.367$$

————————— EXERCISE 19 —————————

Carry out the following correct to three decimal places. (Hint: remember to make the second number a *whole* number before dividing by moving the point the same number of places to the right in both numbers.)

1) 5.2 ÷ 3	7) 8.2 ÷ 0.6
2) 6.2 ÷ 0.09	8) 0.28 ÷ 3
3) 27.8 ÷ 7	9) 42.1 ÷ 0.6
4) 7.1 ÷ 0.9	10) 5.4 ÷ 0.07
5) 0.51 ÷ 0.7	11) 4.51 ÷ 0.06
6) 352 ÷ 3	12) 5.15 ÷ 0.9

CHANGING FRACTIONS TO
————— DECIMALS —————

Suppose we wanted to share £5 between eight people because an outing cost £5 and eight people each wanted to pay their share.

We should have to divide £5 by 8.

We can write this as £5 ÷ 8 or £$\frac{5}{8}$ but what is £$\frac{5}{8}$?

(It wouldn't be much good to cut a £1 note into eight equal parts and take five!) So we need to convert £$\frac{5}{8}$ into decimal form. The method is to write 5 as a decimal and to divide by 8.

5 is the same as 5.000

$$\begin{array}{r} 0.625 \\ 8\overline{)5.000} \end{array}$$

so that

$$\frac{5}{8} = 0.625$$

and

$$£\frac{5}{8} = £0.625 \text{ or } £0.62\tfrac{1}{2}$$

since the 5 in the third decimal place means $\tfrac{1}{2}$p.

To turn a fraction into a decimal divide the number on top by the number underneath.

EXAMPLE

Turn $\tfrac{3}{4}$ into a decimal.

3 is the same as 3.00

$$\begin{array}{r} 0.75 \\ 4\overline{)3.00} \end{array}$$

so that

$$\frac{3}{4} = 0.75$$

If a whole number is included then *the whole number goes before the decimal point.*

EXAMPLE

Turn $1\tfrac{3}{4}$ into a decimal.

First we deal with the fraction:

3 = 3.00

$$\begin{array}{r} 0.75 \\ 4\overline{)3.00} \end{array}$$

so that

$$\frac{3}{4} = 0.75$$

Then we put in the whole number so that

$$1\frac{3}{4} = 1.75$$

--------------- EXERCISE 21 ---------------

Write these mixed fractions as decimal numbers

1) $3\dfrac{3}{4}$ 9) $2\dfrac{5}{8}$

2) $2\dfrac{1}{2}$ 10) $3\dfrac{1}{2}$

3) $1\dfrac{1}{2}$ 11) $15\dfrac{1}{2}$

4) $1\dfrac{1}{4}$ 12) $3\dfrac{4}{5}$

5) $2\dfrac{3}{4}$ 13) $2\dfrac{2}{5}$

6) $4\dfrac{3}{4}$ 14) $2\dfrac{1}{8}$

7) $5\dfrac{1}{2}$ 15) $5\dfrac{3}{5}$

8) $1\dfrac{3}{8}$ 16) $2\dfrac{1}{5}$

--------------- EXERCISE 20 ---------------

Turn these fractions into decimal form

1) $\dfrac{1}{4}$ 6) $\dfrac{2}{5}$

2) $\dfrac{1}{2}$ 7) $\dfrac{3}{5}$

3) $\dfrac{1}{8}$ 8) $\dfrac{1}{20}$

4) $\dfrac{7}{8}$ 9) $\dfrac{1}{25}$

5) $\dfrac{1}{5}$ 10) $\dfrac{3}{20}$

17) $6\frac{1}{4}$ 19) $11\frac{3}{4}$

18) $10\frac{1}{2}$ 20) $4\frac{7}{8}$

CHANGING DECIMALS TO
FRACTIONS

To change a decimal to a fraction it is necessary to remember the table headings:

Units	.	Tenths	Hundredths	Thousandths	Ten thousandths	etc.
0	.	5				

So

$$0.5 = \frac{5}{10} \text{ (five tenths)}$$

Here are some more examples:

$$0.03 = \frac{3}{100} \text{ (three hundredths)}$$

$$0.42 = \frac{4}{10} + \frac{2}{100} = \frac{40}{100} + \frac{2}{100} = \frac{42}{100}$$

$$0.625 = \frac{6}{10} + \frac{2}{100} + \frac{5}{1000} = \frac{625}{1000}$$

Sometimes it is convenient to reduce these fractions to their lowest terms (by dividing top and bottom by the same number):

$$0.5 = \frac{5}{10} = \frac{1}{2}$$

$$0.03 = \frac{3}{100}$$

which is in its lowest terms already.

$$0.42 = \frac{42}{100} = \frac{21}{50}$$

$$0.625 = \frac{625}{1000} = \frac{125}{200} = \frac{25}{40} = \frac{5}{8}$$

(dividing each time by 5).

EXERCISE 22

Change these decimals to fractions in their lowest terms

1) 0.6   9) 0.62
2) 0.7   10) 0.55
3) 0.09   11) 0.15
4) 0.02   12) 0.23
5) 0.04   13) 0.725
6) 0.05   14) 0.123
7) 0.08   15) 0.513
8) 0.17

When there are whole numbers they go in front of the fraction.

EXAMPLE

Change 4.5 to a mixed fraction.

$$0.5 = \frac{5}{10} = \frac{1}{2}$$

$$4.5 = 4\frac{1}{2}$$

EXERCISE 23

Change these numbers to mixed fractions

1) 2.5   6) 27.5
2) 3.75   7) 3.3
3) 5.25   8) 5.25
4) 6.2   9) 14.5
5) 18.1   10) 22.2

58

The following should be learnt by heart:

$$0.1 = \frac{1}{10} \qquad 0.5 = \frac{1}{2}$$

$$0.25 = \frac{1}{4} \qquad 0.75 = \frac{3}{4}$$

and it is also helpful to remember that:

$$0.2 = \frac{1}{5}$$

—— RECURRING DECIMALS ——

When changing $\frac{1}{3}$ to a decimal it is found that the figures repeat themselves:

1 is the same as 1.000 000

$$\begin{array}{r} 0.333\,333 \\ 3\overline{)1.000\,000} \end{array}$$

so that

$$\frac{1}{3} = 0.333\,3333\ldots$$

This is an example of a *recurring decimal*. 0.333 333 33 ... may be written as $0.\dot{3}$. Recurring decimals are not often of practical use. It is generally more useful to work to so many decimal places.

0.666 66 ... is written as $0.\dot{6}$

and is equal to $\frac{2}{3}$. ($\frac{2}{3} = 0.67$ correct to 2 d.p.)

0.121 212 12 ... is written as $0.\dot{1}\dot{2}$

0.124 581 245 812 458 ... is written as $0.\dot{1}245\dot{8}$

14.504 154 154 154 15 ... is written as $14.50\dot{4}1\dot{5}$

This is called "dot notation".

Write these recurring decimals using dot notation (i.e. dots over the figures as in the examples just given).

1) 0.444 444 ...
2) 0.343 434 34 ...
3) 0.467 534 675 346 753 ...
4) 7.888 888 ...
5) 30.787 878 ...
6) 12.503 093 093 093 09 ...
7) 0.222 222 2
8) 0.191 919 ...
9) 2.314 531 453 145 3145 ...

— SEQUENCE OF OPERATIONS —

Brackets must be worked first then multiplication and division before subtraction and addition.

EXAMPLE

$$8.6 \times 2 + 0.5 \times 0.3$$

We do the multiplication first:

$$\begin{array}{lll} 8.6 & 0.5 & 17.2 \\ \underline{2\times} & \underline{0.3\times} & \underline{0.15+} \\ 17.2 & 0.15 & 17.35 \end{array}$$

$$= 17.2 + 0.15$$

$$= 17.35$$

EXAMPLE

$(1.5 + 2.5) \times (3.2 + 0.8)$
This time the brackets must be done first:

$$\begin{array}{llll} 1.5 & 3.2 & 4.0 = 4 & 4 \times 4 = 16 \\ \underline{2.5+} & \underline{0.8+} & & \\ \underline{4.0} & \underline{4.0} & & \end{array}$$

$$= 4.0 \times 4.0$$

$$= 16$$

EXERCISE 25

1) $4.3 \times 5 + 5.1 \times 2$
2) $0.4 \times 0.5 + 0.2 \times 0.3$
3) $(1.5 + 1.5) \times (3.5 + 3.5)$
4) $0.5 \times (5.4 + 6.6)$
5) $5.1 \times 0.5 + 2.7 \times 0.9$
6) $(0.3 + 0.4 + 0.5) \times 0.05$
7) $5.5 \div 0.5 + 4.5 \div 0.5$
8) $(52.5 - 49.3) \div 4$
9) $(15.6 - 4.9) - (0.3 \times 3)$
10) $(1.335 + 23.45 + 13.1) - (15.7 + 0.3)$
11) $0.2 \times 0.3 - 0.15 \times 0.2$
12) $0.3 + 0.4 \times 5$

EXERCISE 26

1) What does the number 4 mean in the following numbers?
   (a) 42   (b) 1.4   (c) 1.04   (d) 34.131
2) Write the number 17 as a decimal with (a) one zero (b) three zeros after the decimal point.
3) Does (a) 7.06 equal 7.60 (b) 7.6 equal 7.60?
4) Write these numbers leaving out unnecessary zeros
   (a) 000 72.5   (b) 63.100
   (c) 402.0500.
5) Write these fractions as decimals
   (a) $\dfrac{3}{10}$ (b) $\dfrac{6}{100}$ (c) $\dfrac{7}{1000}$ (d) $\dfrac{35}{100}$.
6) (a) Add 2.1, 3.4, 2.5 and 1.3.
   (b) Take 7.04 from 8.16.
7) (a) 2.56   (b) 100.00
       13.21   1.96 $-$
       0.568 $+$ _____
       _____
8) $62.51 + 12.72 - 4.38$
9) Multiply 0.72 by (a) 10 (b) 100.
10) Multiply (a) 0.65×4 (b) 1.3×8.

11) (a) 16.5   (b) 6.03   (c) 10.32
        $0.9 \times$ $0.04 \times$ $0.15 \times$
        ____   ____   ____
12) Divide 17.56 by (a) 100 (b) 1000.
13) Divide 217.8 by 3.
14) (a) $5\overline{)25.60}$ (b) $8\overline{)0.976}$
15) $35.84 \div 0.7$
16) Divide 415.2 by 0.4.
17) $0.005\overline{)2.500}$
18) Write (a) 4.28 (b) 4.21 correct to one decimal place.
19) Write (a) 14.6295 (b) 14.6291 correct to three decimal places.
20) Write 59.341 56 correct to (a) the nearest whole number (b) one decimal place (c) two decimal places (d) three decimal places (e) four decimal places.
21) Divide 5 by 3 and give your answer correct to three decimal places.
22) Write (a) $\dfrac{4}{5}$ (b) $\dfrac{7}{10}$ (c) $\dfrac{1}{3}$ as decimals.
23) Write the following numbers as decimals
    (a) $2\dfrac{1}{4}$ (b) $5\dfrac{1}{10}$ (c) $4\dfrac{1}{5}$.
24) Write these decimals as fractions
    (a) 0.2   (b) 0.08   (c) 0.45.
25) Change these numbers to mixed fractions in their lowest terms
    (a) 6.5   (b) 4.25   (c) 9.1   (d) 1.75.
26) Write these recurring numbers using dot notation
    (a) 0.111 11 ...   (b) 0.292 929 29 ...
    (c) 0.501 250 125 012 ...
27) (a) $0.1 \times 21.2 + 0.3 \times 0.5$
    (b) $(6.2 + 3.1) \times (0.1 + 0.2)$
    (c) $(5.60 - 2.79) - (3.41 - 2.38)$

The questions in this exercise are all of a practical nature. They all depend on decimals for their solution.

1) A lorry weighs 3.5 tonnes when empty. It is loaded with 48 metal ingots each weighing 0.075 tonnes. What is the total weight of the lorry when loaded?

2) What is the total weight carried by a train consisting of 40 trucks if 20 of them carry 19.75 tonnes per truck and the remainder carry 18.5 tonnes per truck?

3) A herd of cows yields 19.8 litres of milk per cow. If the herd consists of 28 cows, what is the total amount of milk obtained?

4) A farmer feeds his cattle at the rate of 1.6 kilograms of concentrate per 5 litres of milk produced per day. If he has a herd of 24 cows, each producing 19.25 litres per day, calculate the amount of concentrate required per day.

5) The diagram shows a shaft for a diesel engine. Calculate its overall length.

6) Rivets are placed 35.2 millimetres apart. If 28 rivets are placed in an assembly, calculate the distance between the first and last rivets.

7) An operator takes 0.74 minutes to make a soldered joint. Work out the time required to make 379 such joints.

8) The resistance of a copper wire 27.6 metres long is 1515.24 ohms. What is the resistance per metre?

9) An oil tank contains 1750 litres. How many full tins each containing 0.6 litres can be filled from this tank?

10) It takes 29 strips of wallpaper to paper a room, each piece being 2.35 metres long. What length of wallpaper is needed?

11) The cost of telephone calls is 4.2 pence per call. Work out the cost of making 204 calls.

12) 125 sheets of metal, all of the same thickness, are in a stack which is 37.500 millimetres high. What is the thickness of each sheet of metal?

13) Which is the greater, $\frac{7}{8}$ or 0.882, and by how much?

14) A consignment of screws has a total weight of 1757 grams. If each screw weighs 2.51 grams, calculate the number of screws in the consignment.

5

Measurement

We weigh light objects using milligrams or grams
Heavier objects are weighed in kilograms or
metric tonnes.

There are:

    1000 milligrams in 1 gram

    1000 grams in 1 kilogram

    1000 kilograms in 1 metric
    tonne

Milligrams are shortened to mg

Grams are shortened to g

Kilograms are shortened to kg

It is easy to change from one unit to another in
the metric system. We move the decimal point
to the left when changing to larger units and to
the right when changing to smaller units.

EXAMPLE

Change 4000 g to kg.

    $1000\,g = 1\,kg$ so

    $4000\,g = 4\,kg$

To change grams to kilograms divide by 1000
(move the decimal point three places to the
left).

EXAMPLE

Change 5285 g to kg.

$1000\,g = 1\,kg$

$5285\,g = 5285 \div 1000\,kg$

       $= 5.285\,kg$

Notice that it is more usual to write 5.285 kg
rather than 5 kg 285 g.

EXAMPLE

Change 700 g to kg.

$1000\,g = 1\,kg$

$700\,g = 700 \div 1000\,kg$

     $= 0.7\,kg$

EXAMPLE

Change 15 000 g to kg.

$1000\,g = 1\,kg$

$15\,000\,g = 15\,000 \div 1000\,kg$

       $= 15\,kg$

EXERCISE 1

Change to kilograms

1) 3000 g	7) 3850 g
2) 5000 g	8) 5670 g
3) 9000 g	9) 4500 g
4) 1500 g	10) 1654 g
5) 6500 g	11) 3045 g
6) 7500 g	12) 6723 g

13) 423 g	16) 25 000 g
14) 560 g	17) 40 000 g
15) 305 g	18) 50 000 g

To change kilograms to grams multiply by 1000 (move the decimal point three places to the right).

EXAMPLE

Change (a) 3 kg (b) 3.84 kg (c) 0.2 kg to grams.

$1 \text{ kg} = 1000 \text{ g}$

$3 \text{ kg} = 3 \times 1000 \text{ g} = 3000 \text{ g}$

$3.84 \text{ kg} = 3.84 \times 1000 \text{ g} = 3840 \text{ g}$

$0.2 \text{ kg} = 0.2 \times 1000 \text{ g} = 200 \text{ g}$

——————— EXERCISE 2 ———————

Change to grams

1) 5 kg	10) 5.1 kg
2) 7 kg	11) 4.15 kg
3) 9 kg	12) 3.2 kg
4) 2.34 kg	13) 25 kg
5) 9.16 kg	14) 50 kg
6) 2.08 kg	15) 60 kg
7) 0.5 kg	16) 0.15 kg
8) 0.9 kg	17) 0.35 kg
9) 0.4 kg	18) 0.95 kg

Very small objects are weighed in milligrams (mg). There are 1000 milligrams in 1 gram.

Very heavy objects are weighed in metric tonnes. There are 1000 kg in 1 metric tonne.

——————— EXERCISE 3 ———————

How many mg are there in

1) 2 g	4) 0.5 g
2) 4 g	5) 3.5 g?
3) 10 g	

How many kg are there in

6) 3 metric tonnes
7) 5 metric tonnes
8) 0.5 metric tonnes
9) 8.5 metric tonnes
10) 0.25 metric tonnes?

Imperial units of measurement are ounces, pounds, stones, hundredweights and tons.

There are:

16 ounces in 1 pound
14 pounds in 1 stone
112 pounds in 1 hundredweight
20 hundredweights in 1 ton

Light objects are weighed in pounds and ounces and heavier objects in tons and hundredweights.

An ounce is shortened to 1 oz
A pound is shortened to 1 lb
A stone is shortened to 1 st
A hundredweight is shortened to 1 cwt

Approximate imperial/metric conversions:

2 pounds is slightly less than 1 kilogram
4 ounces is slightly more than 100 grams

Medicines might be weighed in mg.

Sweets are weighed in oz (or grams).

oz or g

Vegetables are weighed in pounds (or kilograms).

lb or kg

A man can carry 1 cwt of coal.

cwt

Lorries are weighed in tons (or metric tonnes).

Tons or tonnes

EXERCISE 4

1) How many ounces are there in
   (a) $\frac{1}{4}$ lb   (b) $2\frac{1}{2}$ lb   (c) 5 lb?

2) How many cwt are there in
   (a) $\frac{1}{2}$ ton   (b) 3 tons   (c) 5.5 tons?

3) Is 1 oz nearly equal to
   (a) 3 g   (b) 30 g   (c) 300 g   (d) 3 kg?

4) Is 1 kg more or less than 2 lb?

5) Is 1 cwt approximately equal to
   (a) 500 kg   (b) 50 kg   (c) 5 kg
   (d) 500 g?

LENGTH

Ruler

Metric tape

Steel rule

Callipers

The "length" of a line gives us a measure of how far a line stretches out from end to end. Some instruments for measuring length are pictured above.

The length of this line is 8 cm.

8

The units of length are:

   kilometres, metres, centimetres or millimetres, in metric measurement

or

   miles, yards, feet or inches in imperial measurement

We measure short distances in millimetres, centimetres or inches and longer distances in metres, kilometres, yards or miles.

Wood might be measured in millimetres, centimetres or inches.

Curtain and dress materials are sold by the metre or the yard.

A metre is about 3 inches longer than 1 yard.

A metre is about the depth of the shallow end of a swimming pool.

You could walk 1 kilometre in about 10 minutes.

   8 kilometres = 5 miles (approx.)

Kilometres are shortened to km
Metres are shortened to m
Centimetres are shortened to cm
Millimetres are shortened to mm

There are:

10 mm in 1 cm
100 cm in 1 m
1000 m in 1 km

EXAMPLE

How many mm are there in

(a) 5 cm   (b) 2.5 cm   (c) 125 cm?

1 cm = 10 mm

so *to change cm to mm we multiply by 10*:

5 cm = 5 × 10 mm = 50 mm
2.5 cm = 2.5 × 10 mm = 25 mm
125 cm = 125 × 10 mm = 1250 mm

EXERCISE 5

How many mm are there in

1) 2 cm   7) 5.5 cm
2) 4 cm   8) 9.5 cm
3) 6 cm   9) 240 cm
4) 9 cm   10) 350 cm
5) 1.5 cm   11) 500 cm?
6) 0.5 cm

EXAMPLE

How many cm are there in   (a) 8 m   (b) 0.5 m (c) 25 m?

1 m = 100 cm

so *to change m to cm we multiply by 100*:

8 m = 8 × 100 cm = 800 cm
0.5 m = 0.5 × 100 cm = 50 cm
25 m = 25 × 100 cm = 2500 cm

EXERCISE 6

How many cm are there in

1) 2 m   5) 0.4 m   9) 40 m
2) 4 m   6) 0.6 m   10) 50 m
3) 7 m   7) 0.8 m   11) 85 m
4) 9 m   8) 0.9 m   12) 95 m?

EXERCISE 7

We write 1 cm 7 mm as 1.7 cm.
This line is 1.7 cm long measured to the nearest mm.

Measure the lines below and give their length in cm to the nearest mm.

1) _____
2) _____
3) _____
4) _____
5) _____
6) _____
7) _____
8) _____
9) _____
10) _____

EXAMPLE

Change to km:
(a) 5000 m   (b) 1500 m   (c) 400 m.

1000 m = 1 km

so to change to km we divide by 1000

5000 m = 5000 ÷ 1000 km = 5 km
1500 m = 1500 ÷ 1000 km = 1.5 km
400 m = 400 ÷ 1000 km = 0.4 km

(Reminder: *To divide by 1000 move the decimal point three places to the left.*)

Change to km

1) 2000 m	7) 4500 m
2) 4000 m	8) 7500 m
3) 7000 m	9) 500 m
4) 9000 m	10) 650 m
5) 2500 m	11) 700 m
6) 3550 m	12) 900 m

There are:

12 inches in 1 foot

3 feet in 1 yard

1760 yards in 1 mile

Inches are shortened to in or ″
Feet are shortened to ft or ′
Yards are shortened to yd

Approximate imperial/metric conversions:

1 inch is slightly more than $2\frac{1}{2}$ cm

1 foot is approximately equal to 30 cm

1 yard is slightly less than 1 metre

$\frac{5}{8}$ mile is approximately equal to 1 km
(or 5 miles = 8 km approx.)

---

1) How many feet are there in 3 yards?

2) How many yards are there in $\frac{1}{2}$ mile?

3) How many inches are there in 3′6″?

4) Change 4 yd 2 ft into feet.

5) Is $\frac{1}{4}$ mile more or less than 800 yd?

6) How many $\frac{1}{16}$″ are there in 1″?

7) Is 1 metre longer or shorter than 1 yard?

8) How many inches are approximately equal to (a) 10 cm (b) 5 cm (c) 20 cm?

9) How many cm are approximately equal to (a) 3 ft (b) 1′6″ (c) 6 in?

10) How many km are approximately equal to (a) 10 miles (b) 15 miles?

11) Is 30 miles approximately equal to (a) 20 km (b) 48 km or (c) 60 km?

12) Are 20 miles more or less than 50 km?

CAPACITY

Capacity is a measure of the amount of space that a liquid takes up.

The metric units in common use are the millilitre and the litre which are shortened to mℓ and ℓ.

There are:

1000 mℓ in 1 litre

Sometimes the centilitre is used. This is shortened to cℓ.

There are:

100 cℓ in 1 litre

The imperial units of capacity are the fluid ounce (fl oz), the pint (pt), the quart (qt) and the gallon (gall). There are others but they are not used so often.

5 mℓ plastic medicine spoon

1 pt milk bottle

Petrol is sold in gallons or litres

Cream is sold in fluid ounces

There are:

20 fl oz in 1 pt
2 pts in 1 qt
8 pts in 1 gall

Approximate imperial/metric conversions:

1 litre is approximately equal to $1\frac{3}{4}$ pints
30 ml is approximately equal to 1 fl oz
1 gallon is approximately equal to $4\frac{1}{2}$ litres

EXERCISE 10

1) How many cl are there in $\frac{1}{2}$ litre?

2) How many 5 ml spoonfuls would make up 1 cl?

3) Are 2 pints more or less than 1 litre?

4) Are 120 ml approximately equal to (a) 1 (b) 2 (c) 3 or (d) 4 fluid ounces?

5) Are 3 gallons of petrol more or less than 15 litres?

6) How many pints are there in (a) $2\frac{1}{2}$ gallons (b) 3 quarts?

7) Change 0.75 litres to cl.

8) Is there more cream in a 5 fl oz pot than a 135 ml pot?

9) Change 2500 ml to litres.

10) I want to buy about 5 gallons of petrol. How many litres should I ask for to make sure of getting at least 5 gallons?

11) How many pints are there in 5 gallons?

12) How many fluid ounces are there in $\frac{1}{4}$ pint?

13) How many ml are there in 0.5 litres?

14) Change 2.5 litres to ml.

15) Are 2 gallons approximately equal to (a) 3 (b) 9 (c) 12 or (d) 15 litres?

In some countries milk is sold in litre packs or 50 cl packs

TIME

In the winter, time in the United Kingdom is measured using Greenwich Mean Time (GMT). In summer the clocks are put forward by 1 hour and this is called British Summer Time.

60 seconds (s) = 1 minute (min)
60 minutes = 1 hour (h)
24 hours = 1 day
7 days = 1 week (wk)
31/30/28 days = 1 month
365 days = 1 year
366 days = 1 leap year
13 weeks = 1 quarter
52 weeks = 1 year
12 months = 1 year
p.a. = per annum = per year
a.m. = ante meridiem = morning
p.m. = post meridiem = afternoon

The time of day can be expressed *either* using the 12 hour clock *or* the 24 hour clock. Our normal clocks and watches use the 12 hour clock and we tell morning from afternoon by the use of a.m. or p.m.

Timetables are usually written using the 24 hour clock which runs from 0000 hours (midnight) through to 2400 hours (midnight again). 8 a.m. would be 0800 hours ("eight hundred hours"), noon would be 1200 hours ("twelve hundred hours") and 5.30 p.m. would be 1730 hours ("seventeen thirty hours").

D

Here is a simplified portion of a railway timetable using the 24 hour clock:

Padlow	Tyford	Maxby	Bixley
0830	0835	0855	0910
0930	⟶	⟶	1000
1030	1035	1055	1110
1130	1137	1159	1215
1200	⟶	⟶	1230
1330	1335	1355	1410
1530	1545	1610	1620
1700	1705	1725	1740

EXERCISE 11

Using the timetable above, answer these questions

1) Which train is the slowest?

2) I wish to catch the next train from Padlow after 4.30 p.m. Which train must I catch?

3) How long must I wait for the first train from Maxby after 9 a.m.?

4) How long does it take the fastest trains to get from Padlow to Bixley?

5) Does the last train run after 6 p.m.?

EXERCISE 12

1) How many minutes are in $2\frac{1}{4}$ hours?

2) How many seconds are in $3\frac{1}{2}$ minutes?

3) Change 150 min to hours and minutes.

4) A 4 lb chicken is to be cooked for 5×20 min. How many hours and minutes is this?

5) How many days are there in
   (a) January   (b) November
   (c) February in a leap year?

6) How many weeks are there in 2 quarters?

7) If a man earns £6000 per annum how much is this per month?

MONEY

There are 100 pence in one pound:

$100\,p = £1$ £1

£5.50 is read as "five pounds fifty" and £6.02$\frac{1}{2}$ as "six pounds two and a half pence". The zero is important as it keeps the place for the missing tens.

Notice that $\frac{1}{2}\,p = £0.005$ so that £3.72$\frac{1}{2}$ could be written as £3.725.

EXAMPLE

Add £6.25$\frac{1}{2}$ and £14.03$\frac{1}{2}$.

$$
\begin{array}{ccc}
6.25\tfrac{1}{2} & \text{or} & 6.255 \\
14.03\tfrac{1}{2}+ & & 14.035+ \\
\hline
20.29 & & 20.290 \\
\hline
\end{array}
$$

so that £6.25$\frac{1}{2}$ + £14.03$\frac{1}{2}$ = £20.29.

EXAMPLE

Subtract £4.07$\frac{1}{2}$ from £5.

$$
\begin{array}{ccc}
5.00 & \text{or} & 5.00 \\
4.07\tfrac{1}{2}- & & 4.075- \\
\hline
0.92\tfrac{1}{2} & & 0.925 \\
\hline
\end{array}
$$

so that £5 − £4.07$\frac{1}{2}$ = 92$\frac{1}{2}$p.

EXERCISE 13

Add

1) £3.71 + £2.03
2) £2.90 + £1.07
3) £54.10 + £3.30
4) £0.65 + £4.18
5) £0.75$\frac{1}{2}$ + £1.30
6) £0.05$\frac{1}{2}$ + £1.07$\frac{1}{2}$
7) £10.95 + £19.13$\frac{1}{2}$
8) £35.47 + £14
9) £23.45$\frac{1}{2}$ + £7.08$\frac{1}{2}$
10) £107 + £235

Subtract

1) £97.53 − £25.22
2) £357.65 − £23.47
3) £405.50 − £203.60
4) £75 − £15.50
5) £34.91$\frac{1}{2}$ − £14.80$\frac{1}{2}$
6) £567.10 − £25.45
7) £45.75 − £15.80$\frac{1}{2}$
8) £30.50$\frac{1}{2}$ − £29.75
9) £55.73 − £35.25$\frac{1}{2}$
10) £40 − £6.50

EXAMPLE

Multiply £2.51$\frac{1}{2}$ by 3.

$$\begin{array}{cc} 2.51\frac{1}{2} & \text{or} \quad 2.515 \\ \underline{3} \times & \underline{3} \times \\ 7.54\frac{1}{2} & 7.545 \end{array}$$

so that £2.51$\frac{1}{2}$ × 3 = £7.54$\frac{1}{2}$.

EXAMPLE

Divide £6.75 by 9.

$$\begin{array}{r} 0.75 \\ 9\overline{)6.75} \end{array}$$

or change to p first

£6.75 = 675 p

$$\begin{array}{r} 75 \\ 9\overline{)675} \end{array} = 75\,\text{p}$$

so that £6.75 ÷ 9 = 75 p.

EXERCISE 15

Multiply

1) £4.50 × 2
2) £3.30 × 3
3) £5.72 × 4
4) £1.05 × 5
5) £16.60 × 5
6) £34.10$\frac{1}{2}$ × 2
7) £10.05$\frac{1}{2}$ × 3
8) £15 × 7
9) £135.50 × 8
10) £0.45 × 9
11) £40 × 7
12) £56.35 × 3
13) £25 × 5
14) £35.50 × 7
15) £0.50$\frac{1}{2}$ × 8
16) £1.50 × 9

EXERCISE 16

Divide

1) £3.36 ÷ 3
2) £4.80 ÷ 4
3) £14.21 ÷ 7
4) £15.60 ÷ 5
5) £7.20 ÷ 6
6) £10.05 ÷ 3
7) £7.10 ÷ 2
8) £1.35 ÷ 5
9) £8.32 ÷ 8
10) £10.50 ÷ 7
11) £2.20 ÷ 4
12) £10.20 ÷ 5
13) £5.01 ÷ 3
14) £9.04 ÷ 8
15) £14 ÷ 4
16) £13.50 ÷ 2
17) £31 ÷ 2
18) £35.70 ÷ 7
19) £25.55 ÷ 5
20) £2.15 ÷ 2

ADDITION AND SUBTRACTION OF METRIC QUANTITIES

EXAMPLE

Add 250 g, 700 g and 325 g giving your answer in kg.

$$\begin{array}{r} 250 \\ 700 \\ 325 + \\ \hline 1275 \end{array} \qquad 1275\,\text{g} = 1.275\,\text{kg}$$

69

EXAMPLE

Subtract 2.8 m from 3.0 m giving your answer in cm.

3.0
2.8 −
0.2   0.2 m = 20 cm

───────── EXERCISE 17 ─────────

1) Add 500 g, 950 g and 750 g giving your answer in kg.
2) Add 200 m, 500 m and 350 m giving your answer in km.
3) Add 450 ml, 500 ml and 750 ml giving your answer in litres.
4) Add 3.2 kg, 4.5 kg and 5 kg giving your answer in kg.
5) Add 50 cm, 20 cm and 140 cm giving your answer in metres.
6) Subtract 500 g from 1750 g giving your answer in kg.
7) Subtract 7.5 km from 8 km giving your answer in metres.
8) Subtract 750 cl from 1500 cl giving your answer in litres.
9) Subtract 8.25 kg from 9.50 kg giving your answer in grams.
10) Subtract 25 mm from 75 mm giving your answer in cm.

In the next exercise make the units the *same* before adding or subtracting.

EXAMPLE

Add 2.5 kg, 500 g and 0.75 kg.

2.5 kg = 2500 g (change to g)

0.75 kg = 750 g (change to g)

2500
 500
 750 +
3750   3750 g

───────── EXERCISE 18 ─────────

1) 1.5 kg + 500 g + 0.25 kg (answer in grams).
2) 20 cm + 1 m + 5.5 m (answer in cm).
3) 50 g + 2 kg + 1.5 kg (answer in grams).
4) 15 mm + 2 cm + 0.3 cm (answer in mm).
5) Add 5 km, 200 m and 1500 m giving your answer in km.
6) Subtract 400 m from 1 km giving your answer in metres.
7) Subtract 550 g from 4 kg giving your answer in grams.
8) 7 m − 600 cm (answer in cm).
9) 1.5 kg − 750 g (answer in grams).
10) 5.5 cm − 25 mm (answer in mm).

MULTIPLICATION AND DIVISION — OF METRIC QUANTITIES —

EXAMPLE

Multiply 250 g by 8 giving your answer in kg.

250
  8 ×
2000   2000 g = 2 kg

EXAMPLE

Multiply 2.5 km by 4 giving your answer in m.

$$\begin{array}{r} 2.5 \\ 4\times \\ \hline 10.0 \end{array}$$ 10.0 km = 10 000 m

or change to metres first

2.5 km = 2500 m

2500 × 4 = 10 000 m

EXAMPLE

Divide 750 km by 3.

750 ÷ 3 = 250   250 km

EXAMPLE

Divide 5 kg by 4 giving your answer in g.

$$4\overline{)5.00}^{1.25}$$ (take care to line up the figures and the decimal point)

1.25 kg = 1250 g

or change to grams first

5 kg = 5000 g

5000 ÷ 4 = 1250 g

─────── **EXERCISE 19** ───────

1) Multiply 200 g by 4 giving your answer in grams.
2) Multiply 500 m by 2 giving your answer in km.
3) Multiply 25 mm by 6 leaving your answer in mm.
4) Multiply 3.5 kg by 5 leaving your answer in kg.
5) Multiply 50 mℓ by 10 giving your answer in litres.
6) Divide 450 km by 3 leaving your answer in km.
7) Divide 6 kg by 4 giving your answer in g.
8) Divide 750 mm by 5 giving your answer in cm.
9) Divide 28 kg by 7 leaving your answer in kg.
10) Divide 3.5 m by 7 giving your answer in cm.
11) 250 g × 3 (answer in g).
12) 450 g ÷ 9 (answer in g).
13) 700 mℓ × 5 (answer in litres).
14) 5 km ÷ 10 (answer in m).
15) 1500 m × 4 (answer in km).
16) 56 mm ÷ 8 (answer in mm).
17) 3.5 kg × 3 (answer in kg).
18) 7.2 m ÷ 9 (answer in cm).
19) 350 cm × 8 (answer in m).
20) 1.8 litres ÷ 6 (answer in cℓ).

─────────────────────

PRACTICAL PROBLEMS USING METRIC AND IMPERIAL ─── MEASUREMENT ───

EXAMPLE

I bought 2 loaves at 42 p each, $\frac{1}{2}$ kg butter at 45 p per 250 g and $\frac{1}{4}$ lb cheese at £1.20 per pound. How much did I pay?

2 loaves
@ 42 p each = 2 × 42 p =   84 p

500 g butter
@ 45 p per 250 g = 2 × 45 p =   90 p

$\frac{1}{4}$ lb cheese

@ £1.20 a lb = $\frac{1}{4}$ × £1.20 =   30 p

I paid $\underline{£2.04}$

EXAMPLE

A man receives "time and a half" for overtime on Sundays and "time and a third" for overtime during the week. If his basic wage is £6 per hour how much per hour does he get for overtime (a) on Sunday (b) on Friday?

For Sunday he gets

$$£6 + \frac{1}{2} × £6 = £6 + £3 = £9 \text{ per hour}$$

For Friday he gets

$$£6 + \frac{1}{3} × £6 = £6 + £2 = £8 \text{ per hour}$$

EXAMPLE

An electricity bill was £65 for 1 quarter (which is 13 weeks). How much was it per week?

£65 ÷ 13 = £5

It was £5 per week.

EXAMPLE

Time in New York is 5 hours behind Greenwich Mean Time (GMT). If it is 1300 hours in New York what time is it according to Greenwich Mean Time?

1300 hours + 0500 hours = 1800 hours

It is 1800 hours or 6 p.m. (GMT)

───────────── **EXERCISE 20** ─────────────

1) Find the cost of 8 tubes of sweets at 7p each.
2) How many days in (a) 2 weeks (b) 5 weeks (c) 7 weeks (d) 9 weeks?
3) Three people share the rent for a flat. It is £30 per week. If they all pay an equal share how much does each person pay?
4) I buy 7 yards of material at £2.50 per yard. How much does this cost?

5) Sugar costs 39 p for 2 kg. How much do 10 kg cost?
6) What is the cost of 3 loaves of bread at 42 p per loaf?

7) 1 dozen = 12. What is the cost of 2 dozen eggs at $42\frac{1}{2}$ p for half a dozen?
8) Taking 4 weeks in 1 month how many weeks are there in (a) 2 months (b) 5 months (c) 7 months?
9) A man receives "time and a quarter" for overtime on weekdays. If his basic wage is £6.40 per hour how much does he get for overtime on Wednesdays?

10) An electricity bill was £52 in 1 quarter (13 weeks). How much was it per week?

11) Three people share the rent for a flat. One pays $\frac{1}{2}$ and a second pays $\frac{1}{3}$ of the total weekly rent of £60. The third pays the rest. How much do each of the three people pay?

12) Find the cost of 3 lb carrots at 20 p per lb, 4 lb eating apples at 40 p per lb, 2 lb cooking apples at 26 p per lb and 5 lb potatoes at 35 p for a 5 lb bag.

13) Rolls cost $8\frac{1}{2}$ p each. Find the cost of 2 dozen.

14) Some dress material costs £5.50 for a metre length. Find the cost of 3 metres of the material.

15) How much is $3\frac{1}{2}$ yards of material at £3.50 per yard?

16) Find the cost of 1.6 kg cheese at £2.40 per kg.

17) Time in New York is 5 hours behind Greenwich Mean Time. Find the time (GMT) when New York time is 1700 hours.

18) Milk costs 20 p per pint. I have 2 pints a day. How much do I pay per week?

19) Find the cost of $2\frac{1}{2}$ lb of beans at 24 p per lb, 10 lb potatoes at 8 p per lb, $3\frac{1}{4}$ lb cabbage at 20 p per lb and 7 oranges at 11 p each.

20) 100 bottles each holding $\frac{2}{5}$ litre are filled from a container holding 150 litres. How much is left in the container?

21) A radio programme of songs, poetry and stories is 1 h 30 mins long. $\frac{3}{5}$ of the time is devoted to songs, $\frac{1}{4}$ to poetry and the rest to stories. How much time is spent on stories?

6

Percentages

% = per cent

per cent = out of 100

5 out of 100 squares have been shaded.

5% of the squares have been shaded.

A percentage is another way of writing a fraction (or a decimal):

$$10\% = \frac{1}{10} = 0.1$$

$$25\% = \frac{1}{4} = 0.25$$

$$33\frac{1}{3}\% = \frac{1}{3} = 0.3\dot{3}$$

$$50\% = \frac{1}{2} = 0.5$$

$$66\frac{2}{3}\% = \frac{2}{3} = 0.6\dot{6}$$

$$75\% = \frac{3}{4} = 0.75$$

These should be learnt by heart.

An increase on wages of 10% means an increase of $\frac{1}{10}$ (for example, £20 wage rises to £22).

A 25% surcharge means paying $\frac{1}{4}$ extra (for example, a £4 bill becomes £5).

A 50% discount means the price is reduced by $\frac{1}{2}$ (for example, a £15 article is sold for £7.50).

To find 10% just divide by 10.

EXAMPLE

Find 10% of £75.

£75 ÷ 10 = £7.50

so that 10% of £75 = £7.50.

─────── **EXERCISE 1** ───────

Find 10% of

1) £30
2) 40 cm
3) 20 p
4) 60 min
5) £5.50
6) 7.5 km
7) 90 m
8) £3.20

CHANGING A PERCENTAGE TO A FRACTION

$$5\% = \frac{5}{100} = \frac{1}{20}$$

(dividing top and bottom by 5).

To change a percentage to a fraction divide by 100 and leave out the % sign.

Harder examples

$$12\frac{1}{2}\% = \frac{12\frac{1}{2}}{100} = \frac{25}{200} \quad \text{(doubling top and bottom)}$$

$$= \frac{1}{8}$$

$$33\frac{1}{3}\% = \frac{33\frac{1}{3}}{100} = \frac{100}{300} \quad \text{(multiplying top and bottom by 3)}$$

$$= \frac{1}{3}$$

$$66\frac{2}{3}\% = \frac{66\frac{2}{3}}{100} = \frac{200}{300} \quad \text{(multiplying top and bottom by 3)}$$

$$= \frac{2}{3}$$

────────── **EXERCISE 2** ──────────

Change these percentages to fractions (cancel where possible)

1) 20%
2) 30%
3) 40%
4) 50%
5) 60%
6) 70%
7) 80%
8) 90%
9) 55%
10) 35%
11) 15%
12) 75%
13) 85%

14) 4%
15) 2%
16) 1%
17) $2\frac{1}{2}\%$
18) $\frac{1}{2}\%$
19) $37\frac{1}{2}\%$
20) $62\frac{1}{2}\%$
21) 150%

CALCULATING PERCENTAGES OF A QUANTITY

EXAMPLE

A coat has been reduced by 15% in a sale. The old price was £40. How much reduction is there?

We have to find 15% of £40:

Method 1

10% of £40 is £4

5% of £40 is £2

15% of £40 is £6 so there is a £6 reduction.

Method 2

$$15\% = \frac{15}{100}$$

so 15% of £40

$$= \frac{15}{100} \times £40 = £\frac{\overset{3}{15} \times 40}{\underset{2}{100}} = £\frac{\overset{12}{60}}{\underset{2}{10}} = £6$$

Method 1 is suitable when working in your head but Method 2 can be used for more complicated numbers.

To calculate a percentage of a quantity, multiply by the number and divide by 100.

────────── **EXERCISE 3** ──────────

1) 15% of £60
2) 25% of 36 cm
3) 50% of 4 km
4) 5% of 20 p
5) 20% of 30 mm
6) 60% of 25 m
7) 40% of £50
8) $33\frac{1}{3}\%$ of £6

9) $12\frac{1}{2}\%$ of £72
10) 75% of 12 kg
11) 50% of £36.56
12) 20% of £300
13) 150% of £40
14) 38% of £1
15) $\frac{1}{2}\%$ of £200

SIMPLE INTEREST

If you save money with a Building Society or the Post Office, or a Bank then *interest* is paid to you for your lending them the money.

EXAMPLE

I save £300 at 10% interest p.a. with a Building Society. How much interest is paid at the end of the year?

10% of £300 is £30

£30 interest will be paid at the end of the year.

If you *borrow* money then you have to *pay* interest for the loan.

EXAMPLE

I borrow £500 at 13% interest p.a. How much do I have to pay back at the end of the year?

$$13\% \text{ of } £500 = \frac{13}{100} \times £500 = £\frac{13 \times 500}{100}$$

$$= £65$$

I have to pay back £500 + £65 = £565 at the end of the year.

Find the interest for 1 year on

1) £600 at 3% p.a.
2) £400 at 5% p.a.
3) £500 at 8% p.a.
4) £1000 at 11% p.a.
5) £500 at 7% p.a.
6) £650 at 9% p.a.
7) £20 at 8% p.a.
8) £75 at 10% p.a.
9) £350 at 8% p.a.
10) £45.70 at 10% p.a.
11) £525 at 10% p.a.
12) £3000 at 15% p.a.

For *simple interest* the interest is the same every year. For 2 years the interest will be doubled. For 3 years it will be multiplied by 3. For 6 months it would be multiplied by $\frac{1}{2}$, for 3 months by $\frac{1}{4}$ and so on. This situation occurs when the interest earned is taken out of the Building Society each year.

Find the simple interest on

13) £100 for 2 years at 15% p.a.
14) £50 for 3 years at 8% p.a.
15) £600 for 6 months at 10% p.a.
16) £200 for 3 months at 10% p.a.

COMPOUND INTEREST

For compound interest the savings and interest are added together at the end of the year. The following year there will be more interest (since there is more capital). This situation occurs when the interest earned is left in the Building Society.

EXAMPLE

A man saves £200 at compound interest of 10% for 3 years. How much will he have at the end of the third year?

1st year

| 10% interest on £200 | = £20 |
| New capital (savings + interest) | = £220 |

2nd year

| 10% interest on £220 | = £22 |
| New capital (savings + interest) | = £242 |

3rd year

| 10% interest on £242 | = £24.20 |
| New capital (savings + interest) | = £266.20 |

He will have £266.20 at the end of the third year.

——— EXERCISE 5 ———

Find the compound interest on

1) £300 at 10% for 2 years
2) £400 at 10% for 3 years
3) £500 at 10% for 3 years
4) £600 at 10% for 2 years
5) £600 at 5% for 2 years
6) £800 at 15% for 2 years

Tables of compound interest are available for more difficult numbers (but this is outside the scope of this book).

CHANGING A FRACTION TO A ——— PERCENTAGE ———

$$\frac{3}{5} = \frac{3}{5} \times 100\% \quad \left(\text{since } 100\% = \frac{100}{100} = 1\right)$$

$$= \frac{3 \times \overset{20}{\cancel{100}}}{\underset{1}{\cancel{5}}}\%$$

$$= 60\%$$

$\frac{3}{5}$ of £100 = £60

60% of £100 = £60.

To change a fraction to a percentage multiply by 100 and put in a % sign.

——— EXERCISE 6 ———

Change these fractions to percentages

1) $\frac{1}{5}$		11) $\frac{2}{5}$
2) $\frac{4}{5}$		12) $\frac{7}{8}$
3) $\frac{1}{4}$		13) $\frac{1}{20}$
4) $\frac{1}{2}$		14) $\frac{1}{40}$
5) $\frac{3}{4}$		15) $\frac{7}{10}$
6) $\frac{1}{3}$		16) $\frac{9}{10}$
7) $\frac{2}{3}$		17) $\frac{1}{10}$
8) $\frac{1}{8}$		18) $\frac{1}{100}$
9) $\frac{3}{8}$		19) $\frac{3}{100}$
10) $\frac{5}{8}$		20) $\frac{1}{50}$

Reminder: To change a fraction to a decimal divide by the number underneath:

$$\frac{3}{4} = 4\overline{)3.00} \quad \frac{0.75}{}$$

To change a decimal to a fraction remember that:

the first place is $\frac{1}{10}$ ths

the second place is $\frac{1}{100}$ ths

the third place is $\frac{1}{1000}$ ths etc.

$$0.125 = \frac{1}{10} + \frac{2}{100} + \frac{5}{1000}$$

$$= \frac{125}{1000} \text{ and } cancel$$

$$= \frac{1}{8}$$

EXERCISE 7

Copy and complete this table

Percentage	Fraction	Decimal
		0.5
	$\frac{3}{4}$	
$33\frac{1}{3}\%$		
	$\frac{2}{3}$	
		0.125
25%		
		0.1
20%		
		0.3
$62\frac{1}{2}\%$		

EXPRESSING ONE NUMBER AS A PERCENTAGE OF ANOTHER NUMBER

To express 36 as a percentage of 50 we say that

$$36 \text{ out of } 50 = \frac{36}{50}$$

and then change this fraction to a percentage:

$$\frac{36}{50} = \frac{36}{50} \times 100\%^{2}$$

$$= 36 \times 2\%$$

$$= 72\%$$

EXAMPLE

A girl gains 14 marks out of 20 in a test. What percentage is this?

$$14 \text{ out of } 20 = \frac{14}{20} = \frac{14}{20} \times 100\%^{5}$$

$$= 14 \times 5\% = 70\%$$

EXERCISE 8

Express the first number as a percentage of the second

1) 10, 50   2) 15, 25
3) 15, 150   4) 20, 125

5) Express 60 as a percentage of 200.

6) Express 75 as a percentage of 150.

7) A boy gains 8 marks out of 10. What percentage is this?

8) 5 out of 30 bolts are defective. What percentage are defective?

9) 15 minutes out of an hour and a quarter TV programme is spent on commercials. What percentage is spent on commercials?

10) There are 12 women in an evening class of 30 adults. What percentage are women? What percentage are men?

11) 3 out of 20 apples are bad. What percentage of apples are bad?

12) There are 50 red tablets, 25 green tablets, 20 yellow tablets and 105 white tablets of soap in a cardboard carton. What percentage are green. What percentage are white? What percentage are coloured?

13) Two girls gain 25 and 30 marks out of 40 in a test, respectively. What percentage does the girl with the higher mark get? What percentage does the other girl obtain?

14) In a survey it is found that out of 400 swans, 350 are Mute swans, 34 are Bewick swans and the rest are Whooper swans. What percentage are Whooper swans?

15) Express $32\frac{1}{2}$ marks out of 50 as a percentage.

COMPARING PERCENTAGES, — FRACTIONS AND DECIMALS —

Since percentages and fractions are different ways of writing decimal numbers, it is possible to see which are smaller or larger by first making them all into decimals.

EXAMPLE

Write in order of size 0.375, 30%, $\frac{1}{3}$.

Changing the percentage first to a fraction and then a decimal we have:

$$30\% = \frac{30}{100} = 0.3$$

Changing the fraction to a decimal (by dividing the bottom number into the top number) we have:

$$\frac{1}{3} = 0.333\ldots \text{ or } 0.3\dot{3}$$

Now, putting them in order of size, smallest first, we have:

$$0.3, \quad 0.3\dot{3}, \quad 0.375$$
$$\text{or} \quad 30\%, \quad \tfrac{1}{3}, \quad 0.375$$

Remember to change the percentage and fraction back to their original forms when you write the answer.

--- **EXERCISE 9** ---

Write in order of size, smallest first

1) $\frac{1}{2}$, 60%, 0.4

2) 25%, $\frac{1}{5}$, 0.22

3) $\frac{4}{5}$, 45%, 0.54

4) 0.67, 66%, $\frac{2}{3}$

5) 0.75, $\frac{3}{4}$, 75%

6) $\frac{3}{20}$, $12\frac{1}{2}\%$, 0.2

7) $\frac{1}{9}$, 9%, 0.9

8) 35%, 0.33, $\frac{3}{8}$

9) 85%, 0.875, $\frac{5}{6}$

10) 150%, 1.75, $1\frac{1}{4}$

PERCENTAGES IN EVERYDAY ——— SITUATIONS ———

VAT

The tax collected on most goods and services is known as Value Added Tax or VAT for short. Some goods, such as food and books, are exempt (no tax is paid). VAT is added on to the end of a bill. The current rate of VAT is 15%.

79

Income Tax

The standard rate of income tax is approximately 30% after allowances have been made. Income tax is collected to pay for large building projects, roads, education, health services, etc.

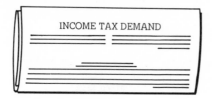

Earnings

Wage increases are often made in terms of percentages. An employee might get an 8%, 10% or 12% increase on his or her earnings. In harder times only a 2% or 3% increase might be paid.

Discounts

If a shop wishes to promote a sale then it will offer a discount of, say, 12%. 12% will be taken off the price. Often regular customers will be allowed a special discount.

Compound Interest

Banks and Building Societies offer compound interest on savings if the interest is left in the account together with the savings at the end of the year. The interest rate is in terms of a percentage.

Rate of Inflation

If goods cost £100 one year and £108 the next year we say the rate of inflation is 8%. If goods then go up by another 10% the following year we say the rate of inflation has increased, but if they only go up by another 6% we say the rate of inflation has decreased (even though the actual price has increased!).

Index Numbers

Index numbers are a way of showing how the *cost of living* rises or falls. If an index number goes up from 50 to 52 we would say it has increased by 4% (2 on 50 being equivalent to 4 on 100).

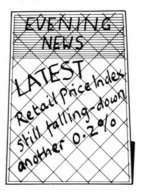

Population Statistics

These are kept to show by how much the number of people in the country (or a particular town or district) increases or decreases each year and they are usually expressed as a percentage.

Birth rate increases by 15% — population rises rapidly

Marks in Examinations

These are often given in percentages. If a student has 35 marks out of 50 this is equivalent to 70 out of a 100, or 70%.

To work out the percentage first work out the fraction·

$$\frac{35}{50}$$

and then multiply by 100%:

$$\frac{35}{\overset{1}{\underset{}{50}}} \times \overset{2}{\cancel{100}}\% = 35 \times 2\%$$
$$= 70\%$$

Tolerances and Efficiency

These are engineering terms. If a bolt must be made to a tolerance of 2% then all measurements must be within 2% of the "standard" bolts. This is often written as ±2%. (Usually the measurement must be much more accurate than this.)

The efficiency of a machine is:

$$\frac{\text{Output}}{\text{Input}} \times 100\%$$

Profit and Loss

If goods are bought for £5 and sold for £7 we say the *profit* is £2. £5 is called the *cost price* and £7 the *selling price*.

The percentage profit is:

$$\frac{\text{Profit}}{\text{Cost price}} \times 100\%$$

In this example the percentage profit is $\frac{2}{5} \times 100\% = 40\%$.

If the selling price is less than the cost price then a loss has been made and the percentage loss is given by:

$$\frac{\text{Loss}}{\text{Cost price}} \times 100\%$$

—————— **EXERCISE 10** ——————

Simple problems involving percentage.

1) 15% VAT is charged on a £300 TV. Find the cost of the TV plus VAT.

£300 (excluding VAT)

2) A man earns £5000 p.a. He is allowed £2000 tax free and pays 30% income tax on the rest. How much income tax does he pay?

3) Wages of £4.50 per hour are increased by 8%. Find the new hourly wage.

WAGE INCREASE AGREED 8%

4) A shop offers 15% discount on a £120 piece of furniture. How much discount is allowed? What is the furniture sold for?

5) A credit card company loans £500 at 2% interest per month. Give the amount of interest payable at the end of the first month.

6) A $12\frac{1}{2}$% reduction is made on a £24 coat. How much does the coat cost?

7) Goods costing £100 one year cost £113 the following year. What is the rate of inflation?

8) A carrycot is bought for £15 and sold for £20. Give the percentage profit.

Secondhand baby goods sold here

Inflation up again % in double figures

9) A car is bought for £400 and sold for £350. Give the percentage loss.

10) An index number is raised by 10%. The index number is 480. What will the new index number be?

11) The population of Tadington is 10 000. Find the population the following year if it is increased by 5%.

12) A boy earns 23 marks out of 50 in a test. What percentage is this?

13) Bolts must be made to a tolerance of ± 2%. If the standard measurement is 10 mm what are the least and most allowable measurements?

14) What is the efficiency of a machine with a 5 kW input and a 3 kW output?

More difficult problems involving percentage will be found in later chapters.

EXERCISE 11

1) Find 10% of (a) £40 (b) £200 (c) £36.50 (d) £18.25 (e) 400 g (f) 2.5 kg (g) 340 m (h) 20 s.

2) Write $12\frac{1}{2}$% (a) as a fraction (b) as a decimal.

3) Find $12\frac{1}{2}$% of (a) £16 (b) £32.

4) Write $33\frac{1}{3}$% (a) as a fraction (b) as a decimal.

5) Find $33\frac{1}{3}$% of (a) £6 (b) £15.

6) Change 95% to (a) a fraction (b) a decimal.

7) Find the simple interest for 1 year on (a) £200 at 3% p.a. (b) £950 at 7% p.a.

8) A man saves £150 at compound interest of 10% for 2 years. Find how much he has at the end of the second year.

9) For savings of £250 at compound interest of 10% for 3 years find (a) the *total* interest earned and (b) the amount of savings (including interest) at the end of the third year.

10) Change (a) $\frac{17}{100}$ (b) $\frac{19}{20}$ to percentages.

11) Write $\frac{3}{10}$ (a) as a decimal (b) as a percentage.

12) 15% VAT is charged on a £45 table. Find the total cost of the table including the VAT.

13) A woman earns £7000 p.a. and is allowed £2000 tax free. How much income tax does she pay if the rate of tax is 30%?

14) Find the new wage when wages of £75 per week are increased by 12%.

15) A price reduction of 17% is made on a three piece suite costing £625. How much does the three piece suite cost?

16) A credit card company makes a loan of £480 at 5% interest for 3 months. Find the amount of interest to be paid at the end of 3 months.

17) An index number is 25. What will the new index number be if it is raised by 20%?

18) The population of a town is 50 000. It is increased by 8% the following year. The year after that the population increases by 10%. What is the new population after 2 years?

19) 3 pupils earn 20, 22 and 24 marks out of 25 in a test. What percentage marks are these?

20) Screws of length 2 cm have to be made to a tolerance of ± 2%. Give the maximum and minimum permissible measurements.

21) Find the efficiency of a heater with a 10 kW input and an 8 kW output.

22) Goods are bought for £50 and sold for £55. Give the percentage profit.

7

Squares and Square Roots

SQUARES OF WHOLE NUMBERS

The square of 4 is $4 \times 4 = 16$. (This can be written as 4^2.)

The square of a number is the number multiplied by itself.

EXERCISE 1

Work out

1) 2^2 4) 7^2
2) 5^2 5) 8^2
3) 6^2 6) 9^2

Long multiplication is needed for the squares of larger numbers.

EXAMPLE

Work out the square of 75.

$75^2 = 75 \times 75$

$$
\begin{array}{r}
75 \\
75 \times \\
\hline
375 \\
5250 \\
\hline
5625 \\
\end{array}
$$

Multiply by the *units* figure. Put a 0 and multiply by the *tens* figure.

EXERCISE 2

Work out

1) 13^2 7) 72^2
2) 26^2 8) 76^2
3) 35^2 9) 77^2
4) 48^2 10) 81^2
5) 57^2 11) 88^2
6) 69^2 12) 95^2

SQUARES OF FRACTIONS

EXAMPLE

Find the square of $\frac{2}{3}$.

$$\frac{2}{3} \times \frac{2}{3} = \frac{2 \times 2}{3 \times 3} = \frac{4}{9}$$

EXAMPLE

Find the square of $1\frac{4}{5}$.

$$1\frac{4}{5} \times 1\frac{4}{5} = \frac{9}{5} \times \frac{9}{5} = \frac{81}{25} = 3\frac{6}{25}$$

Mixed fractions must be made *top-heavy* before multiplying.

Find the squares of these fractions

1) $\dfrac{1}{4}$ 9) $1\dfrac{2}{3}$

2) $\dfrac{5}{7}$ 10) $1\dfrac{1}{3}$

3) $\dfrac{4}{9}$ 11) $2\dfrac{1}{2}$

4) $\dfrac{2}{5}$ 12) $2\dfrac{1}{4}$

5) $\dfrac{5}{8}$ 13) $4\dfrac{1}{2}$

6) $\dfrac{3}{7}$ 14) $5\dfrac{1}{2}$

7) $\dfrac{4}{11}$ 15) $3\dfrac{1}{3}$

8) $\dfrac{7}{12}$

SQUARES OF DECIMALS

EXAMPLE

Find the square of 7.5.

First multiply as if there were no decimal point:

```
  75
  75 ×
 ────
 375
5250
────
5625
```
then

To find where to put the decimal point in the answer:

Count the number of figures after the point in the first number. Add this to the number of figures after the point in the second number. Count back this number of places from the *right* and put in the point.

7.5 one figure after the point
7.5 one figure after the point
────
56.25 count back two figures and put in the
        point

EXERCISE 4

Work out

1) $(1.5)^2$ 6) $(5.5)^2$
2) $(3.5)^2$ 7) $(5.8)^2$
3) $(4.2)^2$ 8) $(6.3)^2$
4) $(4.9)^2$ 9) $(0.5)^2$
5) $(5.1)^2$ 10) $(0.7)^2$

The squares of numbers from 1 to 12 should be learnt by heart:

1 4 9 16 25 36 49 64 81 100 121 144

SQUARE ROOTS OF WHOLE NUMBERS

The *square* of 6 is $6 \times 6 = 36$.

The *square root* of 36 is 6

$$\sqrt{36} = 6$$

$\sqrt{}$ is the square root sign and it means "the square root of".

We read $\sqrt{25}$ as "the square root of 25" and it has a value of 5.

EXERCISE 5

Write down the square roots of these numbers

1) 64   5) 16
2) 49   6) 25
3) 81   7) 100
4) 9   8) 36

SQUARE ROOTS OF FRACTIONS

To find the square root of a fraction we find the square roots of the two numbers separately:

EXAMPLE

Find $\sqrt{\dfrac{9}{16}}$.

$$\sqrt{\dfrac{9}{16}} = \dfrac{\sqrt{9}}{\sqrt{16}} = \dfrac{3}{4}$$

─────────── EXERCISE 6 ───────────

Find

1) $\sqrt{\dfrac{9}{25}}$

2) $\sqrt{\dfrac{16}{49}}$

3) $\sqrt{\dfrac{49}{64}}$

4) $\sqrt{\dfrac{36}{121}}$

5) $\sqrt{\dfrac{49}{100}}$

6) $\sqrt{\dfrac{25}{36}}$

7) $\sqrt{\dfrac{25}{81}}$

8) $\sqrt{\dfrac{9}{100}}$

9) $\sqrt{\dfrac{16}{25}}$

To find the square root of a decimal, say 50.4, we either *make an estimate* or use tables of square roots.

SQUARE ROOTS OF DECIMALS BY ── ESTIMATION ──

EXAMPLE

Estimate $\sqrt{50.4}$ correct to 1 decimal place.

50.4 lies between the whole number squares 49 and 64. 49 is *the square of 7* and 64 is *the square of 8* so that $\sqrt{50.4}$ will be a decimal number which lies between 7 and 8.

Try 7.1:

$$\begin{array}{r} 7.1 \\ 7.1 \times \\ \hline 71 \\ 4970 \\ \hline 50.41 \end{array}$$ *Estimate* means "make a good guess".

so 7.1 is slightly too big.
However, $7.0 \times 7.0 = 49.0$, so that 7.1 is a better estimate than 7.0.

$\sqrt{50.4} = 7.1$ correct to one decimal place

─────────── EXERCISE 7 ───────────

Estimate (correct to one decimal place) the square roots of

1) 10.5   7) 83.8
2) 30.2   8) 86
3) 45.1   9) 90.3
4) 50.9   10) 35
5) 62.0   11) 29
6) 75   12) 60.

Since this process is rather laborious it is usually easier to use tables to find square roots.

Tables may also be used to find the *squares* of numbers.

THE USE OF TABLES

Here is part of the *table of squares*:

	0	1	2	3	4	5	6	7	8	9
					Table of squares					
1.0	1.00	1.02	1.04	1.06	1.08	1.10	1.12	1.14	1.17	1.19
1.1	1.21	1.23	1.25	1.28	1.30	1.32	1.35	1.37	1.39	1.42
1.2	1.44	1.46	1.49	1.51	1.54	1.56	1.59	1.61	1.64	1.66
1.3	1.69	1.72	1.74	1.77	1.80	1.82	1.85	1.88	1.90	1.93
1.4	1.96	1.99	2.02	2.04	2.07	2.10	2.13	2.16	2.19	2.22
1.5	2.25	2.28	2.31	2.34	2.37	2.40	2.43	2.46	2.50	2.53
1.6	2.56	2.59	2.62	2.66	2.69	2.72	2.76	2.79	2.82	2.86
1.7	2.89	2.92	2.96	2.99	3.03	3.06	3.10	3.13	3.17	3.20
1.8	3.24	3.28	3.31	3.35	3.39	3.42	3.46	3.50	3.53	3.57
1.9	3.61	3.65	3.69	3.72	3.76	3.80	3.84	3.88	3.92	3.96
2.0	4.00	4.04	4.08	4.12	4.16	4.20	4.24	4.28	4.33	4.37
2.1	4.41	4.45	4.49	4.54	4.58	4.62	4.67	4.71	4.75	4.80
2.2	4.84	4.88	4.93	4.97	5.02	5.06	5.11	5.15	5.20	5.24

To find the square of 1.6 look *along* the row labelled 1.6 and *down* the column labelled 0 to find $1.6 \times 1.6 = 2.56$.

EXAMPLE

Find $(2.16)^2$.

Look *along* the row labelled 2.1 and *down* the column labelled 6 to find from tables that:

$$(2.16)^2 = 4.67$$

(Notice that this is only approximate — there is not enough room to put all the figures in the table.)

EXERCISE 8

Find (using a complete table of squares) the squares of

1) 1.2
2) 2.7
3) 3.5
4) 4.2
5) 5.1
6) 7.9

7) 3.19
8) 9.75
9) 2.18
10) 4.35
11) 6.26
12) 8.19.

For squares of numbers *greater than 10 or less than 1* we find the figures from the table and put in the decimal point either by common sense or using the method shown in the following examples.

EXAMPLE

Find 16^2 from tables.

$$16 = 1.6 \times 10$$

so

$$16^2 = (1.6)^2 \times 10^2$$
$$= 2.56 \times 100 \quad \text{(finding the square of 1.6}$$
$$= 256 \quad \quad \text{from tables)}$$

87

EXAMPLE

Find 240^2 from tables.

$$240 = 2.4 \times 100$$

so

$$240^2 = (2.4)^2 \times 100^2$$

$$= 5.76 \times 10\,000 \quad \text{(finding the square of}$$
$$2.4 \text{ from tables)}$$

$$= 57\,600$$

EXAMPLE

Find 0.17^2 from tables of squares.

$$0.17 = 1.7 \div 10$$

so

$$0.17^2 = (1.7)^2 \div 10^2$$

$$= 2.89 \div 100 \quad \text{(finding the square of}$$
$$1.7 \text{ from tables)}$$

$$= 0.0289$$

─────────── **EXERCISE 9** ───────────

Using a complete table of squares find the squares of these numbers

1) 19		17) 5600
2) 27		18) 3500
3) 35		19) 4000
4) 45		20) 5670
5) 150		21) 0.311
6) 280		22) 0.455
7) 780		23) 0.512
8) 520		24) 0.674
9) 0.28		25) 138
10) 0.37		26) 399
11) 0.57		27) 563
12) 0.25		28) 754
13) 0.56		29) 21
14) 0.45		30) 37
15) 0.2		31) 52
16) 0.9		32) 88

There are *two square root* tables.

One is for numbers from 1 to 10. The other is for numbers from 10 to 100.

(Part of the) *Table of square roots from 1 to 10*							
	0	*1*	*2*	*3*	*4*	*5*	*6*
2.5	1.58	1.58	1.59	1.59	1.59	1.60	1.60
2.6	1.61	1.62	1.62	1.62	1.62	1.63	1.63
2.7	1.64	1.65	1.65	1.65	1.66	1.66	1.66
2.8	1.67	1.68	1.68	1.68	1.69	1.69	1.69
2.9	1.70	1.71	1.71	1.71	1.71	1.72	1.72

(Part of the) *Table of square roots from 10 to 100*						
	.0	*.1*	*.2*	*.3*	*.4*	*.5*
25	5.00	5.01	5.02	5.03	5.04	5.05
26	5.10	5.11	5.12	5.13	5.14	5.15
27	5.20	5.21	5.22	5.22	5.23	5.24
28	5.29	5.30	5.31	5.32	5.33	5.34
29	5.39	5.39	5.40	5.41	5.42	5.43

Parts of the two tables are shown above.

To find $\sqrt{2.75}$ look in the *first* table because 2.75 lies between 1 and 10.

Look *along* the row headed 2.7 and *down* the column labelled 5, from tables:

$$\sqrt{2.75} = 1.66$$

To find $\sqrt{27.5}$ look in the *second* table because 27.5 lies between 10 and 100.

Look *along* the row headed 27 and *down* the column labelled 5, from tables:

$$\sqrt{27.5} = 5.24$$

─────────── **EXERCISE 10** ───────────

Find the square roots of these numbers using a complete set of *square root* tables

1) 3.8	3) 5.22
2) 4.3	4) 12.0

88

5) 15.2   12) 52.9
6) 33.5   13) 35
7) 3.2   14) 83
8) 32.0   15) 7
9) 45.3   16) 6.8
10) 4.53   17) 21.9
11) 5.29   18) 44.2

The method of "marking-off in pairs" is useful to find the square root of numbers more than 100 or less than 1.

EXAMPLE

Find $\sqrt{570\,000}$.

Mark off in pairs from the decimal point (for a whole number the decimal point is at the end):

57|00|00.

Look at the left hand pair.

This is 57 which is between 10 and 100, so to find the figures of the answer we use the square root table from 10 to 100:

$\sqrt{57} = 7.55$

To find where to put the decimal point in the answer, put one figure over each pair starting with 7 over 57 and put a decimal point over the other point:

```
   7    5    5   .
  57   00   00   .
```

$\sqrt{570\,000} = 755$

EXAMPLE

Find $\sqrt{0.0125}$.

Mark off in pairs from the decimal point:

0 . 01|25

Look at the left hand *non-zero* pair.

This is 01 which we take to equal 1 so look in square root tables from 1 to 10 to find the figures of the answer:

$\sqrt{1.25} = 1.12$

To find where to put the decimal point in the answer put one figure over each pair starting with 1 over 01 and letting the figures spill over. Line up the decimal points:

```
0  .   1    1   2
0  .   01   25
```

$\sqrt{0.0125} = 0.112$

EXAMPLE

Find $\sqrt{0.0025}$.

Mark off in pairs from the decimal point:

0.00|25

and find the square root of 25 which is 5. *In this example a nought must be put above the pair of zeros*:

```
0.0   5
0.00  25
```

so that $\sqrt{0.0025} = 0.05$

--- **EXERCISE 11** ---

Using a complete set of tables find the square roots of

1) 23 000   12) 25 000
2) 230   13) 0.064
3) 0.0023   14) 6400
4) 52 000   15) 640
5) 520   16) 490
6) 0.52   17) 0.49
7) 17 500   18) 4900
8) 175   19) 600
9) 0.0175   20) 0.60
10) 0.25   21) 6000
11) 250

1) Work out (a) 3^2 (b) 10^2.

2) Write down the squares of whole numbers from 7 to 12.

3) Work out (a) 14^2 (b) 20^2 (c) 150^2.

4) Find (a) $\left(\dfrac{1}{2}\right)^2$ (b) $\left(\dfrac{3}{5}\right)^2$ (c) $\left(1\dfrac{1}{2}\right)^2$.

5) Find (a) $(0.2)^2$ (b) $(1.1)^2$ (c) $(0.04)^2$.

6) In these examples you must square before adding or subtracting. Find (a) $3^2 + 4^2$ (b) $11^2 - 9^2$.

7) Write down the square roots of (a) 121 (b) 144.

8) Estimate, correct to one decimal place the square root of (a) 12 (b) 28.

9) Find (a) $\sqrt{\dfrac{4}{9}}$ (b) $\sqrt{\dfrac{25}{64}}$.

10) In these examples you must add or subtract before finding the square root. Find (a) $\sqrt{9+16}$ (b) $\sqrt{25-9}$.

11) Work out from tables of squares
    (a) $(2.5)^2$ (b) $(0.19)^2$ (c) 450^2.

12) Work out from tables of squares
    (a) $(5.42)^2$ (b) 542^2 (c) $(0.542)^2$.

13) Work out from tables of square roots
    (a) $\sqrt{3.4}$ (b) $\sqrt{340}$ (c) $\sqrt{0.34}$.

14) Work out from tables of square roots
    (a) $\sqrt{53.9}$ (b) $\sqrt{539}$ (c) $\sqrt{5390}$
    (d) $\sqrt{0.539}$.

8

Approximation and Estimation

If you ask a builder to put an extension on your house then you would expect him to give you an estimate of the final cost. (If he tells you exactly how much the work will cost this is called a "quotation".) An estimate may be a little more or a little less than the actual cost.

To make his estimate the builder would have to work out roughly what he would charge for building materials, electrical work, plumbing, labour, etc.

Building
materials . £2000
Plumbing
work £400
Electrical
work £200
Labour.... £2400
Final
estimate...£5000

His costs would only be approximate (i.e. not exactly correct but nearly correct). The costs might be rounded to the nearest £100, £50 or the nearest £10.

ROUNDING

£298 rounded to the nearest £100 would be £300

£445 rounded to the nearest £50 would be £450

£179 rounded to the nearest £10 would be £180

EXERCISE 1

Round these numbers to the nearest £100

1) £598
2) £602
3) £730
4) £890
5) £1520
6) £23 890

Round these numbers to the nearest £50

7) £45
8) £135
9) £190
10) £240
11) £780
12) £15 595

Round these numbers to the nearest £10

13) £82
14) £176
15) £181
16) £292.50
17) £475.85

Round these numbers to the nearest £1

18) £45.69
19) £72.85
20) £31.10
21) £173.55
22) £273.99

ROUGH CHECKS FOR CALCULATIONS

Always make sure your answers are sensible!

This can be achieved by rounding the numbers and doing a rough check.

E

EXAMPLE

How much money would I need to be able to buy 19 small presents each costing 18 p?

Rough estimate:

    20 × 20 p

    = 400 p

    = £4

Accurate calculation:

```
   19
   18×
  ───
  152
  190
  ───
  342
```

    342 p = £3.42

I would need £3.42.

EXAMPLE

What is the weight of 28 nails at 1.9 g each?

Rough estimate:

    30 × 2 g

    = 60 g

Accurate calculation:

```
    28
   1.9×
  ────
   252
   280
  ────
  53.2
```

The weight of the 28 nails is 53.2 g.

───────── **EXERCISE 2** ─────────

First make a rough estimate and then perform these calculations accurately.

1) Find the total length of 9 planks of wood each of length 1.9 metres.

2) Calculate the cost of 21 notebooks at 9 p each.

3) What is the weight of 39 books each weighing 102 g?

4) A length of rope 801 cm long is cut into 9 equal pieces. Find the length of each piece.

5) I pay for 11 items each costing $9\frac{1}{2}$ p with a £10 note. Find the change I should receive.

6) I buy goods at £11.99, £4.02, £6.03 and £2.98. What is the total bill?

7) 399 sweets are divided equally between nine children. How many sweets does each child get and how many are left over?

8) How heavy are 401 books each weighing 2.1 kg?

9) If the diameter of a coin is 2.9 cm, how far would 99 coins stretch if laid end to end?

10) The weight of 11 boxes is 319 g. How much does each box weigh?

─────────────────────────

EXAMPLE

$$\frac{20.1 \times 1.9}{0.9}$$

Rough estimate:

$$\frac{20 \times 2}{1}$$

    = 40

Accurate calculation:

```
   20.1
    1.9×
  ─────
   1809
   2010
  ─────
  38.19
```

$38.19 \div 0.9 = 381.9 \div 9$

$$\begin{array}{r} 42.433\ldots \\ 9\overline{)381.900} \end{array}$$

Accurate answer $42.4\dot{3}$ or 42.4 to one decimal place.

───────── **EXERCISE 3** ─────────

First perform a rough estimate and then an accurate calculation

1) $\dfrac{11 \times 9}{3}$

2) 149×9

3) $99 \div 1.1$

4) $64.8 \div 9$

5) 10.5×0.9

6) $\dfrac{30.1 \times 1.9}{0.7}$

7) $\dfrac{11 \times 19}{9}$

8) $99 \div 11 + 11 \times 9$

9) 2.1×1.1

10) 7.01×3.02

11) $11 \times 9\dfrac{1}{2}$

12) 4.05×1.1

───────── **INDICES** ─────────

$2 \times 2 \times 2 \times 2$ may be written as 2^4.

This is known as "index form". The small raised number, 4, is called the *index*. Another word that may be used instead of index is *power*.

We read 2^4 as "2 to the power 4" or "2 to the fourth".

Brackets may be used for clarity so 2^4 and $(2)^4$ are the same.

Numbers to the power 2 are known as *square numbers* so 8^2 is called 8 *squared*. Numbers to the power 3 are *cubic* numbers so 7^3 is called 7 *cubed* or the cube of 7.

EXAMPLE

(a) Write $9 \times 9 \times 9$ in index form.
(b) Write out $(8)^4$ as a product.
(c) Evaluate $(7)^3$.

(a) $9 \times 9 \times 9 = 9^3$
(b) $(8)^4 = 8 \times 8 \times 8 \times 8$
(c) $(7)^3 = 7 \times 7 \times 7 = 49 \times 7 = 343$

Notice that "evaluate" means "work out to a single number".

Similarly $3^5 = 3 \times 3 \times 3 \times 3 \times 3$, with 3 being multiplied by itself 5 times and $2^7 = 2 \times 2 \times 2 \times 2 \times 2 \times 2 \times 2$, and so on.

───────── **EXERCISE 4** ─────────

Write in index form

1) 3×3
2) $4 \times 4 \times 4$
3) $6 \times 6 \times 6 \times 6$
4) $5 \times 5 \times 5 \times 5 \times 5 \times 5$
5) 10×10
6) $9 \times 9 \times 9 \times 9 \times 9 \times 9 \times 9 \times 9 \times 9 \times 9$
7) $11 \times 11 \times 11$

Write out as a product

8) $(3)^4$ 11) 10^6
9) 7^2 12) 12^3
10) 8^3

Evaluate

13) 2^3 16) 3^4
14) 5^4 17) 8^3
15) 6^3

18) Add together 4 squared and 2 cubed.

19) What is twice the cube of 3?

20) Subtract the square of 4 from the cube of 3.

93

WAYS OF WRITING VERY LARGE AND VERY SMALL NUMBERS

In atomic physics measurements may be very small whereas in astronomy measurements may be very large. It is inconvenient to write very large or very small numbers out in full.

The short way of writing these numbers is known as *standard index form* (or *standard form*). Some calculators are able to store standard form numbers and they do this by storing two numbers: one that gives the figures and the other that shows where the decimal point should go.

To understand standard form you need to know the meaning of 10^0, 10^1, 10^2, 10^3, etc., and also 10^{-1}, 10^{-2}, etc.

$$10^3 = 10 \times 10 \times 10 = 1000$$

$$10^2 = 10 \times 10 = 100$$

$$10^1 = 10$$

$$10^0 = 1$$

$$10^{-1} = 0.1$$

$$10^{-2} = 0.01$$

etc.

so that $10^5 = 10 \times 10 \times 10 \times 10 \times 10 = 100\,000$

and $10^{-5} = 0.000\,01$

— EXERCISE 5 —

Convert from index form to single numbers

1) 10^2 6) 10^1

2) 10^0 7) 10^{-2}

3) 10^{-1} 8) 10^{-3}

4) 10^3 9) 10^{-4}

5) 10^6 10) 10^4

Standard Form Numbers

The first number has a value between 1 and 10. (It is either a single figure or a decimal point follows the first figure.)

It is followed by "$\times 10^3$" or "$\times 10^{-2}$", etc., to show the *size* of the number. The small raised number is called *the index*.

Here are some examples of standard form numbers:

$$2.56 \times 10^2$$

$$3.7 \times 10^3$$

$$5 \times 10^{-1}$$

$$2.7 \times 10^{-2}$$

$$3.56 \times 10^0$$

$$5.3 \times 10^1$$

EXAMPLE

Write 256 in standard form.

$$256 = 2.56 \times 100 = 2.56 \times 10^2$$

EXAMPLE

Write 3700 in standard form.

$$3700 = 3.7 \times 1000 = 3.7 \times 10^3$$

Write these numbers in standard form

1) 248	6) 4100
2) 6800	7) 5200
3) 781	8) 343
4) 563	9) 230
5) 7800	10) 4560

EXAMPLE

Write 0.5 in standard form.

$$0.5 = 5 \times 0.1 = 5 \times 10^{-1}$$

EXAMPLE

Write 0.34 in standard form.

$$0.34 = 3.4 \times 0.1 = 3.4 \times 10^{-1}$$

EXAMPLE

Write 0.06 in standard form.

$$0.06 = 6 \times 0.01 = 6 \times 10^{-2}$$

EXAMPLE

Write 0.027 in standard form.

$$0.027 = 2.7 \times 0.01 = 2.7 \times 10^{-2}$$

────── **EXERCISE 7** ──────

Write these numbers in standard form

1) 0.6	7) 0.054
2) 0.2	8) 0.061
3) 0.09	9) 0.1
4) 0.05	10) 0.087
5) 0.45	11) 0.08
6) 0.56	12) 0.3

The two numbers which are stored in a calculator are, of course, the first number (between 1 and 10) and the index. If the index is large then the number is large and if the index is low (negative) then the number is small:

5.6×10^9 is a large number

3.28×10^{-8} is a small number

Quick Rule for Finding the Index

Count the number of places you need to move the decimal point until it is just after the first figure. (If you move to the *right* the index will be negative.)

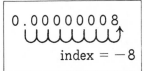

So from the diagrams above:

$$3638 = 3.638 \times 10^3$$

$$0.0075 = 7.5 \times 10^{-3}$$

$$853.2 = 8.532 \times 10^2$$

$$4\,560\,000 = 4.56 \times 10^6$$

$$0.000\,000\,08 = 8 \times 10^{-8}$$

Write these numbers in standard form

1) 58 000
2) 3400
3) 156 000
4) 63
5) 597
6) 0.0078
7) 0.0543

8) 0.000 452
9) 567 000 000
10) 0.000 000 59
11) 497 000
12) 0.000 35
13) 0.000 026
14) 635 124 000

It is important to be able to work out *the value* of standard form numbers.

EXAMPLES

Evaluate (a) 5.2×10^4 (b) 6.11×10^{-3}.

$$5.2 \times 10^4 = 5.2 \times 10\,000$$
$$= 52\,000$$
$$6.11 \times 10^{-3} = 6.11 \times 0.001$$
$$= 0.006\,11$$

EXERCISE 9

Evaluate these numbers

1) 5.3×10^3
2) 3.4×10^2
3) 6.9×10^5
4) 9.2×10^{-1}
5) 9.43×10^{-1}
6) 3.11×10^{-2}

7) 4.7×10^0
8) 5.66×10^1
9) 4.505×10^{-1}
10) 3.2×10^6
11) 1.4×10^{-2}
12) 8×10^{-3}

SIGNIFICANT FIGURES

Sometimes a number has far too many figures for practical use. This is overcome by putting the number "correct to 3 significant figures"

(or "correct to 2 significant figures" or "correct to 4 significant figures" or however many figures are required).

For example

70.196 754 02

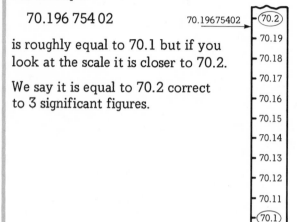

is roughly equal to 70.1 but if you look at the scale it is closer to 70.2.

We say it is equal to 70.2 correct to 3 significant figures.

"Significant figures" is generally shortened to "sig.fig." or to "S.F.".

EXAMPLE

Put 65.712 34 correct to 3 S.F.

The first three figures are 6, 5 and 7. The number is closer to 65.7 than 65.8, so:

$$65.712\,34 = 65.7 \text{ correct to } 3\,\text{S.F.}$$

(Since all figures after the fourth are ignored, the following examples only have 4 figures to start with.)

EXAMPLE

Put (a) 3.268 (b) 3.265 (c) 3.264 correct to 3 S.F.

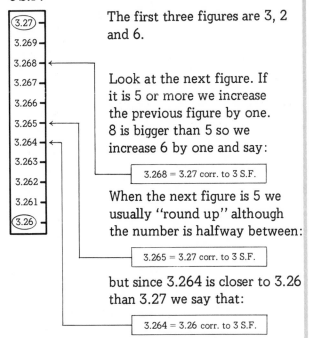

The first three figures are 3, 2 and 6.

Look at the next figure. If it is 5 or more we increase the previous figure by one. 8 is bigger than 5 so we increase 6 by one and say:

| 3.268 = 3.27 corr. to 3 S.F. |

When the next figure is 5 we usually "round up" although the number is halfway between:

| 3.265 = 3.27 corr. to 3 S.F. |

but since 3.264 is closer to 3.26 than 3.27 we say that:

| 3.264 = 3.26 corr. to 3 S.F. |

EXAMPLE

Put 4571 correct to 3 S.F. Count three figures and then look at the figure in the next place:

4   5   7   1
①   ②   ③   ↑

It is a 1 so we leave the figure before alone.

It may be tempting to say 4571 = 457 correct to 3 S.F. but this is quite wrong as you can see if you look at the scale. It is obvious then that 4571 is nowhere near 457!

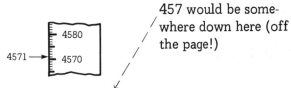

457 would be somewhere down here (off the page!)

The correct answer is 4571 = 4570 correct to 3 S.F. We have to put in a nought. It is called a "trailing zero".

EXERCISE 10

Put these numbers correct to 3 S.F.

1) 3.261
2) 3.269
3) 3.263
4) 3.262
5) 3.266
6) 3.260
7) 3.267
8) 62.89
9) 62.83
10) 62.87
11) 62.86
12) 62.85
13) 62.81
14) 62.84
15) 62.88
16) 62.82

EXERCISE 11

Put these numbers correct to 3 S.F. (Don't forget the trailing zeros – sometimes there will be more than one.)

1) 1351	11) 5563
2) 6732	12) 4325
3) 5674	13) 6072
4) 6789	14) 4516
5) 7128	15) 3399
6) 24 561	16) 1199
7) 145 881	17) 4599
8) 3009	18) 23 410
9) 4028	19) 567 889
10) 5421	20) 4561

Further examples:

12 151 = 12 200 correct to 3 S.F.

5009 = 5010 correct to 3 S.F.

6699 = 6700 correct to 3 S.F.

Reminder: Putting a number correct to 3 significant figures is simply a way of getting a *rough value of the number which is good enough for most purposes.*

When the number has a value less than 1 we start counting at the first non-zero figure.

EXAMPLE

Put (a) 0.5121 (b) 0.5128 (c) 0.5125 correct to 3 S.F.

(a) 0 . 5 1 2 1 = 0.512 correct to 3 S.F.
    ①②③↑

(b) 0 . 5 1 2 8 = 0.513 correct to 3 S.F.
    ①②③↑

(c) 0 . 5 1 2 5 = 0.513 correct to 3 S.F.
    ①②③↑

EXAMPLE

Put (a) 0.008 127 (b) 0.008 025 (c) 0.008 199 correct to 3 S.F.

(a) 0 . 0 0 8 1 2 7 = 0.008 13 correct to 3 S.F.
      ①②③↑

(b) 0 . 0 0 8 0 2 5 = 0.008 03 correct to 3 S.F.
      ①②③↑

We do count the zero "inside" the number.

(c) 0 . 0 0 8 1 9 9 = 0.008 20 correct to 3 S.F.
      ①②③↑

When 1 is added to 819 it becomes 820.

Put these numbers correct to 3 S.F.

1) 0.4121	9) 0.089 13
2) 0.4129	10) 0.089 19
3) 0.4125	11) 0.080 91
4) 0.4123	12) 0.080 99
5) 0.006 112	13) 0.005 199
6) 0.006 118	14) 0.005 191
7) 0.006 115	15) 0.006 099
8) 0.006 111	16) 0.006 092

EXAMPLES

3.61 = 3.6 correct to 2 S.F.

4.92 = 4.9 correct to 2 S.F.

389 = 390 correct to 2 S.F.

Put these numbers correct to 2 S.F.

1) 5.61	7) 279
2) 3.92	8) 0.369
3) 6.15	9) 1499
4) 7.29	10) 0.512
5) 2.31	11) 63.9
6) 5.38	12) 5.81

Round

1) £43.98 to the nearest £

2) £780 to the nearest £100

3) £6.72 to the nearest 10 p

4) 1.95 m to the nearest metre

5) 485 g to the nearest 100 g

6) 3 h 55 min to the nearest hour

7) 25.41 cm to the nearest cm

8) 7950 ml to the nearest litre (1000 ml = 1 litre)

9) 5.7 kg to the nearest kg

10) 3959 m to the nearest km (1000 m = 1 km).

First make a rough estimate and then work out accurately

11) the weight of 9 boxes each weighing 190 g

12) the total length of 2 ropes each 1.95 m long

13) a shopping bill of 5 items at £3.96, £4.02, £2.10, £1.98 and £0.96.

Make a rough estimate and then perform these calculations accurately.

14) A length of wood is sawn into 7 equal pieces. The wood is 490 cm long. How long is each piece?

15) $\dfrac{21 \times 9}{3}$

16) 119×9

17) $810 \div 8$

18) Write out (a) 10^2 (b) 10^{-1} (c) 10^0 (d) 10^1.

19) Write these numbers in standard form
(a) 372   (b) 45   (c) 0.65
(d) 0.09.

20) Write (a) 57 000 (b) 0.000 05 in standard form.

21) Write these numbers correct to 3 significant figures
(a) 2.561   (b) 0.6592   (c) 8.079
(d) 5723.

22) Write these numbers correct to 2 significant figures
(a) 0.125   (b) 7280   (c) 0.0366
(d) 4.5152.

9

Ratio and Proportion

Concrete is made by mixing sand and cement in the ratio 3:1 (three to one) and then mixing this with water. You could put three *bags* of sand to one *bag* of cement:

or three *bucketfuls* of sand to one *bucketful* of cement:

or three *cups* of sand to one *cup* of cement:

These ratios are all 3:1.

As long as sand and cement are kept "in the same proportion", when mixed with water they will make concrete. The actual amounts of sand and cement only affect the total *amount* of concrete made.

Jam is made by mixing fruit to sugar in a given ratio according to a recipe:

Recipe

4 lb blackcurrants
2 pts water
6 lb sugar

To make *twice* as much jam you would *double* the amounts given in the recipe. To make *half* the amount of jam you would *halve* the amounts in the recipe. The recipe gives the proportion of fruit to water to sugar. Here three quantities are involved, fruit, water and sugar.

Model trains are usually made to a "scale of 1:72". Every measurement on the model is 1/72th of the real measurement. They are in a ratio of 1:72.

The ratio shows how many times bigger one quantity is than another. The real measurements are 72 times bigger.

Sometimes problems are made easier by first putting ratios into "simpler terms". These ratios are already in their *simplest terms*:

3:1   5:7   10:9   1:100   500:3

The numbers in the ratios are all *whole numbers*. *No* number divides exactly into both sides of the ratio.

These ratios are *not* in their simplest terms:

6:4   15:3   100:50   40 cm:50 cm

1 m:1 cm $1\frac{1}{4}:\frac{1}{3}$

2 will divide into both 6 and 4. We can simplify the ratio 6:4 by dividing both sides by 2:

6:4 is the same ratio as 3:2

In the second example, 3 divides into both 15 and 3:

15:3 is the same ratio as 5:1

(If you put 15 cups to 3 cups you would get the same "mix" as if you put 5 cups to 1 cup.)

In the third example, 50 divides into both 100 and 50 (50 is a "common factor"):

100:50 is the same ratio as 2:1

To simplify a ratio you may divide both sides by the same number.

EXERCISE 1

Simplify the following ratios

1) 3:6		19) 45:81
2) 5:20		20) 33:44
3) 8:16		21) 48:60
4) 4:12		22) 72:84
5) 4:10		23) 50:60
6) 7:21		24) 45:50
7) 3:9		25) 100:150
8) 3:15		26) 200:300
9) 42:49		27) 1400:2100
10) 25:30		28) 1500:3000
11) 35:42		29) 175:200
12) 16:24		30) 5000:7500
13) 25:20		31) 900:1000
14) 36:24		32) 350:400
15) 40:50		33) 50:60:70
16) 15:18		34) 25:30:35
17) 21:24		35) 40:50:60:70
18) 56:64		

The above exercise should bring out the similarities between ratios and fractions.

Compare 3:6 = 1:2 with $\frac{3}{6} = \frac{1}{2}$

and   5:20 = 1:4 with $\frac{5}{20} = \frac{1}{4}$

SIMPLIFYING RATIOS WITH UNITS

We can simplify the ratio 40 cm:50 cm by

(a) removing the units (because they are the same) and

(b) dividing both sides by 10

40 cm : 50 cm is the same ratio as 4 : 5

The ratio 1 m : 1 cm can be simplified by making the units the same and then removing them

1 m : 1 cm is the same ratio as 100 cm : 1 cm (because 1 m = 100 cm)

100 cm : 1 cm is the same ratio as 100 : 1

To simplify a ratio make the units the same and then remove them. Then simplify as before if possible.

EXAMPLE

Simplify (a) 5 cm : 1 mm (b) 5 km : 1 m
(c) £2.50 : 50 p.

(a) 5 cm : 1 mm is the same as 50 mm : 1 mm which is the same as 50 : 1.
(b) 5 km : 1 m is the same as 5000 m : 1 m which is the same as 5000 : 1.
(c) £2.50 : 50 p is the same as 250 p : 50 p which is 250 : 50 or 5 : 1 (dividing by 50).

─────────── **EXERCISE 2** ───────────

Simplify the following ratios

1) 300 cm : 100 cm
2) 500 cm : 1 m
3) 40 g : 1 kg
4) £1.50 : 50 p
5) 6 kg : 60 g
6) 2 km : 500 m
7) 100 g : 0.5 kg
8) 30 p : 90 p
9) 75 p : 25 p
10) 75 p : £1.00
11) 400 cm : 4 km
12) $2\frac{1}{2}$ km : 1000 m
13) 75 p : £1.50
14) 40 cm : 4 m

15) 1 cm : 5 mm
16) £2.80 : £3.50
17) 5.5 cm : 20 mm
18) 60 g : 100 g
19) £5.00 : £1.00
20) 3 km : 2.5 km
21) 2 kg : 500 g
22) 30 m : 27 m
23) 12 p : 8 p
24) 3 hours : 30 min
25) £12.50 : £2.50
26) 16 kg : 8 kg
27) 5 g : 50 g
28) 2 hours : 45 min
29) £3.00 : 30 p
30) 3 kg : 300 g

───────────────────────

To simplify a ratio such as $1\frac{1}{4} : \frac{1}{3}$ change mixed fractions to top-heavy fractions and make them fractions of the same type.

The smallest number that 4 and 3 will go into without leaving a remainder is 12, so change the fractions to twelfths:

$$1\frac{1}{4} : \frac{1}{3} = \frac{5}{4} : \frac{1}{3} = \frac{15}{12} : \frac{4}{12} = 15 : 4$$

You may multiply both sides of a ratio by the same number.

(To change $\frac{15}{12} : \frac{4}{12}$ to 15 : 4 we have multiplied both sides by 12.) A picture may help to make this clearer so look at this diagram:

There are
15 shaded
parts

There are
4 parts which
are shaded

102

EXAMPLE

Simplify (a) $\dfrac{3}{5}:\dfrac{7}{10}$ (b) $1\dfrac{1}{2}:3$ (c) $1\dfrac{2}{3}:\dfrac{1}{3}$.

(a) $\dfrac{3}{5}:\dfrac{7}{10} = \dfrac{6}{10}:\dfrac{7}{10} = 6:7$

(b) $1\dfrac{1}{2}:3 = 3:6$ (doubling both sides)

$\qquad = 1:2$ (dividing both sides by 3)

(c) $1\dfrac{2}{3}:\dfrac{1}{3} = \dfrac{5}{3}:\dfrac{1}{3} = 5:1$

EXERCISE 3

Simplify these ratios

1) $\dfrac{3}{4}:\dfrac{1}{3}$

2) $\dfrac{1}{5}:\dfrac{1}{10}$

3) $\dfrac{1}{2}:\dfrac{3}{8}$

4) $\dfrac{1}{6}:\dfrac{1}{12}$

5) $2\dfrac{1}{4}:\dfrac{1}{4}$

6) $1\dfrac{4}{5}:\dfrac{3}{10}$

7) $1\dfrac{1}{2}:\dfrac{1}{3}$

8) $1\dfrac{1}{2}:\dfrac{1}{2}$

9) $3\dfrac{1}{2}:1\dfrac{1}{2}$

10) $\dfrac{5}{6}:1\dfrac{2}{3}$

11) $10:2\dfrac{1}{2}$

12) $5:2\dfrac{1}{2}$

13) $2\dfrac{3}{4}:1\dfrac{1}{2}$

14) $3\dfrac{1}{4}:2\dfrac{1}{4}$

15) $\dfrac{1}{2}:5$

16) $1\dfrac{1}{3}:1\dfrac{1}{4}$

17) Multiply the quantities in this recipe by
(a) 2 (b) 6 (c) $\frac{1}{2}$.

Recipe

3 oz butter
$2\frac{1}{2}$ oz caster sugar
1 egg separated
6 oz SR flour
pinch salt
$1\frac{1}{2}$ oz currants
$\frac{1}{2}$ oz mixed peel

18) Multiply the quantities in this recipe by
(a) 4 (b) 10 (c) $\frac{1}{2}$.

Recipe

1 onion
2 carrots
2 sticks celery
250 g cooked beef
a 340 g can
  oxtail soup
salt and pepper
4 tsp curry
  powder
50 g raisins

Measure the lines below.

Copy the table and put your measurements into it. Then simplify the ratio. (The first one has been done for you.)

1) (a) _____
   (b) _____
2) (a) _____
   (b) _____
3) (a) _____
   (b) _____
4) (a) _____
   (b) _____
5) (a) ___
   (b) _____
6) (a) _____
   (b) _____
7) (a) _____
   (b) ____
8) (a) _____
   (b) _____
9) (a) _____
   (b) ___
10) (a) ____
    (b) _____

	(a)	(b)	Simplified ratio of Length (a): Length (b)
1)	1.5 cm	3 cm	1:2
2)			
3)			
4)			
5)			
6)			
7)			
8)			
9)			
10)			

CHANGING RATIOS FRACTIONS AND PERCENTAGES

A ratio may be expressed as either a fraction or a percentage.

EXAMPLE

Express the ratio $4:5$ (a) as a fraction, (b) as a percentage.

(a) $4:5 = \dfrac{4}{5}$

(b) changing this to a percentage:

$$\frac{4}{5} = \frac{4}{5} \times 100\% = 80\%$$

EXAMPLE

Express the ratio $9:27$ first as a fraction in its lowest terms and then as a percentage.

$$9:27 = \frac{9}{27} \text{ or } \frac{1}{3} \text{ in its lowest terms}$$

$$\frac{1}{3} = \frac{1}{3} \times 100\% = 33\tfrac{1}{3}\%$$

Express these ratios (a) as a fraction in its lowest terms, (b) as a percentage

1) $1:5$
2) $8:16$
3) $6:9$
4) $7:10$
5) $12:15$
6) $5:8$
7) $3:20$
8) $100:300$
9) $8:64$
10) $100:150$
11) $11:20$
12) $6:120$.

13) Two steel bars have lengths 15 cm and 25 cm respectively. Give the ratio of the two lengths in its simplest form. What fraction is this? Convert this fraction to a percentage.

14) The area of a lawn is 16 m^2 and the area of a surrounding flowerbed is 40 m^2. Write down the ratio of the two areas and simplify it. Write down in its simplest form the ratio of the area of the lawn to the *total* area of the lawn and the flowerbed. What percentage is this?

15) Two girls share £3 pocket money with the younger girl getting less than the older. What percentage of the *total* pocket money does the younger girl receive if they share the pocket money in the ratio 2:3? How much does the younger girl receive? How much does the older girl get?

PROPORTIONAL PARTS

EXAMPLE

Divide £20 in the ratio 3:2.

$3 + 2 = 5$ so there are 5 parts altogether.

Divide £20 by 5 to find each part:

$20 \div 5 = 4$ so each part is £4

3 parts is $3 \times £4 = £12$

2 parts is $2 \times £4 = £8$

£20 in the ratio 3:2 is £12:£8.

EXERCISE 6

1) Divide £15 in the ratio 2:1.
2) Divide £16 in the ratio 3:1.
3) Divide £125 in the ratio 1:4.
4) Divide £20 in the ratio 3:1.
5) Divide 300 g in the ratio 3:2.
6) Divide 3000 g in the ratio 1:2.
7) Divide 400 g in the ratio 5:3.
8) Divide £35 in the ratio 4:3.
9) Divide 60 min in the ratio 3:1.
10) Divide 45 min in the ratio 4:5.
11) Divide 6 km in the ratio 5:1.
12) Divide 42 p in the ratio 2:1.
13) Divide 50 p in the ratio 1:4.
14) Divide 40 g in the ratio 5:3.
15) A man divides £500 between his two children in the ratio 2:3. How much does each child get?
16) 700 g of alloy is made up of copper, tin and nickel in the ratio 2:3:2. How many grams of each metal are there?
17) If 75 cm is divided in the ratio 4:1 how long is each part?

DIRECT PROPORTION

Two quantities are in *direct proportion* if an increase (or decrease) in one quantity is matched by an increase (or decrease) in the same ratio in the second quantity. Thus if 8 pens cost 56 p then 16 pens will cost 112 p (we have doubled the number of pens and we have also doubled the cost). Also 4 pens will cost 28 p (we have halved the number of pens and we have also halved the cost).

EXAMPLE

If 7 pencils cost 28 p how much will 5 pencils cost?

The cost is in *direct proportion* to the number of pencils. There are two methods for solving this problem:

Method 1 (the method of unity)

  7 pencils cost 28 p
  1 pencil costs $28 \div 7 = 4$ p
  5 pencils cost $5 \times 4 = 20$ p

Method 2 (fractional method)

  7 pencils cost 28 p

  5 pencils cost $\dfrac{5}{7} \times \overset{4}{\cancel{28}} = 5 \times 4 = 20$ p

────────────── **EXERCISE 7** ──────────────

1) 5 pens cost 15 p. What do 6 cost?

2) 3 oranges cost 30 p. What do 7 cost?

3) 9 pencils cost 27 p. What do 8 cost?

4) 2 kg potatoes cost 24 p. What do 12 kg potatoes cost?

5) 3 bananas cost 24 p. What do 6 cost?

6) 5 hooks cost 25 p. Find the cost of 8 hooks.

7) 9 bolts cost 36 p. Find the cost of 27 bolts.

8) 2 televisions cost £500. What do 3 cost?

9) 4 bowls cost £3.00. What do 5 cost?

10) 3 rubbers cost 33 p. What do 9 cost?

11) 2 bottles of ink cost £1.20. What do 7 bottles of ink cost?

12) 6 sweets cost 12 p. Find the cost of 18 sweets.

13) 5 razor blades cost 35 p. Find the cost of 15 razor blades.

14) 8 plates cost £8.80. What do 3 cost?

15) A car travels 60 miles in 2 hours. How far will it travel in (a) 4 hours (b) 1 hour?

16) 3 boxes weigh 12 kg. Find the weight of 5 similar boxes.

17) A machine makes 12 articles in $\frac{1}{2}$ hour. How many articles will it make in (a) 1 hour (b) 2 hours (c) 6 hours?

18) A man earns £6 in two hours. Find how much he earns in (a) $\frac{1}{2}$ hour (b) 5 hours.

19) What is the weight of 20 books if 4 similar books weigh 800 g?

20) 100 g of sweets cost 28 p. Find the cost of 400 g.

21) Copy these tables and fill in the spaces

Weight	Cost
50 kg	£1.00
100 kg	
10 kg	
20 kg	

Weight	Cost
8 kg	£9.60
4 kg	
24 kg	
1 kg	

Weight	Cost
7 kg	£8.40
1 kg	
$3\frac{1}{2}$ kg	
14 kg	

Weight	Cost
2 kg	£6.30
1 kg	
$\frac{1}{2}$ kg	
$2\frac{1}{2}$ kg	

Weight	Cost
5 kg	£5.15
1 kg	
20 kg	
40 kg	

Weight	Cost
3 kg	£2.70
1 kg	
9 kg	
18 kg	

Weight	Cost
15 kg	£3.00
5 kg	
1 kg	
30 kg	

Weight	Cost
20 kg	£1500
10 kg	
1 kg	
$\frac{1}{2}$	

Weight	Cost
$3\frac{1}{2}$ kg	£7.00
7 kg	
1 kg	
21 kg	

—— INVERSE PROPORTION ——

If an increase (or decrease) in one quantity produces a decrease (or increase) in a second quantity in the same ratio, the two quantities are in *inverse proportion*. For example, suppose 3 men working on a job take 6 days. Then 6 men working on a similar job will take *less* time — they will take 3 days if they work at the same rate.

EXAMPLE

5 men building a wall take 20 days. How long will it take 4 men?

   5 men take 20 days

   1 man takes $20 \times 5 = 100$ days

(1 man takes *longer* so *multiply* by 5)

   4 men take $100 \div 4 = 25$ days

(4 men take *less time* so *divide* by 4).

—— EXERCISE 8 ——

1) 6 men building a wall take 12 days. How long would it take 2 men?

2) A farmer employs 12 men to pick apples. It takes them 2 days. How long would it take 8 men?

3) A bag of sweets is shared between 5 children and each child gets 3 sweets. How many sweets would each get if the same bag were shared between 3 children?

4) 7 men make 21 toys in 1 hour. How long would it take 21 men?

5) 5 men dig up a row of potatoes in 20 minutes. How long will it take 10 men?

6) 3 men dig a hole in the road in 1 hour. How long would it take 12 men?

7) 3 men take 6 hours to complete some work. How long will it take 5 men?

8) A bag of sweets is shared among 6 children and each child gets 8 sweets. How many sweets would each child get if the same bag were shared among 12 children?

9) 8 people take 3 hours to pick a field of strawberries. How long would it take 6 people?

These problems are answered by using direct proportion.

EXAMPLE

Which is the best buy:

   40 g for £2.80   150 g for £9.00

   100 g for £8.00   200 g for £10.00?

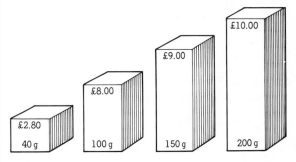

The best way to tackle this is to put the ratios of the weights in their lowest terms:

   40 g : 100 g : 150 g : 200 g

is the same as $4 : 10 : 15 : 20$. We have divided through by 10 g.

107

Now find the price for 10 g of each item:

40 g for £2.80 means that 10 g will cost 70 p

100 g for £8.00 means that 10 g will cost 80 p

150 g for £9.00 means that 10 g will cost 60 p

200 g for £10.00 means that 10 g will cost 50 p

We can see that 200 g for £10.00 is the best buy.

EXERCISE 9

Which is the best buy?

1) 20 g at 60 p or 50 g at £1.00

2) 100 mℓ shampoo at 35 p
   150 mℓ shampoo at 42 p or
   200 mℓ shampoo at 70 p

200 mℓ   100 mℓ   150 mℓ

3) 100 g at £1.50
   200 g at £2.20
   300 g at £3.18 or
   400 g at £4.28

4) 850 g of washing powder at 51 p or 2500 g at £1.75

5) Is 50 g of cornflour at 35 p better value than 80 g at 64 p?

6) 250 g of cornflakes cost 35 p. A 500 g packet of cornflakes cost 60 p. How much do I save by buying one 500 g packet rather than two 250 g packets?

7) I can buy single nails at 2 p each or 5 for 9 p or 10 for 17 p. I need 36 nails. What is the least I would have to pay? How much do I save over buying them all singly?

— MAPS AND SCALE MODELS —

EXAMPLE

The scale on this map is 1 : 100. 1 cm on the map represents 100 cm = 1 m.

(a) What would 5 cm represent?

(b) What would 0.5 cm represent?

(a) 5 cm would represent
   5 × 100 cm = 500 cm = 5 m.

(b) 0.5 cm would represent
   0.5 × 100 cm = 50 cm.

1) A model car is 50 times smaller than a real car.
   (a) 100 cm on the real car would be represented by how much on the model?
   (b) What length on the real car does 3 cm on the model represent?

2) A map has a scale of 1 cm : 1 km. What distance does 2 cm on the map represent? What distance would 5 cm represent? What distance would 2.5 cm represent?

3) A model train is built 72 times smaller than the real train. What is the real measurement represented by (a) 3 cm (b) 0.5 cm (c) 20 cm (d) 25 cm on the model?

4) On a map 5 km is represented by 1 cm. What distance is represented by (a) 2 cm (b) 0.5 cm (c) 5 cm (d) 11 cm?
   What length on the map represents (e) 10 km (f) 30 km (g) 2.5 km (h) 7.5 km?

FOREIGN CURRENCY

When people travel abroad they need to change their money into the currency of the country they are visiting.

They might use a calculator to work out the exact amount of money they would get, but it is useful to be able to do a rough check. The methods of direct proportion are used to work out foreign currency exchange. The rate of exchange may vary from day to day, so to find exactly how much foreign money you would get for £1 you would need to look at a *rate of exchange table* such as the one below:

Country	Rate of exchange
France	£1 = 11 French francs
Germany	£1 = 4.7 German marks
Italy	£1 = 2270 lire
Spain	£1 = 192 pesetas
Switzerland	£1 = 4.3 Swiss francs

EXAMPLE

If £1 is roughly 2000 lire, find approximately how many lire you would get for £7.

£1 = 2000 lire

£7 = 7 × 2000 = 14 000 lire

EXAMPLE

If £1 is roughly 4 Swiss francs, find how many pounds you would get for 24 Swiss francs.

4 Swiss francs = £1

1 Swiss franc = £1 ÷ 4 = 25 p

24 Swiss francs = 25 p × 24 = £1 × 6 = £6

1) If £1 = 11 French francs find how many francs you would get for £2.

2) If £1 is approximately 5 German marks find how many marks you would get for £3.

3) If £1 is roughly 2000 lire find approximately how many lire you would get for £9.

4) If £1 is roughly 200 pesetas find approximately how many pesetas you would get for £8.

5) If £1 is roughly 4 Swiss francs find approximately how many Swiss francs you would get for £15.

6) If 4 Swiss francs is roughly £1 how much approximately is 20 Swiss francs worth in pounds?

7) If 2000 lire is roughly £1 find how much approximately 1000 lire is worth in pounds and pence.

8) If 11 French francs is roughly £1 find out how much roughly 44 French francs is worth in pounds.

9) If 200 pesetas is roughly £1 find approximately how much 500 pesetas is worth in pounds and pence.

10) If 2000 lire is roughly £1 find how much 10 000 lire is worth in pounds.

11) If 5 German marks is roughly £1 find how much 40 German marks is worth in pounds.

12) If 2000 lire is roughly £1 find approximately how much 50 000 lire is worth in pounds.

13) If 4 Swiss francs is roughly £1 find how much 25 Swiss francs would be worth in pounds and pence.

EXERCISE 12

1) Simplify (a) $5:25$ (b) $30:24$ (c) $150:200$ (d) $42:14$.

2) Simplify (a) $3\,cm:5\,cm$ (b) $1\,m:20\,cm$ (c) $3\,mm:1\,cm$ (d) $2\,hours:1\,hour$.

3) Simplify (a) $5\,kg:500\,g$ (b) $200\,g:1\,kg$.

4) Simplify (a) $1\frac{1}{8}:\frac{1}{8}$ (b) $\frac{3}{5}:\frac{9}{10}$.

5) (a) Double, (b) treble, (c) halve the quantities in this recipe for meringue
   4 egg whites
   200 g caster sugar.

6) Measure these lines and simplify the ratio of their lengths.
   (a) _____ (b) _____

7) Divide £50 in the ratio $3:2$.

8) Divide 16 in the ratio $5:3$.

9) Divide 150 g in the ratio $4:1$.

10) Divide 2 hours in the ratio $1:3$.

11) Divide £40 in the ratio $1:2:1$.

12) Divide 52 p in the ratio $6:7$.

13) 5 pencils cost 30 p. How much do 7 pencils cost?

14) 6 rubbers cost 42 p. How much do 5 rubbers cost?

15) 9 articles cost 18 p. How much do 12 articles cost?

16) 2 men take 4 hours to do a job. How long will 5 men take?

17) Which is the best value: (a) 35 g for 70 p or (b) 15 g for 45 p?

18) Which is the best value: (a) 12 g for 36 p or (b) 10 g for 20 p?

19) If £1 is roughly 5 German marks how much is £20 worth in marks?

20) If 4 Swiss francs is roughly £1 how much approximately is 48 Swiss francs worth in pounds?

21) If 10 cm on a map represents 40 km how much will 7 cm represent?

22) If the scale on a map is $1:400$ how much will 1 cm represent?

110

10

Averages

The average of a set of numbers is the number typical of that set. The most common sort of average is the *arithmetic mean*.

EXAMPLE

Find the mean of these numbers:

6, 6, 7, 8, 10, 11.

To find the mean we add the numbers and then divide the sum by the number of numbers in the set:

$$\frac{6+6+7+8+10+11}{6}$$

$$= \frac{48}{6}$$

$$= 8$$

So the mean of the set of numbers is 8.

Where the word "average" is used alone, it is the arithmetic mean that is required.

EXAMPLE

Find the average height of five women whose heights are: 4 ft 5 inches, 5 ft 2 inches, 6 ft 1 inch, 5 ft 2 inches and 5 ft exactly.

First we add up their heights:

ft	inches
4	5
5	2
6	1
5	2
5	
25	10

Average height

and then, because there are five women, we divide by 5. Thus:

Average height = (25 ft 10 inches) ÷ 5
                = 5 ft 2 inches

Note carefully that:

$$\text{Average} = \frac{\text{Sum}}{\text{Number in set}}$$

EXERCISE 1

Find the mean of these numbers

1) 2, 3, 5, 6
2) 2, 5, 6, 7, 10
3) 5, 0, 2, 1
4) 2, 6, 7
5) 3, 8, 2, 7
6) 5, 1, 7, 2, 2, 1
7) 8, 1, 1, 2, 3

8) 15, 9, 12
9) 12, 16, 13, 15
10) 2, 5, 1, 3, 4, 5, 1
11) 12, 17, 29, 23, 34
12) 68, 72, 61
13) 0.5, 0.7, 0.3
14) 1.2, 1.8, 1.9, 1.5
15) 0.7, 0.6, 0.8, 0.3
16) 0.9, 0.9, 0.6, 1.7, 1.8, 0.8, 1.7
17) 90, 92, 78, 84
18) 1.58, 2.72, 4.10
19) 7.5, 7.2, 7.2, 7.5, 7.1
20) 8.0, 7.2, 6.1, 3.5, 4.2

Here give your answers as fractions

21) 4, 2, 3, 1
22) 5, 1, 4
23) 8, 1, 0, 5, 2, 1
24) 1, 0, 0, 5, 2
25) $\dfrac{1}{4}, \dfrac{1}{8}, \dfrac{1}{2}, \dfrac{1}{8}$
26) $1\dfrac{1}{2}, 2\dfrac{1}{2}, 3\dfrac{1}{4}, 5\dfrac{3}{4}$
27) $\dfrac{1}{3}, \dfrac{5}{6}, \dfrac{1}{12}$
28) 1, 3, 4, 1, 9, 1, 3

Here give your answers to 3 significant figures

29) 4, 3, 1, 1, 1, 3, 9
30) 2, 5, 0, 3, 4, 0, 0, 1, 1

Here give your answers to three decimal places

31) 5.602, 4.117, 3.281
32) 0.103, 0.105, 0.109

Here give your answers to one decimal place

33) 1.7, 1.3, 1.4, 1.6, 1.2, 1.1
34) 5.2, 5.3, 5.5, 5.6, 6.7, 8.1, 5.5

In Exercises 2, 3 and 4:

Average = Mean

EXERCISE 2

1) Ten families have 0, 0, 1, 1, 2, 2, 2, 2, 3 and 7 children. Find the average number of children in each family.

2) A batsman scores 25, 30, 110, 80 and 45 runs in five different innings. Find his average score.

3) The weights of six apples are 90 g, 92 g, 93 g, 94 g, 97 g and 92 g. Find their mean weight.

4) The marks given in an examination were 35, 45, 47, 52, 55, 60 and 70. Find the average mark.

5) The hourly wages of seven people are £3.40, £4.20, £2.50, £3.35, £2.10, £4.30 and £5.21. Find their average hourly wage.

6) Four children are aged 11 years, 11 years 1 month, 11 years 3 months and 11 years 4 months. Find their average age.

7) Find the arithmetic mean of 9 cm, 9 cm, 11 cm, 13 cm, 15 cm and 15 cm.

8) Five boxes have weights 120 g, 210 g, 250 g, 300 g and 320 g. Find (a) their total weight (b) their mean weight.

9) Find the mean of 12.3, 12.4, 12.5, 12.5, 12.6, 12.9 and 13.0.

10) Find the mean of three 9s, five 10s and one 13.

Note also that:

Sum = Number in set × Average

EXERCISE 3

1) A batsman scores an average of 50 runs in 4 innings. What was his total number of runs?

2) Three children have an average age of 11 years 4 months. What is their total age in years?

3) Seven people have a mean hourly wage of £3.10. What is the total wages paid per hour?

4) Six numbers have an average of 13. What is their total?

5) Sixteen families have an average of two children per family. How many children are there altogether?

6) What is the total weight of 11 apples each with average weight of 92 g?

7) Four parcels have an average weight of 200 g. What is their total weight?

8) Five children have an average weekly pocket money of 50 p. What is the total pocket money of these children?

EXAMPLE

A girl gains 10, 15, 20, 30 and 40 marks in five different tests.

(a) What is her average mark?

(b) What mark must she get in her next test to improve her average by 2 marks?

(a) $\dfrac{10 + 15 + 20 + 30 + 40}{5} = \dfrac{115}{5} = 23$

Her average mark is 23.

(b) To improve this by 2 marks her average mark over six tests must be 25, so her total marks over six tests must be:

$6 \times 25 = 150$ marks

Her total marks over five tests were $5 \times 23 = 115$ marks. $150 - 115 = 35$.

She must gain 35 marks in her sixth test.

1) A batsman scores 16, 25, 32 and 63 runs in four innings. What is his average score and what must he score in the next innings to improve his average by 1 run?

2) The average age of five girls is 11 years 2 months. What is their total age in years and months? What must be the age of a sixth girl if their new average age is 11 years 3 months?

3) Five workers earn £80, £95, £95, £100 and £120 a week. What is their average wage? What must a sixth worker earn if the average wage of the six is to be £1 more.

4) The average of five numbers is 11. What must a sixth number be if the average of the six numbers is to be 12?

5) Two parcels weigh 30 g and 45 g. What must a third parcel weigh if the average weight of the three parcels is 40 g?

6) The average length of three gardens is 90 m. What is the length of a fourth garden if the average length of the four gardens is 100 m?

7) In six different tests a boy gains 10, 10, 13, 15, 16 and 14 marks. What is his average mark? What is his total mark for the six tests? What must he get in his seventh test to improve his average by 1 mark?

8) If the average of five numbers is 10 and the average of six numbers is 9, what is the sixth number?

9) Five boxes weigh 500 g in total. One box weighing 140 g is taken away. What is the average weight of the remaining four boxes?

MIXTURES

Grocers often mix two or three types of coffee together and the price will depend on the quantity and price of each type.

EXAMPLE

Coffee at 80 p for 100 g is mixed with coffee at 95 p for 100 g in the ratio 3 : 2. Find the price of 100 g of the mixture.

Since they are mixed in the ratio 3 : 2 and 3 + 2 = 5, it will be useful to find the total cost of 500 g of the mixture:

300 g at 80 p per 100 g costs 3 × 80 p = £2.40

200 g at 95 p per 100 g costs 2 × 95 p = £1.90

500 g of the mixture will cost
£2.40 + £1.90 = £4.30

so

100 g of the mixture will cost
£4.30 ÷ 5 = 86 p

EXERCISE 5

1) 3 kg of pears at 20 p a kg are mixed with 2 kg at 15 p per kg. Find the price of 1 kg of the mixture.

2) 5 kg of apples at 25 p a kg are mixed with 5 kg of apples at 33 p a kg. Find the price of 1 kg of the mixture.

3) 2 litres of petrol at 25 p a litre are mixed with 3 litres at 30 p a litre. Find the price of 1 litre of the mixture.

4) Coffee at 90 p for 100 g is mixed with coffee at 100 p for 100 g in the ratio 2 : 3. Find the price of 100 g of the mixture.

5) A brass consists of copper and zinc in the ratio 3 : 1. Find the cost of 1 kg of brass if copper costs 30 p per kg and zinc costs 20 p per kg.

6) Three types of wine are mixed in the ratio 5 : 3 : 2. Their prices per litre are £1.00, £2.00 and £3.00 respectively. Find the cost per litre of the mixture.

7) Tea at 70 p per 100 g is mixed with tea at 80 p per 100 g in the ratio 3 : 7. Find the price of 100 g of the mixture.

8) 4 kg of grapes at 60 p a kg are mixed with 6 kg of grapes at 80 p a kg. Find the price of 1 kg of the mixture.

WEIGHTED AVERAGES

Sometimes some of the numbers are repeated several times.

EXAMPLE

Find the average of:

7, 7, 8, 8, 8, 9, 9, 10.

7 is repeated *twice*, 8 is repeated *three times*, 9 is repeated *twice* and 10 occurs only *once*. We say the "weight" for 7 is 2, for 8 is 3, for 9 is 2 and for 10 is 1. (Sometimes the weights are called "the frequency".)

There are 8 numbers altogether.

The information could have been given in a table like this:

Number	Frequency (or weight)
7	2
8	3
9	2
10	1

To find the total we multiply 7 by 2, 8 by 3, 9 by 2, 10 by 1 and add:

Sum = (7 × 2) + (8 × 3) + (9 × 2) + (10 × 1)

= 14 + 24 + 18 + 10 = 66

Average $\dfrac{66}{8} = 8\dfrac{2}{8} = 8\dfrac{1}{4}$ (or 8.25)

Notice that the number of numbers in the set is $2 + 3 + 2 + 1 = 8$ (the sum of the weights).

The calculations can be recorded in a table:

Number	Frequency (or weight)	Number × frequency
7	2	14
8	3	24
9	2	18
10	1	10
Total	8	66

Average $= 66 \div 8 = 8\frac{1}{4}$ or 8.25.

─────────── **EXERCISE 6** ───────────

Find the average for these numbers

1)

Number	Frequency (or weight)
2	5
3	2
4	1
5	2

2)

Number	Frequency (or weight)
19	2
20	5
25	1
30	3

3)

Number	Frequency (or weight)
1.5	2
3.5	4
5.5	3
6.5	1

4)

Number	Frequency (or weight)
6	4
9	6
11	5
15	5

5)

Number	Frequency (or weight)
33	2
35	2
37	3
38	3

6)

Number	Frequency (or weight)
56	3
62	1
65	1
67	3

─────────────────

EXAMPLE

At 2 football matches no goals were scored, at 5 matches 1 goal was scored, at 9 matches 2 goals were scored and at 4 matches 3 goals were scored. Put this information in a table and find the average number of goals scored per match.

Number of goals	Number of matches
0	2
1	5
2	9
3	4

Total number of goals scored
$$= (0 \times 2) + (1 \times 5) + (2 \times 9) + (3 \times 4)$$
$$= 0 + 5 + 18 + 12$$
$$= 35$$

115

F

Number of matches is $2 + 5 + 9 + 4 = 20$

Goal average $= \dfrac{35}{20} = 1\dfrac{15}{20} = 1\dfrac{3}{4}$

1) The wages of ten people are shown by this table:

Wage	Number of people earning this wage
£65	4
£72	5
£80	1

Find:

(a) the total wages paid to all ten people
(b) the average wage.

2) The weights of ten bolts are given by this table:

Weight	Number of bolts with this weight
5 g	2
7 g	3
8 g	3
9 g	2

Find:

(a) the total weight of all ten bolts
(b) the average weight of the bolts.

3) The lengths of five bars of steel are given by this table:

Length	Number of bars of steel with this length
250 cm	3
300 cm	1
400 cm	1

Find the average length of the bars of steel.

4) In 10 hockey matches the goals scored were: no goals in 1 match, 1 goal in 3 matches, 2 goals in 3 matches, 3 goals in 2 matches and 4 goals in 1 match. Put this information in a table. Find (a) the total number of goals scored and (b) the goal average.

5) 3 apples have a weight of 50 g and 7 apples have a weight of 70 g. What is the average weight of an apple?

6) 2 tins are sold at 15 p per tin, 3 tins are sold at 20 p per tin and 5 tins are sold at 30 p per tin. What is the average price per tin?

7) Find the average length using the information in this table:

Length	Number with this length
20 cm	3
24 cm	4
30 cm	2
35 cm	1

8) Find the average weight of a box using the information in this table:

Weight	Number of boxes with this weight
500 g	7
550 g	8
600 g	5

9) Using the information given in this table find the average mark:

Mark	Number with this mark
5	22
6	30
7	18
8	20
9	10

10) Copy this table and fill in the missing spaces. Find the total wage. Find the total number of people and then find the average wage (to the nearest whole pound).

Wage	Number of people with this wage	
£72	15	$72 \times 15 =$
£75	20	$75 \times 20 =$
£80	40	$80 \times 40 =$
£85	35	$85 \times 35 =$
£90	17	$90 \times 17 =$
£92	13	$92 \times 13 =$
£95	60	$95 \times 60 =$

——— AVERAGE SPEED ———

There are three formulae to remember:

$$\text{Average speed} = \frac{\text{Distance}}{\text{Time}}$$

(For two-part questions you must find the *total distance* and divide by the *total time*.)

$$\text{Time} = \frac{\text{Distance}}{\text{Average speed}}$$

and

$$\text{Distance} = \text{Average speed} \times \text{Time}$$

As a way of remembering these, try thinking of a simple example such as "If a car travels at 4 miles per hour for 3 hours how far will it travel?" Obviously it will travel 12 miles. The three formulae can be worked out from:

$$4 \, \text{miles/hour} = \frac{12 \, \text{miles}}{3 \, \text{hours}}$$

$$3 \, \text{hours} = \frac{12 \, \text{miles}}{4 \, \text{miles/hour}} \quad \text{and}$$

$$12 \, \text{miles} = 4 \, \text{miles/hour} \times 3 \, \text{hours}$$

where 4 miles/hour (mph) is the speed, 12 miles is the distance and 3 hours is the time.

EXAMPLE

If a car travels for 120 miles at an average speed of 40 miles/hour how long does it take?

$$\text{Use Time} = \frac{\text{Distance}}{\text{Average speed}} = \frac{120 \, \text{miles}}{40 \, \text{miles/hour}}$$

$$= 3 \, \text{hours}$$

EXAMPLE

A car travels at 50 miles/hour for 3 hours; how far has it gone?

$$\text{Use Distance} = \text{Average speed} \times \text{Time}$$

$$= 50 \, \text{miles/hour} \times 3 \, \text{hours}$$

$$= 150 \, \text{miles}$$

EXAMPLE

What is the average speed of a car that travels for 90 miles and takes $2\frac{1}{2}$ hours?

$$\text{Use Average speed} = \frac{\text{Distance}}{\text{Time}} = \frac{90 \, \text{miles}}{2\frac{1}{2} \, \text{hours}}$$

$$= 90 \div 2\frac{1}{2}$$

$$= 90 \div \frac{5}{2}$$

(turn second fraction upside down and multiply)

$$= \overset{18}{90} \times \frac{2}{\underset{1}{5}}$$

$$= 36 \, \text{miles/hour}$$

Find the times taken to travel
1) 8 miles at an average speed of 2 mph
2) 12 miles at an average speed of 4 mph
3) 25 miles at an average speed of 5 mph
4) 30 miles at an average speed of 10 mph.

Find the times if the distances and average speeds are as follows
5) Distance 90 miles, average speed 30 mph
6) Distance 120 miles, average speed 40 mph
7) Distance 200 miles, average speed 50 mph.

In some countries, distances are measured in kilometres (km) and speeds in kilometres per hour (km/h or $km\,h^{-1}$).
8) Find the time taken to travel 12 km at 3 km/h.
9) How long does it take to travel 15 km at 5 km/h?

Give your answers in hours and minutes.
10) Find the time to travel 10 miles at 4 mph.
11) How long does it take to go 24 miles at 10 mph?
12) 150 miles are travelled at an average speed of 60 mph. How long does this take?
13) How long does it take if you go 2 mph for $4\frac{1}{2}$ miles?

Find the distances travelled if the average speeds and times are as follows
14) Average speed 2 mph, time 4 hours
15) Average speed 5 mph, time 2 hours
16) Average speed 8 mph, time 3 hours.
17) How far do you go if you travel at 20 mph for 3 hours?
18) How far do you go if you travel at 50 mph for $1\frac{1}{2}$ hours?

For the following questions your answers should be in kilometres.
19) Give the distance travelled if you go for $2\frac{1}{2}$ hours at 60 km/h.
20) How many kilometres are travelled in $3\frac{1}{4}$ hours at 40 km/h?

In the following questions you have to find the average speeds.
21) If you travel 2 miles in 1 hour what is your average speed?
22) Find the average speed for a distance of 6 miles in a time of 2 hours.
23) Find the average speed for a distance of 15 miles in a time of 3 hours.

Copy this table and fill in the values for the average speeds.

	Distance	Time	Average speed
24)	6 miles	3 hours	
25)	8 miles	4 hours	
26)	20 miles	5 hours	
27)	56 miles	8 hours	
28)	60 miles	2 hours	
29)	120 miles	3 hours	
30)	200 miles	4 hours	
31)	9 km	3 hours	
32)	27 km	3 hours	
33)	250 km	5 hours	
34)	10 km	4 hours	
35)	100 km	8 hours	

1) A car travels for 2 hours at 40 miles/hour. How far has it gone?
2) How long does it take to travel 120 miles at 30 miles/hour?

3) What is the average speed of a car that takes 3 hours to travel 90 miles?

4) A journey lasts for 3 hours at an average speed of 35 miles/hour. How far is it?

5) If you travel at 40 miles/hour for $2\frac{1}{2}$ hours how far do you go?

6) A car travels for 4 hours and goes 160 miles. What is its average speed?

7) What is the average speed if you travel for $2\frac{1}{2}$ hours and go 80 miles?

8) How long does it take to go 60 miles at an average speed of 40 miles/hour?

9) Give the time for a journey of 90 miles at an average speed of 20 miles/hour.

10) After a $3\frac{1}{2}$ hour journey a car has travelled 210 miles. What is its average speed?

EXAMPLE

A car travels 60 miles at 20 miles/hour and 80 miles at 40 miles/hour. What is its overall average speed?

For two-part questions you must work out the *total distance* and the *total time*:

Total distance = 60 miles + 80 miles
$$= 140 \text{ miles}$$

$$\text{Time} = \frac{\text{Distance}}{\text{Average speed}}$$

$$\text{Time for first part} = \frac{60 \text{ miles}}{20 \text{ miles/hour}} = 3 \text{ hours}$$

$$\text{Time for second part} = \frac{80 \text{ miles}}{40 \text{ miles/hour}}$$
$$= 2 \text{ hours}$$

Total time = 3 hours + 2 hours = 5 hours

$$\text{Overall average speed} = \frac{\text{Total distance}}{\text{Total time}}$$
$$= \frac{140 \text{ miles}}{5 \text{ hours}}$$
$$= 28 \text{ miles/hour}$$

The results may be clearer if they are put in a table like this:

	Time	Distance	Average speed
1st part	3 hours	60 miles	20 mph
2nd part	2 hours	80 miles	40 mph
Totals	5 hours	140 miles	Overall average speed $= \dfrac{140}{5}$ $= 28$ mph

(Put your results into a table like the one shown above.)

1) A car travels 120 miles at 40 miles/hour and 120 miles at 60 miles/hour. Find its overall average speed.

2) For 2 hours of a 100 mile journey the average speed is 30 miles/hour and the average speed of the remainder is 40 miles/miles/hour. Find the overall average speed.

3) On an outward journey of 240 miles a motorist takes 6 hours and on the return journey he takes 2 hours less.
   (a) Calculate the average speed on the outward journey.
   (b) Calculate the average speed on the return journey.
   (c) By first calculating the total distance and then the total time find the overall average speed.

4) An aeroplane travels 100 km in $2\frac{1}{2}$ hours. What is its average speed? It then travels for $5\frac{1}{2}$ hours at an average speed of 800 km/h.

(a) How far has it travelled altogether?

(b) What is the total time taken?

(c) What is the overall average speed?

5) A car travels for 2 hours at 25 miles/hour and 90 miles at 30 miles/hour.

(a) What is the total time?

(b) Find the total distance.

(c) Find the overall average speed.

6) A plane travels for 3 hours at 500 km/hour and for 2 hours at 650 km/hour. Find the total distance travelled and the overall average speed.

7) Calculate the overall average speed of a journey of 180 miles where the first 120 miles are travelled at an average speed of 40 miles/hour and the remainder at an average speed of 30 miles/hour.

STATISTICAL AVERAGES — — MEAN, MEDIAN AND MODE —

The *mean* is found by adding the numbers and dividing by the number in the set.

The *median* is found by putting the numbers in order and selecting the middle one or the average of the two middle ones.

The *mode* is the number that occurs most frequently.

EXAMPLE

Find the mean, median and mode of these numbers:

6, 6, 6, 7, 7, 8, 8, 10.

The mean is

$$\frac{6+6+6+7+7+8+8+10}{8} = \frac{58}{8} = 7\frac{2}{8}$$
$$= 7\frac{1}{4}$$

The numbers are already in order; the middle ones are both 7, so the median is 7.

The mode is 6 (there are more 6s than any other number).

The mean is the ordinary average that we have already met. Sometimes the median and mode give more suitable information than the mean. The mean can sometimes be distorted by very large or very small numbers.

EXAMPLE

A shop sells 2 pairs of shoes of size 3, 3 pairs of size 4, 5 pairs of size 5 and 2 pairs of size 6 and 1 pair of size 8. Putting these numbers in order:

3, 3, 4, 4, 4, 5, 5, 5, 5, 5, 6, 6, 8

we see that the median is 5. The mode is also 5. More shoes of size 5 are sold than of any other size.

EXERCISE 11

Find the mean, median and mode of these sets of numbers

1) 2, 2, 3, 3, 3, 3, 4, 8

2) 12, 12, 13, 13, 13, 15

3) 1, 1, 1, 1, 5, 10, 10, 11
4) 15, 16, 17, 18, 18
5) 33, 33, 34, 34, 34, 35, 37, 40, 41, 42.
6) A shoe shop sells 3 pairs of shoes of size 4, 5 pairs of size 5, 4 pairs of size 6, 2 pairs of size 7 and 1 pair of size 8. Find the median and the mode.
7) 2 pairs of shoes size 3, 3 pairs size 4, 4 pairs size 5 and 3 pairs size 6 are sold. Find the mean, median and mode.
8) In 8 innings a batsman scores 6, 18, 0, 12, 3, 15, 12 and 10 runs. Find the mean and the median.
9) The numbers of children in 10 neighbouring houses are 2, 3, 3, 5, 0, 1, 2, 6, 0 and 2. Find the mean, median and mode.
10) The weights of 6 apples are 90 g, 90 g, 92 g, 92 g, 92 g and 94 g. Find the mean, median and mode.

The *range* of a set of numbers is the largest minus the smallest.

EXAMPLE

The range of 11, 11, 13, 15, 15, 17 is:

$17 - 11 = 6$

1) Find the range of 15, 15, 17, 18, 21, 24.
2) Find the range of 17, 17, 19, 24, 26.
3) Find the range of 15, 13, 11, 9, 17.
4) Find the range of 62, 65, 67, 69.
5) Find the range of 51, 48, 47, 54, 51.
6) Find the range of 20, 19, 18, 21, 24.

1) Find the average of 0, 2, 3, 5 and 5.
2) Find the average of 14 cm, 15 cm, 17 cm and 19 cm.
3) If the average of 4 numbers is 7 what is their total?
4) 4 boxes have average weight of 512 g. What is their total weight?
5) A batsman scores a total of 255 runs in 5 innings. What is his average?
6) A motorist travels 80 miles at an average speed of 40 miles/hour and spends 2 hours travelling the remaining 60 miles.
   (a) What is the total distance?
   (b) What is the total time?
   (c) What is the overall average speed?

7) A motorist does the first 50 miles of a 90 mile journey at an average speed of 25 miles/hour. In what time must she do the other 40 miles for her overall average speed to be 30 miles/hour?
8) Find the average price per can of:
   3 cans at 30 p
   5 cans at 35 p
   2 cans at 40 p.
9) 400 g of tea at 90 p per 100 g are blended with 500 g of tea at 99 p per 100 g. Find the price of 100 g of the mixture.
10) The numbers of marks gained in seven tests were
    40, 42, 42, 45, 47, 48 and 51.
    (a) Find the mean.
    (b) Find the mode.
    (c) Find the median.
    (d) Find the range.

121

11) A girl gains 6, 7, 7, 7 and 8 marks in five different tests. Find her average mark. Her mark in a sixth test meant that her new average was 1 mark lower than it had been before. Find the mark she obtained in her sixth test.

12) A motorist drives for $3\frac{1}{2}$ hours at an average speed of 50 miles/hour. How far has he travelled? He then travels for $2\frac{1}{2}$ hours at an average speed of 60 miles/hour. What is the total distance he has now travelled? What is the total time? What is his overall average speed?

13) Find the mode of these numbers
2, 3, 0, 0, 1, 2, 0, 0, 4, 0, 5.

14) Find the median of these numbers
7, 5, 4, 6, 11, 2, 3, 0, 12.

15) Find (a) the mean, and (b) the range, of
3, 5, 7, 2, 7, 8, 1, 0, 5 and 4.

11

Money in Business

It is important to keep careful records of all money transactions in business. Each business has its own way of keeping records and the forms will all look slightly different but the ideas behind bookkeeping are the same.

A record must be kept of money coming in (from sales, etc.) and of money going out (for expenses, etc.). These records are kept in special books called *ledgers* (or, more likely nowadays, in *computer files*).

Computer files are stored on tapes or disc.

CASH STATEMENTS

Cash statements are usually in two parts: one for money coming in (*income*) and the other for *expenses* (as shown below).

The three items of *essential information* are
1) the date

2) where the money has come from, or where it is going
3) the amount of money.

This is entered into the statement *being careful to put the information on the correct side.*

The left hand side is totalled. This is the total income.

The right hand side is *made to come to the same total* by including "balance carried down" which is worked out by adding the total expenses and taking this away from the total income.

This working out is not done on the statement but will be done on another piece of paper as shown here:

$$
\begin{array}{ll}
80.00 & 470.00 \\
15.00 & 220.00 - \\
\underline{125.00+} & \underline{250.00} \\
\text{Total expenses } \underline{220.00} & \\
& \text{Balance} = £250
\end{array}
$$

INCOME			EXPENSES		
Date	Particulars	Receipts	Date	Particulars	Payments
		£			£
1 June	Sale of 100 tickets @ £2	200.00	2 June	Hire of hall	80.00
3 June	Sale of 50 tickets @ £3	150.00	5 June	Printing of tickets	15.00
9 June	Sale of 40 tickets @ £4	160.00	11 June	Cost of entertainment	125.00
11 June	Raffle ticket sale	10.00			
				Balance carried down	250.00
	Total	£470.00			£470.00

Draw up a cash statement (in the same way as just shown) for each of these events

1) Village Fete

1 Aug	Hire of six lorries @ £5 per lorry
3 Aug	Paid to farmer for use of his field £35
3 Aug	Hire of stalls from village hall £15
15 Aug	Donation received from local traders £75
24 Aug	Income from sale of tickets at gate £124
24 Aug	Income from raffle £11
24 Aug	Income from stalls £50

2) Sports Club Gymnastic Display

3 May	Hire of hall £50
7 May	Cost of printing tickets £3.75
11 May	Sale of 20 tickets @ £2 each
15 May	Hire of equipment for event £10
17 May	Sale of 25 tickets @ £2 each
20 May	Income from sale of programmes £14
20 May	Sale of tickets at door £50

3) Annual Works Outing

5 July	Received £2 from each of 70 employees
10 July	Hire of two coaches and drivers £75
10 July	Received £35 subsidy from works
15 July	Cost of 72 teas @ £1 each
15 July	Cost of entertainment £25

4) School Sale of Work

10 Jan	Hire of stalls £15
15 Jan	Cost of decorating stalls £7
17 Jan	Income from raffle tickets £15
17 Jan	Income from tickets at door £12
17 Jan	Good-as-new stall profit £56
17 Jan	Other stalls profit £75

PETTY CASH BOOK

The money that offices keep for small everyday expenses, such as stamps, parcel post, etc., is known as *petty cash*. The record of how the money is spent is kept in a petty cash book which might be set out as shown on the opposite page.

The petty cash book is usually ruled into columns so that it is easy to see how much has been spent on postage, travelling expenses, etc.

The office has some money in the petty cash box at the beginning of the week and this is known as "cash in hand" and is entered as *balance in hand* in the petty cash book. (In our example it is £30.00.)

In this example the total week's expenses are £25.31.

So that the cash in hand will be the *same at the start of the following week*, £25.31 will be put into the petty cash box. This is entered in the petty cash book as *reimbursement*. Since the money *goes into* the box it is entered in the left hand column under "receipts".

£25.31

The book is then balanced in a similar way to the cash statement on the previous page. The "balance carried down" is calculated on a separate piece of paper by taking the total payments away from the total receipts:

	£
Total receipts	55.31
Total payments	25.31 −
Balance carried down	30.00

This is then put into the petty cash book as shown.

Receipts	Date	Particulars	Payments	Postage	Stationery	Travelling expenses	Office expenses	Cleaning
30.00	3 May	Balance in hand						
	4 May	Postage	1.24	1.24				
	5 May	Envelopes	0.55		0.55			
	5 May	Bus fares	1.70			1.70		
	5 May	String	0.62		0.62			
	6 May	Window cleaner	4.00					4.00
	6 May	Parcel post	0.70	0.70				
	6 May	Pencils	0.40		0.40			
	7 May	Office tea	0.60				0.60	
	7 May	Rail fares	3.50			3.50		
	7 May	Cleaners' wages	12.00					12.00
		Totals	25.31	1.94	1.57	5.20	0.60	16.00
25.31	7 May	Reimbursement						
		Balance carried down	30.00					
55.31			55.31					

EXERCISE 2

1) Rule lines as shown in the example above and enter these items as if you were writing them into a petty cash book

   5 Jan   Petty cash balance in hand £40.00
   6 Jan   Postage £3.10
   6 Jan   Window cleaner £3.50
   6 Jan   String 65 p
   7 Jan   Ballpoint pens 35 p
   7 Jan   Rail fares £4.50
   8 Jan   Cleaners' wages £10
   8 Jan   Taxi fares £4.50
   9 Jan   Office coffee 95 p
   9 Jan   Telegram £2.10
   9 Jan   Envelopes 65 p
   9 Jan   Reimbursement £30.30

2) Draw up a page of a petty cash book with these items

   4 May   Cash in hand £30.00
   4 May   Envelopes 60 p
   4 May   Office tea 70 p
   5 May   Pencils 35 p
   5 May   Window cleaner £2.50
   5 May   Taxi fare £1.75
   5 May   Postage £1.35
   6 May   Typewriter ribbon £1.10
   6 May   Wages for cleaning £15
   6 May   Bus fares £1.45
   7 May   Parcel post £1.35
   7 May   Office coffee 92 p
   8 May   Photocopying £1.04
   8 May   Ballpoint pens 55 p
   8 May   Reimbursement £28.66

125

INVOICES

An invoice is a record of goods supplied to a customer, together with the cost. It is *not* a bill although it looks similar.

The invoice has the supplier's name, address and telephone number, the cost, number and type of articles and various totals and reference numbers. Space is also left for discounts and VAT. (By law discounts must be applied before VAT is calculated.)

The column labelled "gross" is calculated by multiplying "qty" (quantity) by "unit cost".

INVOICE

D. THORNEYCROFT
14 PRINCES ST
WILDON
GB6 8LX

125-6301

Ref. No	Qty	Description	Unit Cost	Gross	Discount	VAT
A/501	3	Ladies coats	£45	£135.00	10%	15%
A/603	5	Mens jackets	£60	£300.00	10%	15%

	£435
Less 10% discount	43.50
	391.50
Plus 15% VAT	58.72½
	£450.22½

Despatched
by Harvey &
Peters Deliveries

126

Copy these simplified invoices and complete
the last column in each.

1)

	J. SMITH & CO **17 LONDON RD** **TAXERBY** **TEL 62-1251**		
Qty	**Description**	**Unit Cost**	**Gross**
20	Children's dresses	£2.50	
15	Prs. children's socks	£0.50	
10	Children's cardigans	£1.50	
20	Small woolly hats	£0.50	
Discount 0.00%			
VAT 0.00%			
SALES INVOICE			

2)

	P. WILLIAMS LTD **44 SMITH ST** **BAXBY** **TEL 28-1134**		
Qty	**Description**	**Unit Cost**	**Gross**
40	Small cakes	6 p	
20	Loaves bread	30 p	
60	Buns	5 p	
25	Pkts. biscuits	4 p	
Discount 0.00%			
VAT 0.00%			
SALES INVOICE			

Copy each of the simplified invoices below and
fill in the last column. Calculate the total. Work
out 10% discount (by dividing by 10) and take
this away from the total. Fill in the final box.

1)

SELBERTON 5428	**INVOICE**		**J. GREEN** **24 ASH AVE.** **SELBERTON**
Qty	**Description**	**Unit cost**	**Gross**
4	Bags apples	£2.00	
5	Boxes oranges	£8.00	
3	Crates pears	£5.00	
TOTAL GROSS			
LESS 10% **DISCOUNT**			
VAT ZERO RATED			

2)

RANDALLS **3 LONG LA** **TYDFORD**	**INVOICE**		**TYDFORD 121**
Qty	**Description**	**Unit Cost**	**Gross**
20	Single sheets	£ 5.25	
25	Double sheets	£ 8.00	
10	Pillow cases	£ 4.75	
15	Bedspreads	£24.00	
TOTAL GROSS			
LESS 10% **DISCOUNT**			
VAT 0.00%			

Make up your own invoices for each of the following suppliers

3) From: R. Evans
101 Dark Street
Bevington
Tel. Bevington 3035

Discount 10%
VAT zero rated
33 jars coffee @ 50 p per jar
20 tins soup @ 15 p per tin
10 boxes biscuits @ £2 per box
50 tins fruit @ 20 p per tin
40 pkts sugar @ 30 p per pkt

4) From: J. Saunders
45 James Street
Oxminster
Tel. Oxminster 1139

Discount 10%
VAT zero rated
10 Maths books @ £2.10
30 French books @ £3
15 English books @ £2
10 Geography books @ £4.35
25 History books @ £2.50

THE ELECTRONIC CALCULATOR

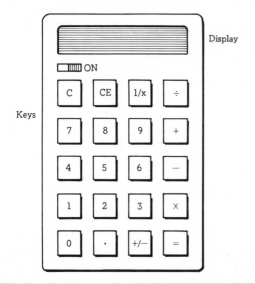

C "Clear" key — this clears the calculator

CE "Clear last entry" key — this only clears the last entry

Most offices have a calculator available for working out sums of money quickly and, if used properly, it can be a most valuable tool.

To work out the sum of £6.50, 75p and £4.35 the keys pressed would be

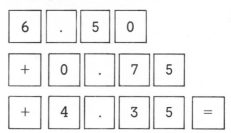

and the answer which is £11.60 would appear on the calculator as $\boxed{11.6}$ in the display.

To work out the cost of 7 items @ £4.37$\frac{1}{2}$ the keys pressed would be

and the answer which is £30.62$\frac{1}{2}$ would appear on the calculator as $\boxed{30.625}$ in the display.

Notice especially that:

£11.60 on a calculator is 11.6 and

£30.62$\frac{1}{2}$ on a calculator is 30.625

Since each calculator is slightly different it is advisable to read the maker's instructions very carefully because these will tell you the meaning of all the different buttons and what happens if you make an error.

6 p would be entered on a calculator as 0.06

2$\frac{1}{2}$ p would be entered as 0.025

Using a calculator work out the following

1) £5.23 + £3.15 + £4.89
2) £4.50 + £6.25 + £3.75
3) £15.88 + £0.72 + £43.95
4) £6.47 + 72 p + £1.20
5) £5.62½ + £3.12½
6) £124 + £356 + £780
7) £0.52½ + £1.27 + £0.17½ + £0.03½
8) £5600 + £340 + £279.50
9) £64.57½ + £32.57 + £45.11
10) £507 899 + £43 777
11) 56 p + 45 p + 13 p + 79 p + 5 p
12) 85 p + £4.50 + 25 p + 4½ p

Using a calculator work out the following

13) 6 × £3.50
14) 9 × £35.12
15) 11 × £45
16) 24 × £72.35½
17) 30 × £0.35
18) 257 × £51.60
19) the cost of 3 items @ £5.67
20) the cost of 7 items @ £0.88
21) the cost of 15 items @ 45 p
22) the cost of 90 items @ £5.60½
23) the cost of 208 items @ £0.03
24) the cost of 500 items @ 7½ p

Using a calculator work out the following

25) A man saws a plank of wood 171 cm long into 5 equal pieces. How long is each piece? Each piece is sold for £0.87½. What is the cost of 3 pieces?

26) 12 000 beads are made into 250 necklaces. How many beads are there in each necklace? Each bead is worth 3 p. How much is each necklace worth?

27) Which is the best buy: 2 oz coffee @ 53 p; 4 oz coffee @ 95 p; 8 oz coffee @ £1.72 or 1 lb coffee @ £3.04? (Hint: work out the price per oz for each.)

28) Find the change from a £10 note after spending £5.21, £4.18 and 14 p.

29) £7.65½ is subtracted from £214.12. How much is left?

30) A firm pays £1050 in wages equally to 25 people. How much does each get?

Since $15\% = \dfrac{15}{100} = 0.15$ we can work out 15% (for VAT calculations) by *multiplying by 0.15.*

EXAMPLE

Find 15% of £76.52.

We press the keys:

| 0 | . | 1 | 5 |

| × | 7 | 6 | . | 5 | 2 | = |

and find that the display reads:

| 11.478 |

Since 11.478 is nearer to 11.48 than 11.47, then 15% of £76.52 = £11.48 to the nearest penny.

Find (to the nearest penny) 15% of

1) £100
2) £200
3) £500
4) £750
5) £960
6) £2525
7) £533.45
8) £970.21
9) £3350.40
10) Copy the simplified invoice opposite. Fill in the last column. Calculate the total gross. Calculate 10% discount and *take this away*. Calculate 15% VAT and *add this on*. Fill in the final box.

P. SMITH 2 OAK LANE SELBY	INVOICE			SELBY 141 FURNITURE

Ref No	Unit cost	Qty	Description	Gross
A/71	£185.00	3	Cupboards	
A/62	£169.00	7	Tables	
A/43	£40.00	14	Chairs	

TOTAL GROSS	
LESS 10% DISCOUNT	
PLUS 15% VAT	

12

Wages and Salaries

If you work for an employer you are paid a wage or a salary. Wages are usually paid weekly and salaries monthly.

PAYMENT BY THE HOUR

The amount paid per hour up to a certain limit (called the *basic week*) is known as the hourly or *basic rate*. After that overtime is paid.

EXAMPLE

A man works a basic week of 38 hours at a basic rate of £3 per hour. Calculate his total wage for the week.

38 hours at £3 per hour = 38 × £3 = £114

His total wage is £114.

EXAMPLE

£164 is paid for a basic week of 40 hours. What is the hourly rate?

$$\text{Hourly rate} = \frac{£164}{40} = £4.10$$

EXERCISE 1

1) A woman works a basic week of 40 hours and her basic rate is £3 an hour. Calculate her total wage for the week.

2) £200 is paid for a basic week of 40 hours. Calculate the hourly rate.

3) Calculate the total wage for a 38 hour week if the basic rate is (a) £2 (b) £2.50 (c) £3 (d) £4.25.

4) Calculate the hourly rate for a 40 hour week if the total wage is (a) £120 (b) £160 (c) £180 (d) £200.

5) The basic week is 37 hours and the basic rate is £3 an hour. Find the total wage for a basic week.

6) What is the total wage for a basic week of $37\frac{1}{2}$ hours at a basic rate of (a) £3 (b) £3.50 (c) £4 (d) £4.50 per hour?

OVERTIME

Work done extra to the basic week is usually paid at "time and a quarter", "time and a third", "time and a half" or "double time".

EXAMPLE

Find the hourly rate of overtime at (a) time and a half (b) time and a third on a basic rate of £4.80.

Overtime at time and a half $= 1\frac{1}{2} \times £4.80$

$$= £4.80 + £2.40$$

$$= £7.20$$

Overtime at time and a third $= 1\frac{1}{3} \times £4.80$

$$= £4.80 + £1.60$$

$$= £6.40$$

EXAMPLE

A basic rate of £5.60 is paid. Find the hourly rate of overtime at (a) double time (b) time and a quarter.

Overtime at double time $= 2 \times £5.60$

$$= £11.20$$

Overtime at time and a quarter $= 1\frac{1}{4} \times £5.60$

$$= £5.60$$

$$+ £1.40$$

$$= £7.00$$

EXERCISE 2

1) Find the hourly overtime rate at time and a half on a basic rate of (a) £4 (b) £7 (c) £6.20 (d) £3.60.

2) What is the hourly overtime rate at time and a third on a basic rate of (a) £6 (b) £9 (c) £3.30 (d) £4.20?

3) A basic rate of £3.20 is paid. Find the hourly overtime rate at (a) double time (b) time and a quarter.

---

4) Time and a quarter is paid for overtime. What is the hourly overtime rate on a basic rate of (a) £4 (b) £8 (c) £2 (d) £3?

5) Find the hourly overtime rate at time and a half on a basic rate of (a) £7.56 (b) £5.98 (c) £3.79 (d) £4.57.

PIECEWORK

Sometimes people are paid a fixed amount for each piece of work they make.

Often if they can make more than a certain amount they are paid a *bonus*.

EXAMPLE

A seamstress in a factory is paid 5 p for each handpuppet she makes up to 200 per day. For each handpuppet over 200 she is paid a bonus of 2 p. Calculate how much she earns if she makes 250 handpuppets.

Money earned on first 200 $= 200 \times 5p$

$$= £10.00$$

Money earned on next 50 $= 50 \times 7p = £3.50$

Total earned $= £13.50$

EXERCISE 3

1) A woman is paid 3 p for each lb of sausages that she packs up to a limit of 500. After that she earns a bonus of 1 p. Calculate how much she earns if she packs 600 lb of sausages.

2) A man is paid 4 p for each spot weld he makes up to a limit of 400. After that he earns a bonus of 2 p. Calculate how much he earns if he makes 600 spot welds.

3) 3 p is paid for each handle fixed up to a limit of 300 after which 4 p is paid per handle. Calculate how much is paid if 350 handles are fixed.

4) A pieceworker receives $3\frac{1}{2}$ p for each buttonhole sewn up to a limit of 80. After that she earns $4\frac{1}{2}$ p per buttonhole. Find how much she earns if she sews 150 buttonholes.

5) For each article up to a limit of 250 a pieceworker is paid 6 p. After that she is paid 7 p per article. Find how much she earns for completing 300 articles.

6) A man is paid 15 p for each plate he decorates up to a limit of 100 plates. After that he is paid a bonus of 5 p per plate. Find how much he earns if he decorates 120 plates.

COMMISSION

Sales people are usually paid a commission on top of their basic wage. This is calculated as a percentage of the value of the goods they sell.

EXAMPLE

A salesman is paid a commission of 2% on goods sold. Calculate the commission if he sells goods worth £500.

$$2\% \text{ of } £500 = \frac{2}{100} \times £500 = £10$$

The commission is £10.

EXAMPLE

A shop assistant is paid a basic wage of £80 and she sells goods to the value of £1000 on which she gets 2% commission. How much does she earn?

$$\text{The commission} = 2\% \text{ of } £1000$$

$$= \frac{2}{100} \times £1000 = £20$$

She earns £80 + £20 = £100.

EXERCISE 4

1) Find the commission at 2% on goods worth
   (a) £100 (b) £200 (c) £250 (d) £300
   (e) £575.

2) A car is sold for £2000 and the salesman gets 3% commission. How much does the salesman get?

3) 3% commission is paid on goods worth £400. How much is this?

4) Furniture worth £800 is sold by a salesman who gets $2\frac{1}{2}$% commission. Find the amount the salesman gets.

5) A woman earns £50 a week and gets 2% commission on goods sold worth £300. Find her earnings for the week.

6) Commission of 2% is paid on a sale of £400. How much is the commission?

SALARIES

Salaried workers, such as teachers or civil servants, earn a fixed amount per year. The money is usually paid monthly. They do not earn commission or get paid for overtime.

EXAMPLE

A civil servant earns £7200 p.a. How much is this per month?

Monthly salary = £7200 ÷ 12 = £600

— EXERCISE 5 —

These are the salaries of eight people. How much is each paid monthly?

1) £3600
2) £6000
3) £9000
4) £9600
5) £9648
6) £3720
7) £4080
8) £5400

Of course these are not the amounts that are actually taken home. To work out someone's *take home pay* certain amounts have to be deducted first. The main items are income tax (see Chapter 13), National Insurance and payments towards a pension fund.

Before deductions the wage (or salary) is known as the GROSS wage (or salary).

After deductions the wage (or salary) is known as the NET wage (or salary)

— NATIONAL INSURANCE —

Both employers and employees pay National Insurance. Employees pay a certain percentage of their gross wage (9% in 1983). Married women and widows can pay at a reduced rate (3.85% in 1983). There are upper and lower limits fixed by the Chancellor of the Exchequer. These limits and the rate of National Insurance can vary from year to year. National Insurance pays for such things as sick pay and unemployment benefit.

— PENSION FUND —

Because the state pension is small, many firms operate their own private pension fund schemes to provide extra pensions. (*This used to be called superannuation.*) Both employer and employee contribute. The employee's contribution is about 5% or 6% of his or her annual (yearly) salary before deductions. The amount of pension received depends on length of service and earnings at the time of retirement. Some schemes are "transferable" when an employee changes jobs, but many are not.

			NET £690
Payslip	**Totals to date**	**Deductions**	**This payment**
Mr. P.W. Green Assist. Sales Mngr.	Gross £12 000 Tax £2640 Pen £480 NI £600	NI(D) £50 Tax £220 Pen £40	Basic £1000
Pay Mar 81 by C/T			
			Total £1000 Dedns £310
Tax month 12 J. Smith Ltd	NI BK415002B	Code 320H	Net £690
Joined 14 01 74	1 mth @ £12 000 p.a.		

EXAMPLE

A manager earns £12 000 a year. £2640 are deducted for income tax, £600 for National Insurance and £480 for the pension fund. Calculate the take home pay per month.

$$£$$

The deductions are   2640
                       600
                       480
                      ―――
                      3720

Yearly salary after deductions is

£12 000 − £3720 = £8280

Monthly take home pay is

£8280 ÷ 12 = £690

The manager's payslip for the last month of the year is shown at the bottom of the previous page.

―――――――― EXERCISE 6 ――――――――

(A calculator will be useful for some of these questions.)

1) A man earns £6000 a year. £1200 are deducted for income tax, £465 for National Insurance and £300 for his pension fund. Find his yearly take home pay after deductions. Divide this by 12 to find his monthly take home pay.

2) Calculate the amount paid into a pension fund at a rate of 5% on a yearly salary of £7000.

3) How much National Insurance is paid at the rate of 8% on an annual salary of £8500?

4) A woman earns £85 per week. Her deductions are £14 for income tax, £6.50 for National Insurance and £4.25 for the pension fund. Calculate her take home pay for the week.

5) National Insurance is paid at the rate of 7% on an annual salary of £6400. How much National Insurance is paid? With a calculator find how much National Insurance would be paid at a rate of $7\frac{3}{4}$%.

6) How much is paid into the pension fund scheme if the rate is 6% on an annual salary of £6500?

7) An employer pays 14% of an employee's wage of £8000 towards National Insurance. How much does the employer pay?

8) A man's weekly wage is £105.75 and his total deductions are £34.73. What is his weekly take home pay?

9) Income tax of £76.50, National Insurance of £31.50 and payment to a pension fund scheme of £25.20 are deducted from a monthly salary of £420. What is the take home pay?

10) A woman is paid £3 per hour for a 40 hour week. Calculate her total weekly wage. Calculate the amount she pays weekly towards her pension if she pays 6% of her total weekly wage.

―――――――― EXERCISE 7 ――――――――

1) A man works a 40 hour basic week at £2.50 an hour. Calculate his total weekly wage.

2) £156 is paid for a basic week of 39 hours. Calculate the hourly rate.

3) Find the hourly overtime rate at (a) time and a half (b) time and a third on a basic rate of £6.60.

4) A man works a basic week of 40 hours at £2 an hour. He then earns overtime at time and a half. Find his weekly wage for 44 hours' work.

5) A woman earns £86. Her basic rate is £2 for a 40 hour week. She works 2 hours overtime. What is her overtime hourly rate?

6) A pieceworker earns 2 p for each article she makes up to a limit of 40 articles. She then earns 3 p per article. How much is she paid for 50 articles?

7) 2% commission is paid on a sale worth £600. How much is this?

8) How much commission at 2% would a salesman get if he sold £350 worth of goods?

9) What is the monthly gross salary of a manager who is paid £9600 per year?

10) Find the weekly take home pay of a woman who earns £90 gross per week and has £6.30 deducted for National Insurance, £15.46 deducted for income tax and pays £5.40 towards her pension fund.

13

Money in the Community

Rates are paid by owners and tenants of property. This money is used by Local Authorities to pay for such things as education and libraries. Every property has a *rateable value* (RV) dependent on its size and condition.

Rateable value £700

Rateable value £250

Rateable value £375

Yearly rates = Rateable value × Rate in the £

EXAMPLE

The RV of a house is £400. If the rate is 80p in the £ how much must the owner pay in rates?

The yearly rates = 400 × 80p = £320

The owner pays £320 per year in rates.

EXAMPLE

If the rate is £1.20 in the £ and the RV of a house is £300 what are the yearly rates?

The yearly rates = 300 × £1.20 = £360

EXERCISE 1

1) The RV of a house is £200. If the rate is 40 p in the £ how much must the owner pay per year?

2) If an owner pays £70 rates per quarter (13 weeks) how much is paid per year?

3) An owner pays £200 in rates per year. The RV is £400. What is the rate in the £?

4) Copy and complete this table

Rateable value (RV)	Rate in the £	Yearly rates
£200	50 p	
£200	80 p	
£200	£1.20	
£300	50 p	
£300	£1.50	
£350	70 p	
£400	75 p	
£400	£1.20	
£400	£1.50	
£500	75 p	
£500	85 p	
£500	£1.20	

MORTGAGES

If a person buying a house cannot pay outright, he or she arranges a loan called a *mortgage* from a Building Society or a Bank. They generally have to pay a *deposit* of about 5% or 10% although occasionally 100% mortgages are available.

Cost £30 000

Deposit £3000
Mortgage £27 000
(loan from the Building Society)

Repayments about £348 a month @ 15% interest over 25 years

The loan + interest is paid back over perhaps 20 or 25 years. The interest rate sometimes varies according to whether the Building Society has plenty of money available or not. (If more people save with a particular Building Society it will have more money for mortgages.)

EXAMPLE

A woman wishes to buy a house costing £24 000. She pays 10% deposit. How much mortgage does she need?

Deposit = 10% of £24 000 = £2400 (to find 10% divide by 10)

She needs £24 000 − £2400 = £21 600 mortgage

EXAMPLE

The monthly repayments of a mortgage are £352. What is paid per year?

Yearly repayments = 12 × £352 = £4224

EXERCISE 2

Copy and complete this table

House price	Deposit @ 10%	Mortgage needed	Monthly repayments	Yearly repayments
£15 000			£174	
£20 000			£232	
£25 000			£290	
£30 000			£348	
£37 500			£435	
£42 500			£493	
£53 000			£615	
£55 000			£638	

INSURANCE

The loss from being burgled or suffering fire damage can be so serious that many people take out *insurance policies*. (They are then called *policy holders*.) They pay an insurance *premium* each year. The Insurance Company collects the premiums from thousands of people and invests the money to earn interest. This money is then available to pay out to the people who *claim* for their loss.

People can also insure against injury and car accidents. A car has to be insured by law. Car owners who have had no accidents are usually allowed a *no claims bonus* which means they do not have to pay so much premium.

EXAMPLE

A house and its contents are valued at £30 000. An insurance company charges a premium of £3 per £1000 of insurance. How much premium is charged per year?

Yearly premium = 30 × £3 = £90

EXAMPLE

The insurance on a car is £120 but the owner is allowed $33\frac{1}{3}$ % no claims bonus. How much does he pay per year?

$$33\frac{1}{3}\% = \frac{1}{3} \text{ so he allowed } \frac{1}{3} \text{ of £120} = £40$$

He has to pay £120 − £40 = £80 per year

EXERCISE 3

1) An insurance company charges £1.50 per £1000 of insurance. Find the yearly premium to insure for £3000.

2) An insurance company charges £1.50 per £1000 of insurance. Find how much has to be paid per year to insure for £8000.

3) The insurance on a car is £100 but 20% no claims bonus is allowed. How much premium is paid per year?

4) 20% no claims bonus is allowed on insurance for a car of £120. What is the premium?

G

5) If the premium on £5000 is £10 how much would the premium be on (a) £1000 (b) £10 000 (c) £4000?

6) If the premium on £6000 is £9, what would it be on (a) £1000 (b) £7000?

LIFE ASSURANCE

A person may take out life assurance if, when he or she dies, they want their *dependants* (widow/widower, children) to receive a lump sum of money.

The premiums depend on (a) *age* (the older the person, the more money he or she has to pay) and (b) *the amount of money the widow/widower and children are to receive* (the larger the amount the larger the premium).

With *Endowment Assurance*, at the end of a fixed period of time a lump sum is paid anyway. With *Whole Life Assurance* there is no fixed time.

Some assurance schemes include a *bonus that is based on the profits* that the Insurance Company makes.

EXERCISE 4

Look at the table at the foot of this page, which is for a 10 year Endowment Plan with bonus and then answer the questions.

1) What is the minimum guaranteed sum assured if a man pays a net monthly premium of £10 from age (a) 30 (b) 35 (c) 37 (d) 40?

2) What is the possible maturity value if a woman pays a net monthly premium of £50 from age (a) 25 (b) 29 (c) 36 (d) 39?

10 YEAR BONUS ENDOWMENT PLAN					
The *Guaranteed Sum Assured* is the minimum amount your policy is guaranteed to pay. The *Possible Maturity Value* is the possible return with bonus.					
Age today		For net monthly premium of £10		For net monthly premium of £50	
Male	Female	Guaranteed sum assured	Possible maturity value	Guaranteed sum assured	Possible maturity value
Up to	Up to	£	£	£	£
28	32	1257	2133	6649	11 283
29	33	1257	2133	6648	11 281
30	34	1256	2132	6646	11 278
31	35	1256	2132	6643	11 273
32	36	1255	2129	6641	11 270
33	37	1255	2129	6638	11 264
34	38	1254	2128	6634	11 258
35	39	1253	2126	6630	11 251
36	40	1252	2125	6624	11 241
37	41	1251	2123	6618	11 231
38	42	1249	2119	6610	11 217
39	43	1248	2118	6601	11 202
40	44	1246	2115	6592	11 187

3) What is (a) the minimum guaranteed sum assured and (b) the possible maturity value if a man pays £10 a month from age 32?

4) If a man pays £10 a month over 10 years how much has he paid to the insurance company altogether?

5) What is (a) the minimum guaranteed sum assured and (b) the possible maturity value if a woman pays £50 a month from age 40?

6) If a woman pays £50 a month over 10 years how much has she paid in premiums altogether?

INCOME TAX

Every person who earns money above a certain level pays income tax. The government uses the tax revenue to pay for the National Health Service, roads, the Civil Service, etc.

Tax is not paid on the whole income. Allowances are made for some expenses incurred during work, interest paid on life assurance and mortgages, dependent relatives, etc. A *personal allowance* is made which varies according to whether the tax payer is single or married.

The income left after the allowances have been deducted is known as *taxable income*:

(the Chancellor of the Exchequer may vary the rate of tax in the Budget).

EXAMPLE

A man's salary is £9000. He is allowed a personal allowance of £2445 and income tax relief of £594 on interest on his Building Society mortgage and relief on his pension fund

payments of £540. Calculate his taxable income. He pays tax at the standard rate of 30%. Find the amount he has to pay in income tax.

Allowances:	£
Personal	2445
Interest on Building Society mortgage	594
Pension fund payments (superannuation)	540
Total allowances	3579

Taxable income = £9000 − £3579 = £5421

Tax payable = 30% of £5421 = $\dfrac{30}{100} \times £5421$

= £1626.30

"PAYE"

Most people pay income tax by a method known as "Pay As You Earn" or PAYE for short. The tax is taken off their wage or salary before they receive it.

The tax payer and the employer receive a notice of coding which gives the employee's allowances (based on forms he or she has filled in) and gives a code number. The employer then knows from tax tables the amount of tax to deduct from the wages of the employee. (A typical notice of coding is shown overleaf.)

EXERCISE 5

1) A man has a taxable income of £2000 and pays tax at the rate of 30%. How much does he pay in income tax?

2) From an income of £6000, allowances of £3355 are deducted. Tax is paid on the rest at a rate of 30%. Find the taxable income and the amount of income tax paid.

3) A man earns £8000. He has a personal allowance of £2445 and an allowance of £590 for a loan. He is allowed relief on

his mortgage interest payments of £360. Find his total allowable deductions. Work out his taxable income. Find the amount of income tax he pays at 30% on his taxable income.

4) The total (gross) income of a woman is £5600. Her allowances are

Personal allowance	£1565
Expenses	£55

Calculate her total allowances. Find her taxable income.

She pays income tax at 30%. Find the amount of income tax she pays. Find her take home pay when she pays £392 National Insurance.

5) Deductions of £3415 are allowed on an income of £7435. Find the amount of income tax paid at 30% and the take home pay.

──────────── **EXERCISE 6** ────────────

1) The rateable value of a house is £350. The rate is 80p in the £. How much does the owner of the house pay in rates per year?

2) The tenant of a house pays £280 in rates per year. How much does he pay per quarter?

3) A woman pays 10% deposit on a house costing £17 500. How much mortgage does she need?

4) The monthly repayments of a mortgage are £320. How much is this per year?

5) How much has to be paid to insure for £7500 if the insurance company quotes £1.50 per £1000?

6) $33\frac{1}{3}$% no claims bonus is allowed on car insurance of £150. What is the premium after the no claims bonus has been deducted?

7) If a man pays £10 a month for life assurance over 15 years how much has he paid altogether?

8) Calculate the income tax to be paid at 30% on a taxable income of £4150.

This is a typical notice of coding:

NOTICE OF CODING	
FOR 1983 YOUR CODE IS 276 H	
Your Allowances	£
Expenses	
Death and Superannuation Benefits	15
Building Society interest payable	595
Loan, etc. interest payable	
Personal	2154
Age (estimated total income £ . . . . . .)	
Wife's earned income	
Additional personal	
Dependent relative	
Widow's bereavement	
. . . .	
. . . .	
Total Allowances	2764
LESS: Allowances given against other income	
Untaxed interest	
Occupational pensions	
National Insurance benefits	
. . . .	
. . . .	
Net Allowances	2764
LESS: Adjustments	
. . . .	
Tax unpaid for earlier years	
ALLOWANCES GIVEN AGAINST PAY/OCCUPATIONAL PENSION	2764

(Pension fund payments are deducted before tax is calculated but do not now appear on this form.)

14

Household Bills and Personal Loans

GAS BILLS

Overleaf is a typical gas bill. It gives the name and address of the Gas Company, the name and address of the gas user, the present and previous gas meter readings, the amount of gas used in both cubic feet and therms, the cost per therm, and the total cost of gas used. There is also a *standing charge* (of £8.00). The total gas bill to be paid is in the "total due" box at the bottom of the bill. Gas is "zero rated" which means that no VAT is added to a gas bill. At the top of the bill is a date labelled "consumption to" and on this bill it is 15 12 82 which means the bill is for the quarter ending 15 December 1982. Bills are paid *quarterly* so you get *four* bills a year.

EXERCISE 1

1) Look at the gas bill overleaf and answer these questions

   (a) How much does the customer have to pay?

   (b) Write down the present meter reading and subtract from it the previous meter reading. How many cubic feet have been used?

(c) Add the standing charge to the cost of gas used and check that the bill is correct.

2) Gas is measured first in cubic feet and this is changed into therms. *To find the cost of gas used we multiply the number of therms used by the charge per therm.* Copy and complete this table

Charge per therm	Number of therms used	Cost of gas used	
		In pence	In pounds
20 p	100		
24 p	100		
24 p	200		
24 p	250		
24.8 p	100		
24.8 p	200		
24.8 p	300		
24.8 p	350		

3) Some gas meters look like this

which shows a reading of 1720 cubic feet.

143

NEGAS

A PART OF THE BRITISH GAS CORPORATION

**Central Accounts Office
Gower St. Leeds LS2 7RG**

Account queries
Telephone
Leeds:

MR J BROWN
14 Smith Street
Skelmanthorne
Huddersfield   HD2 1JP

Tax point & date of account 18 12 82

Consumption to
15 12 82

VAT Ref No 232 177091

346 Domestic Credit Tariff

Declared Calorific Value 39.0 MJ/m³ (1045 Btu's per cu ft)

*	Meter reading		'C'	†	Gas supplied		Pence per therm	Amount	VAT code
	Present	Previous			Cubic ft (Hundreds)	Therms			
	1119	784			335	350.08			
						350.08	27.20	95.22	1
STANDING CHARGE								8.00	1
								103.22	

VAT analysis	Goods	Rate	Amount	
Code 1	103.22	0.00%	0.00	

Account Ref for Enquiries			
D51	D32	0691	0002

Due £103.22

TOTAL

* Estimated reading
'C' Customers reading
† Deducted consumption

For unreasonable estimate
complete details on back
and return within 7 days

Copy these sets of dials and put in arrows to show readings of

(a) 3541 cubic feet

(b) 1500 cubic feet

(c) 9513 cubic feet

4) Write down how many cubic feet these meters show

(a)

(b)

(c)

Take care! If the arrows are *between* two numbers then take the smaller number *except* when the arrow is between 9 and 0. In this case take 9 as the reading.

5) Gas meters are read every quarter. If the reading was 2500 at the beginning of the quarter and 3712 at the end of the quarter how many cubic feet were used?

_____

ELECTRICITY BILLS

Electricity is charged according to the number of units used. There is also a *fixed charge* which is added to the bill. Like gas, electricity is zero rated, so no VAT is charged. Bills are paid every quarter so there will be four bills per year.

EXERCISE 2

Look at the electricity bill overleaf and answer these questions

1) How much does the customer have to pay?
2) How many units were used?
3) What is the cost per unit?
4) What is the fixed charge?
5) Multiply the cost per unit by the number of units used and give your answer in pounds and pence (to the nearest penny).
6) Add the fixed charge to the cost of electricity used and check that the bill is correct.
7) Give the total amount payable for these bills

	£
(a) fixed charge	5.82
1000 units @ 5.17 p per unit	____
	____
(b) fixed charge	5.82
1500 units @ 5.17 p per unit	____
	____

8) On what date was the meter read?

_____

145

Yorkshire Electricity Board

PBXG2 Limewood Approach Leeds LS15
VAT Registration Number 238 5679 21

Please quote this reference
when making enquiries
3   191   6132   63

MR D JONES
148 Oak Lane
Leeds LS24 1JP

Meter reading date 9 Dec 1982

Tax point and
date of issue 15 Dec 1982

Meter readings		Units supplied	Units and unit rates charged						Fixed charges	Amount £	VAT %
Present	Previous		@	p	@	p		5.17p			
44989	43544	01445						1445	5.82	80.53	0

E – estimated
R – customers own
    reading

AMOUNT NOW DUE AND PAYABLE £ 80.53

TELEPHONE BILLS

Telephone bills are paid quarterly so there will be four bills a year. There is a charge for *rental* (under rental and other standing charges) and a charge is made for the number of units used. VAT is charged at the rate of 15%.

You will notice that although the exact amount £28.638 appears on the bill as £28.63½, the ½ p is not in fact charged to the customer. (Compare this with the "rounding up" that occurred on the electricity bill.)

EXERCISE 3

Give the total cost of these telephone bills

                  £

1) (a) standing charge   16.15
       100 units @ 4.3 p per unit   ———

                    ———

  (b) standing charge   16.15
       600 units @ 4.3 p per unit   ———

                    ———

  (c) standing charge   16.15
       450 units @ 4.3 p per unit   ———

                    ———

  (d) standing charge   16.15
       325 units @ 4.3 p per unit   ———

                    ———

2) The meter reading on 13 May is 009850 and on 10 Feb is 008950. How many units have been used between 10 Feb and 13 May?

3) If 566 units have been used between 13 May and 4 Aug and the meter reading on 13 May is 009850, what will the meter reading be on 4 Aug?

4) Telephone bills for the year were £48.70, £31.90, £46.50 and £35.90. How much was spent on the telephone during the whole year?

5) A family expects to pay about £156 a year on their telephone. How much would they expect to pay per quarter?

This is a typical telephone bill:

British Telecom

BRADFORD AREA TELEPHONE HOUSE 11 BROADWAY BRADFORD W YORKSHIRE B2 LLW P8	MR. A. EVANS 2 LONDON RD DENBY DALE HUDDERSFIELD HD1 2IB
Telephone Number Huddersfield . . .	DATE OF BILL 15 FEB 82

	£
Rental and other standing charges From 1 FEB – 30 APR	16.15

Metered units	Date	Meter reading	
	2 NOV	008284	
	10 FEB	008950	
Units used		666 at 4.30p	28.63½

Total (exclusive of VAT)	44.78½
Value Added Tax at 15 %	6.71
TOTAL PAYABLE	51.49

Tick box if *receipt required*	☐

— COST OF RUNNING A CAR —

To find how much it costs to run a car, *tax*, *insurance*, *petrol*, *repairs and maintenance*, and *depreciation* must all be taken into account. "Depreciation" means by how much the car has gone down in value during the year.

EXAMPLE

A car is bought for £2500 and after 1 year is valued at £2000. During the year it did 7500 miles at an average of 25 miles to the gallon. Petrol cost £1.80 a gallon on average through the year. Insurance cost £120, tax £80 and repairs and maintenance £250. Find the total cost of the year's motoring.

	£
Depreciation	500
Insurance	120
Tax	80
Repairs and maintenance	250
Cost of petrol $\dfrac{\overset{300}{\cancel{7500}}}{\underset{1}{\cancel{25}}} \times £1.80$	
	540
Total cost of year's motoring	£1490

1) A man estimates the cost of his motoring as follows

Depreciation	£650
Insurance	£135
Tax	£80
Cost of petrol	£650
Repairs	£242

Find the total cost of the year's motoring.

2) A car is bought for £3000 and sold the next year for £2050. It travelled 5200 miles at 26 miles to the gallon and petrol cost £1.80 per gallon on average. Insurance was £110. Tax was £80 and repairs and maintenance £85. Find (a) the depreciation and (b) the cost of petrol for 5200 miles. (c) Calculate the total cost of the year's motoring.

3) How much does it cost to travel 150 miles at the average cost of 6p per mile?

4) If a man travels 2600 miles at a total cost of £130 find the average cost per mile.

5) A car is bought for £3500 and sold 4 years later for £1500. Find by how much the car has depreciated in value per year.

6) A woman travels 320 miles a week. She uses 8 gallons of petrol. How many miles per gallon is this?

7) How much does it cost to buy 7 gallons of petrol at £1.80 per gallon?

8) If £12 a week are spent on petrol how much is spent per year?

9) A car averages 25 miles to the gallon. How far will it travel on 8 gallons? How many gallons are needed to travel 300 miles? If petrol costs £1.80 per gallon how much does it cost to travel 300 miles? The car is changed for a new one that does 30 miles to the gallon. How far will the new car travel on 8 gallons? How many gallons will be needed to travel 300 miles? How much will it cost to travel 300 miles in the new car at £1.80 per gallon for petrol? How much money is saved over 300 miles by having the new car?

VALUE ADDED TAX

Value Added Tax (VAT for short) is a tax which is added to some goods and services such as furniture and telephone bills. Some goods and services are exempt (bear no tax). Food and electricity bills and gas bills are exempt from VAT.

BRITISH **TELECOM**	
TOTAL (excluding V.A.T.)	£ 44 78
VALUE ADDED TAX	£ 6 71
TOTAL	£ 51 49

EXAMPLE

A table costs £40. VAT at 15% is charged. Calculate the cost of the table plus VAT.

VAT = 15% of £40

$$= \frac{\overset{3}{\cancel{15}}}{\underset{2}{\cancel{100}}} \times \cancel{£40}^{2} = £6$$

Cost of the table + VAT

= £40 + £6 = £46

Sometimes it is easier to work out VAT this way:

10% of £40 = £4 (divide by ten)

5% of £40 = £2 (half of 10%)

15% of £40 = £6 (15% = 10% + 5%)

With a calculator it is more straightforward to say $15\% = \frac{15}{100} = 0.15$ so to find 15% of £40 we multiply by 0.15:

press keys

| 0 | . | 1 | 5 |

| × | 4 | 0 | = |

to get the result | 6 | . |

─────── **EXERCISE 5** ───────

1) Find 15% of (a) £60 (b) £400 (c) £612 (d) 90p.

2) A woman buys a fridge for £120 but VAT at 15% is charged on top of this. Find how much she pays altogether.

3) Find the VAT payable on a restaurant bill of £20 if the rate of VAT is 15%.

4) A telephone bill excluding VAT is £50. Find the cost when VAT is added on. The rate of VAT is 15%.

5) A man buys some tools for £4.60 but VAT at 15% has to be added to the bill. How much did the tools cost with VAT?

6) VAT at 15% is added to a bill for a meal which came to £3.60. How much was paid altogether?

7) Calculate the VAT payable on a garage bill of £240 if the rate of VAT is 15%.

8) How much VAT is there on a bill of (a) £30 (b) £300 (c) £3000 if the rate of VAT is 15%?

9) A lawnmower is priced at £80 plus VAT. How much is the lawnmower with VAT if the rate of VAT is 15%?

10) A washing machine costs £110 exclusive of VAT. VAT is charged at 15%. How much is actually paid for the washing machine?

If you know the price *including* VAT and wish to know the cost without VAT then you have to use the following method:

EXAMPLE

The price of a coat is £23 including VAT. The rate of VAT is 15%. How much does the coat cost without VAT?

Let 100% be the price without VAT, so 115% is the price with VAT:

$$115\% = £23$$
$$1\% = £23 \div 115$$
$$100\% = 100 \times (£23 \div 115)$$

This can be worked out easily using a calculator, but in this example the numbers cancel (first by 5 and then by 23)

$$= £\frac{\overset{20}{\cancel{100}} \times \overset{1}{\cancel{23}}}{\underset{\underset{1}{\cancel{23}}}{\cancel{115}}}$$

$$= £20$$

so the coat costs £20 without VAT.

─────── **EXERCISE 6** ───────

(These questions have all been chosen so the numbers cancel, as in the example just given.)

Take the rate of VAT to be 15%.

1) If a table costs £69 with VAT how much does it cost without VAT?

2) A radio costs £46 inclusive of VAT. What is the cost without VAT?

3) The cost of a box of chocolates is £2.30 with VAT. Find the cost of the chocolates exclusive of VAT.

4) A restaurant bill is £115 with VAT included. How much is it without VAT?

5) With VAT included a telephone bill came to £92. How much was the bill with VAT excluded?

6) A carpet cost £230 with VAT. How much was it without VAT?

HIRE PURCHASE

Hire purchase (or HP for short) is used when we buy things *now* but pay for them over the next few months. Some money is usually paid straight away. This is called a *deposit*. The remaining money to be paid is called the *balance*. *Interest* is charged on the balance.

EXAMPLE

A woman buys a washing machine for £120 and pays a deposit of 20%. 10% interest is charged on the balance. The balance + interest is paid in 12 equal amounts per month for 1 year.

Find (a) the deposit, (b) the balance, (c) the interest, (d) the total to be repaid and (e) the amount of each instalment.

Deposit = 20% of £120

$$= \frac{\overset{2}{\cancel{20}}}{\underset{10}{\cancel{100}}} \times \cancel{£120}^{12} = £24$$

Balance = £120 − £24 = £96

Interest = 10% of £96 = £9.60

Total to be repaid = £96 + £9.60

$$= £105.60$$

Monthly instalments = £105.60 ÷ 12

$$= £8.80$$

BANK LOANS

Many people take out personal loans from a Bank. The Bank charges *interest*. The *loan + interest* is usually paid back in equal monthly instalments.

EXAMPLE

A man borrows £300 from his Bank. The Bank charges 20% interest. He pays back the loan + interest in 12 equal amounts. Find each amount.

Loan = £300

Interest = 20% of £300 (or say 10% = £30)

$$= \frac{20}{100} \times £300 \quad \text{(so that 20\% = £60)}$$

$$= £60$$

Total amount to be repaid = £300 + £60

$$= £360$$

Amount of each instalment = £360 ÷ 12

$$= £30$$

─────────── **EXERCISE 7** ───────────

1) If the HP payments on a record player are £4 per month, how much will be paid at the end of 3 years?

2) A woman buys £120 worth of kitchen equipment. She pays a deposit of £20. She is charged 10% interest on the balance.
   (a) How much is the balance?
   (b) How much is the interest?
   (c) If the balance + interest is paid back in 10 equal instalments how much is each instalment?
   (d) How much has she paid altogether?

3) The cash price of some furniture is £200. To buy on HP a deposit of 25% is made followed by 10 equal payments of £21. Find
   (a) the total paid for the furniture on HP
   (b) the difference between the cash price and the HP price.

4) A man borrows £100 from a Bank. 20% interest is charged. If he repays the loan plus interest in 12 equal amounts find how much he pays each time.

5) A Bank lends a woman £600. They charge interest at 20%. She pays the loan + interest back in 12 equal amounts. Find how much she pays back each time.

─────────── **EXERCISE 8** ───────────

1) What is the cost of 300 therms of gas at 20 p per therm?

2) Find the amount to be paid on these gas bills

		£
(a) standing charge		8.00
500 therms @ 28 p per therm		_____
		_____
(b) standing charge		8.00
100 therms @ 28 p per therm		_____
		_____
(c) standing charge		8.00
50 therms @ 28 p per therm		_____
		_____
(d) standing charge		8.00
250 therms @ 28 p per therm		_____
		_____

3) How many cubic feet do these meters show?
   (a)

   (b)

4) Give the total amount to be paid on this electricity bill

	£
fixed charge	5.82
1000 units @ 5.2 p per unit	_____
	_____

5) If a family pays about £52 per year on their telephone bill find how much they would expect to pay per quarter.

6) Give the total cost of this telephone bill

	£
standing charge	15.00
350 units @ 4 p per unit	_____
VAT @ 15%	_____
Total:	_____

7) The cost of a year's motoring is

	£
depreciation	750
insurance	145
tax	80
cost of petrol	750
repairs	95

Find the total cost of the year's motoring.

8) A car is bought for £2000 and sold 2 years later for £1000. Find the depreciation per year.

9) How much does it cost to buy 5 gallons of petrol at £1.88 per gallon?

10) VAT at 15% is added to a bill of £500. How much VAT is paid? How much is the total bill?

11) With VAT included, electrical goods cost £2300. How much do they cost without VAT?

12) A woman borrows £500 from her Bank. The Bank charges 20% interest. She pays back the loan + interest in 10 equal amounts. Find (a) the interest (b) the total she pays back (c) the value of each of the 10 equal amounts.

15

Graphs and Charts

AXES, SCALES AND COORDINATES

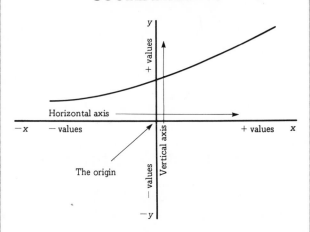

A graph is a picture of numerical information.

There are two axes: the horizontal axis and the vertical axis. The point where the axes cross is called the *origin.*

If all the numbers on the graph are positive (greater than zero) then the graph will look like this:

The horizontal and vertical axes should both be labelled.

There should be a *heading* at the top of the graph.

It is important when drawing a graph to choose a sensible *scale* so the graph fills the whole page (without going over the edge or being squashed into one corner!).

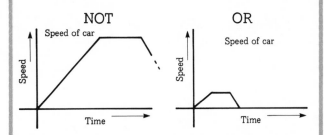

The *scale* on a graph is the *spacing* between the labels on the axes. Number labels on the axes should always be spaced *evenly.*

The scale of a graph can be used to deceive!

On the graph on the left it looks as if wages have risen a great deal from 1978 to 1980 but on the graph on the right they don't seem to have risen by very much.

The *coordinates* say where the points are on a graph.

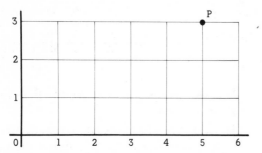

The point P has coordinates (5, 3). The first number, 5, says how far *along* and the second number, 3, says how far *up*.

——— EXERCISE 1 ———

1) Give the coordinates of the points A, B, C, D, E and F.

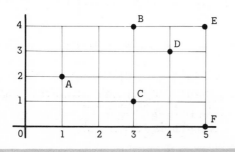

2) Give the coordinates of the points A, B, C, D, E, F, G, H, I and J. Copy the graph on to squared paper and draw a smooth curve through the points.

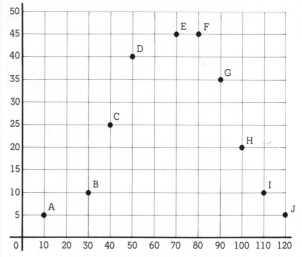

——— **DRAWING A GRAPH** ———

Graphs are drawn on squared paper. They show a relationship between two sets of numbers.

EXAMPLE

This table shows the average wage in J. Brown & Co. over 16 years:

Year	1950	1952	1954	1956	1958
Wage	£10	£12	£14	£16	£21

Year	1960	1962	1964	1966
Wage	£24	£29	£33	£40

Plot these points on a graph and from it estimate (a) the average wage in 1955 (b) the probable wage in 1968.

First draw two axes and then choose a suitable scale. (Our scale is 1 cm for 2 years and 1 cm for £10.)

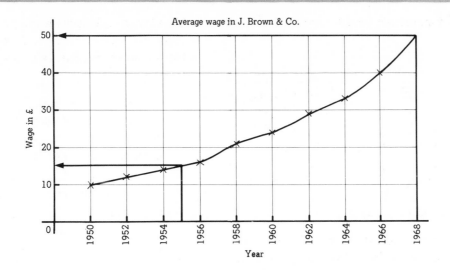

Average wage in J. Brown & Co.

Plot the points with a sharp pencil and mark them neatly with a small cross. For this graph you can draw a smooth curve through the points.

A graph may be used to find values not given in the table.

Reading from the graph: the average wage in 1955 was £15, the probable average wage in 1968 was £50.

Of course it is not always possible to draw a smooth curve through the points – some graphs are best drawn with straight lines joining the points. This must be decided by using common sense.

─────── **EXERCISE 2** ───────

1) Plot these points on a graph choosing suitable scales for the axes.

Age of child in years	2	4	6	8	10
Average height in cm	85	101	115	129	140

Draw a smooth curve through the points.

From your graph estimate (a) the height of a 5 year old child (b) the age of a child whose height is 135 cm.

2) A car was tested for petrol consumption at various speeds.

Speed in mph	10	30	50	70	80
Consumption in miles/gallon	20	35	40	30	23

Plot the points and draw a smooth curve through them.
(a) Give the petrol consumption at 40 mph.
(b) At what speeds is the consumption 25 miles to the gallon?
(c) What is the most efficient speed at which to drive the car?

3) Temperature can be measured in degrees centigrade (°C) or degrees Fahrenheit (°F). This diagram can be used to change °C to °F.

Plot a graph with this information. Join the points with a straight line. From your graph
(a) what is 20°C in °F?
(b) what is 98°F in °C?

155

4) This is part of a table to change cm to inches.

Cm	60	70	80	90	100
Inches	23.6	27.6	31.5	35.4	39.4

Plot these points on a graph and join them with a straight line. Use your graph to convert
(a) 65 cm to inches (correct to one decimal place)
(b) 37.5 inches to the nearest cm.

Look at the following sketches of graphs and then answer the questions.

5) (a) How many ounces in 250 grams (approximately)?
(b) How many grams in 14 ounces (approximately)?

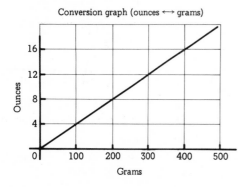

Conversion graph (ounces ⟷ grams)

6) (a) What is the fastest speed?
(b) How long does it take to achieve the fastest speed?

Speed–time graph

(c) For how long is it travelling at this speed?
(d) How long does it take to come to rest?

7) (a) How old was the tree when it measured 50 cm round its trunk?
(b) When the tree was 50 years old what was its measurement round its trunk?

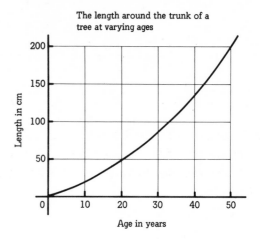

The length around the trunk of a tree at varying ages

8) (a) How far has the motorist driven?
(b) For how long did the motorist stop driving?
(c) What was the average speed between 6 and 7 p.m.?
(d) What was the average speed between 3 and 5 p.m.?

Distance–time graph showing the distance travelled by a motorist between 3 and 7 p.m.

The *rate of increase* or *slope* of a graph is found by drawing two dashed lines as shown and working out the value of:

Distance up ÷ Distance along

using the units of the graph.

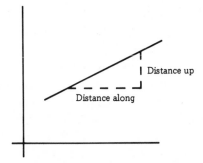

For a straight line graph this value should be the same no matter where the triangle is drawn.

This value is sometimes known as the *gradient* of the graph.

EXAMPLE

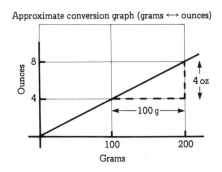

The rate of increase of ounces to grams is:

$$\frac{4\,oz}{100\,g} = 0.04\,oz/g$$

EXAMPLE

The slope of the next graph is $\dfrac{30\text{ miles}}{1\text{ hour}}$

$= 30\,\text{mph}$

For a distance-time graph the slope gives the speed.

————— **EXERCISE 3** —————

1) Find the rate of increase of wages with respect to time in J. Smith Ltd.

2) Find the slope of this graph during the first 3 seconds.

(The slope of a speed–time graph gives the acceleration.)

3) Find the gradient of this graph.

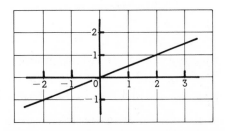

157

4) The slope of this graph gives a car's average speed. What is the average speed of the car?

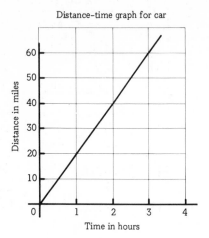

Distance-time graph for car

CHARTS

Charts should present information in a clear and easily understood form.

Bus fare charts are set out in this way:

The Grange

25	Royal Parade						
40	25	Queen St					
60	40	25	Fir Tree Drive				
64	60	40	25	West Road			
72	64	60	40	25	Mitford St		
76	72	65	60	40	25	The Croft	
80	76	72	64	60	40	25	Southdene St
80	80	76	72	64	60	40	25	Bus Station

To find the cost of travelling from Queen St to The Croft look down the column under the label Queen St until the row containing The Croft is reached. Then read off the fare: 65 p.

Look at the chart and answer these questions.

EXERCISE 4

How much does it cost to travel from

1) West Road to Southdene St?
2) The Grange to the Bus Station?
3) Royal Parade to West Road?
4) West Road to the Bus Station?
5) Queen St to Mitford St?
6) The Croft to Southdene St?
7) A girl has to go by bus from Fir Tree Drive to Mitford St to visit a friend and then go on from there to Southdene St for a meeting. How much more does it cost to break her journey than to go direct from Fir Tree Drive to Southdene St?

The chart opposite shows approximate telephone charges for local calls, calls up to 35 miles and calls over 35 miles at cheap, standard and peak rates.

The next chart shows when the cheap, standard and peak rates apply. For example, it is cheapest to make a call after 6 p.m. and on Saturday and Sunday.

The most expensive time to make a call is between 9 a.m. and 1 p.m. Monday to Friday (peak rate).

Telephone calls are measured in whole "units", the time allowed per unit for the different types of call is also shown on the chart. A unit costs about 5 p and since only *whole units* are measured the minimum cost of a call is 5 p.

EXERCISE 5

Use the telephone charges chart given to answer these questions

1) A 3 minute local call at peak rate is made. What would this cost?

158

		Time allowed for 1 unit	Approximate cost (including VAT) of a call of 1 min to 5 min or 10 min duration					
			1 min	2 min	3 min	4 min	5 min	10 min
Local calls	Cheap	8 min	5 p	5 p	5 p	5 p	5 p	10 p
	Standard	2 min	5 p	5 p	10 p	10 p	15 p	25 p
	Peak	1 min 30 s	5 p	10 p	10 p	15 p	20 p	35 p
Calls up to 35 miles	Cheap	144 s	5 p	5 p	10 p	10 p	15 p	25 p
	Standard	45 s	10 p	15 p	20 p	30 p	35 p	69 p
	Peak	30 s	10 p	20 p	30 p	40 p	49 p	99 p
Calls over 35 miles	Cheap	48 s	10 p	15 p	20 p	25 p	35 p	64 p
	Standard	16 s	20 p	40 p	59 p	74 p	94 p	£1.88
	Peak	12 s	25 p	49 p	74 p	99 p	£1.24	£2.47

	Mon	Tues	Wed	Thur	Fri	Sat	Sun
8 a.m.–9 a.m.	Standard rate						
9 a.m.–1 p.m.	Peak rate						
1 p.m.–6 p.m.	Standard rate						
6 p.m.–8 a.m.	Cheap rate						

2) Give the cost of a 10 minute local call at peak rate.

3) What would you expect a 10 minute local call at standard rate to cost?

4) A man phones for 5 minutes in the evening after 6 o'clock to his aunt who lives 74 miles away. What would the call cost?

5) How much is saved by phoning in the afternoon rather than the morning on a call over a distance of 50 miles if the expected length of call is 10 mins?

6) What would you expect a 20 minute local call at standard rate to cost?

7) What rate (cheap, standard or peak) is charged for a call made on a Thursday at 3 p.m.?

8) Give the approximate cost of a 4 minute call over a distance of 20 miles at standard rate.

9) A woman is telephoned by her grandson who lives 25 miles away. He phones in the evening after 6 p.m. and the call lasts 2 minutes. State the approximate cost of the call.

10) How much time is allowed for 1 unit for a peak rate call over 35 miles?

11) A local call uses 6 units at peak rate. How long was the call?

12) State the number of units used by a local call at standard rate lasting 22 minutes. If the charge is taken as 5p per unit how much would this call cost?

13) How much does a 2 minute cheap rate local call cost?

14) What is the cost of a 3 minute peak rate call over 37 miles?

PIE CHARTS

A pie chart is another way of showing numerical information in picture form.

EXAMPLE

24 pupils were asked what sort of career they would like:

  8 chose work with animals

  3 chose office work

  2 chose teaching

  5 said they would like to work outdoors

  the rest said "don't know"

Hints for drawing pie charts:

(a) use a sharp pencil

(b) draw a reasonable size circle with a pair of compasses

(c) calculate the angles at the centre and put them in a table as shown opposite

(d) use a protractor to draw the angles

(e) label each sector carefully

(f) label the angles.

How to calculate the angles at the centre of the pie chart:

There are $360°$ in the whole circle. *Divide 360 by the total number of pupils.* This gives the angle for *one* pupil. (In our example it works out exactly but usually you have to *round to the nearest whole degree.*)

To find the angle of each section *multiply* by the number of pupils in this section. (It is often not possible to draw a pie chart completely accurately.)

Set the work out like this:

$360 \div 24 = 15$		
There are $15°$ per pupil		
Sector label	*Number of pupils*	*Angle*
Work with animals	8	$8 \times 15° = 120°$
Office work	3	$3 \times 15° = 45°$
Teaching	2	$2 \times 15° = 30°$
Work outdoors	5	$5 \times 15° = 75°$
Don't know	6	$6 \times 15° = 90°$

EXERCISE 6

1) This pie chart shows the proportion of money spent by men, women and children on magazines in a shop.

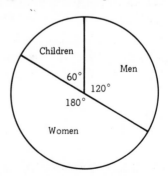

(a) Who spends the most?

(b) If the shop takes about £360 a day on magazines how much is this from
   (i) women (ii) men (iii) children?

160

Hint: The best way to solve this problem is to think in terms of fractions of the circle (e.g. women buy $\frac{1}{2}$ the magazines, men $\frac{1}{3}$ and children the rest).

2) How a boy spends his 64 p pocket money is shown by the pie chart below. How much does he spend on sweets? How much on comics? How much does he save? How much does he spend at the swimming pool?

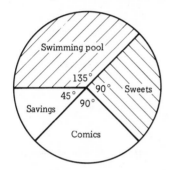

3) Draw a pie chart showing the proportion of trees in Radley Wood, using this table

Oak trees	45
Ash trees	90
Beech trees	120
Fir trees	45
Other	60

4) A family spends their week's money in this way

Food	£24
Clothes	£12
Electricity and gas	£15
Rent and rates	£14
Other	£7

Show their expenditure on a pie chart.

BAR CHARTS

There are three types of bar chart: a single bar chart, a vertical bar chart and a horizontal bar chart.

EXAMPLE

A family spends a monthly wage of £300 in this way:

Food	£100
Clothes	£50
Heating	£40
Rates and mortgage	£90
Other	£20
Total	£300

This information can be shown on:

a *single bar chart* (scale 2 mm to £10) or

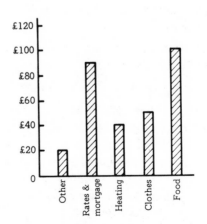

a *vertical bar chart* or

161

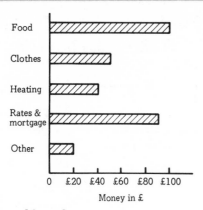

a horizontal bar chart

On a single bar chart the *heights* of the various sections show how much is spent on each item in relation to the other items. The *lengths of the bars* on a vertical or horizontal bar chart show how much is spent.

─────────── **EXERCISE 7** ───────────

1) 100 people were asked how they travelled to work. 50 said by car, 30 said bus, 5 said train and 15 said they walked. Present this information on a single bar chart.

2) A sample survey was done to market a new range of soups. 500 people were questioned. 260 said they preferred Tomato. 140 said they liked Chicken best. 40 preferred Oxtail. 15 preferred Vegetable and 25 liked Mushroom best. The rest didn't know. Show this information on a vertical bar chart.

3) This horizontal bar chart shows how the sales of two types of washing machine varied from 1974 to 1980

 Type A
Type B

(a) Was type A or type B more popular in 1974?
(b) Which was the more popular type in 1980?
(c) How many washing machines of type B were sold in 1978?
(d) How many more washing machines of type A were sold in 1980 than 1974?
(e) Would the manufacturer do better to make more washing machines of type B than type A in 1983?

─────────── **HISTOGRAMS** ───────────

The histogram is a special kind of graph with the area representing the frequency. The simplest type of histogram is a bar chart with all the bars the same width.

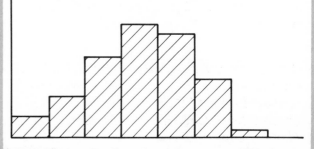

EXAMPLE

The diameters of 50 ball bearings were measured and the readings (in mm) were:

15.01	15.02	14.99	15.00	15.01
15.00	15.01	15.00	15.00	14.99
14.99	15.00	15.00	15.02	14.98
15.01	15.00	15.01	15.00	15.00
15.00	15.00	15.00	15.01	14.99
14.99	15.00	14.99	15.00	15.00
15.00	15.01	15.00	15.00	15.00
15.00	14.99	15.00	14.99	15.01
15.00	15.00	14.99	15.00	15.00
14.98	15.00	15.00	15.02	14.99

These numbers as they stand don't mean very much but if the measurements are grouped and the results put into a table then it is easier to see a pattern emerging.

Measurement	Tally marks	Frequency
14.98	||	2
14.99	⊞ ⊞	10
15.00	{ ⊞ ⊞ ⊞ ⊞ ⊞ ||	27
15.01	⊞ |||	8
15.02	|||	3

Tally marks are simply an aid to counting. Every time a measurement of, say, 15.01, is counted a mark is put by 15.01 in the frequency table. The fifth mark is drawn across a group of four. The *frequency* of 15.01 is simply the number of times 15.01 appears in the above readings.

Once the results are displayed on a histogram it can be seen quite clearly that the most frequent measurement is 15.00 mm with a sharp falling off on either side (so the manufacturing process must be fairly accurate).

A histogram showing the diameters of a sample of 50 ball bearings:

If the shape of the histogram had been more like this:

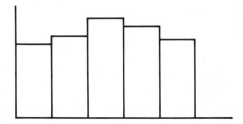

then it would become obvious that the manufacturing process was not so accurate, and the manufacturer would either have to take steps to remedy this or decide whether the limits of accuracy were acceptable.

EXERCISE 8

1) The lengths of 36 steel bars were measured (in centimetres) with these results

35.95	35.98	35.95	35.94	35.96	35.94
35.93	35.96	35.94	35.95	35.92	35.94
35.96	35.97	35.95	35.93	35.93	35.95
35.94	35.95	35.93	35.92	35.95	35.93
35.93	35.97	35.94	35.94	35.94	35.94
35.94	35.92	35.95	35.96	35.93	35.94

Draw up a frequency table and from that draw a histogram.

H

2) These were the results of a "speed of reaction" test given to 72 people. The scores are out of 10.

```
5 3 7 6 1 4   6 3 9 4 9   4
4 5 4 3 4 5   5 6 5 7 8   5
2 3 2 7 6 3   9 5 4 6 4   7
3 4 3 2 5 6   2 8 2 3 2   1
9 3 4 5 7 2   3 7 6 4 8  10
5 6 8 3 5 7  10 8 1 5 4   4
```

Draw a histogram to show this information.

3) This histogram shows the population of six towns:

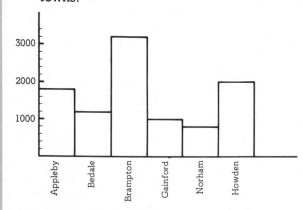

(a) Which town has the most people?
(b) Which town has the least?
(c) Approximately how many people are there in the six towns altogether?

PICTOGRAMS

Suppose a manufacturer sold 3500 cans of soup to a particular supermarket in 1 week. They might want to show this in picture form:

Such a diagram is called a *pictogram*.

1) This is a pictogram showing how many new houses were built in a certain city

How many new houses were built in 1978? in 1979? in 1980?

2) Using the pictogram below say how many days of sunshine (a) Selsea (b) Fulton and (c) Exford received in 1969.

1969		
Selsea	✿✿✿✿✿✿✿✿	
Fulton	✿✿✿✿✿✿✿	✿ = 15 days' sunshine
Exford	✿✿✿✿✿	

3) This pictogram shows car sales for the years 1975 to 1979.

(a) In which year were the most cars sold?
(b) How many cars were sold in 1976?
(c) How many more cars were sold in 1979 than 1975?
(d) Give the increase in sales from 1977 to 1978 and express this as a percentage.

164

1) Plot the following points on a graph choosing a suitable scale for the axes. Draw a smooth curve through the points.

Age of baby in months	Average weight of baby in kg
birth	3.5
3	5.8
6	7.7
9	9.0
12	10.0
15	10.7
18	11.2

From your graph estimate (a) the average weight of a baby aged 2 months (b) the probable age of a baby weighing 10.9 kg.

2) This table is used for changing miles to kilometres

Miles	Km
5	8
10	16
15	24
20	32
25	40
30	48

Plot these points on a graph, putting miles horizontally and kilometres vertically.
Draw a straight line through the points. Use the graph to change
(a) 12 miles to km
(b) 30 km to miles.

What is the rate of increase of km with respect to miles?

3) What is the slope of this graph?

4) Use this bus fare chart to find the fare from
   (a) Oak Lane to Maple St
   (b) Elm Avenue to Ash Close
   (c) Beech Drive to the Bus Station.

Oak Lane

10p	Beech Drive				
13p	10p	Elm Avenue			
15p	13p	10p	Ash Close		
17p	15p	13p	10p	Maple St	
20p	17p	15p	13p	10p	Bus Station

5) Draw a pie chart (and label the angles) to show how a girl spends her time on her hobbies

Music	2 hours
Reading	3 hours
Dancing	1 hour
Skating	5 hours
Judo	1 hour

6) Draw a single bar chart to show the proportion of skilled, unskilled, clerical and managerial workers in a factory if the proportions are: skilled 50%, unskilled 25%, clerical 10% and managerial 15%. Make sure that the height of each section is in the correct proportion.

7) The Local Authority made a survey of how a Leisure Centre was used. 1000 people were asked which facility they thought they used most. The results were

Swimming pool	450
Badminton	150
Table tennis	125
Squash	180
Gymnastics	95

Draw a vertical bar chart to show this information.

8) A tea company made a comparison of tea sold loose and in tea bags during the years 1950 to 1962.

165

In 1950 £600 000 worth of loose tea was sold and £200 000 worth of tea bags

In 1954 £750 000 worth of loose tea was sold and £350 000 worth of tea bags

In 1958 £500 000 worth of loose tea was sold and £550 000 worth of tea bags

In 1962 £450 000 worth of loose tea was sold and £950 000 worth of tea bags

Put this information into a horizontal bar chart (distinguishing between the bars of each type – loose tea and tea bags – by contrasting shading).

9) The marks obtained in a test were as follows

19	15	14	18	17
15	14	18	17	19
20	13	14	19	18
15	15	17	16	17
17	17	13	14	16
12	17	13	15	16
17	17	16	15	13
16	18	16	16	17
17	16	15	18	14

Group these results in a frequency table. Draw a histogram. Which is the most frequent mark?

These are the marks obtained by a second group of people

Mark	Frequency
11	1
12	3
13	5
14	9
15	16
16	11
17	7
18	5
19	3
20	2

Draw a second histogram showing these results and say how they differ from the first set. (The frequency should be plotted vertically and the mark horizontally.)

16

Maps and Timetables

ROAD MAPS

EXERCISE 1

1) Smith St is in square C2. Which squares are these streets in?
   (a) John William St
   (b) West Road
   (c) Finchley Avenue
   (d) Charles St
   (e) Orchard Close

2) All distances on the map opposite are in miles.
   (a) Which is shorter: Leeds to Huddersfield via Brighouse or Leeds to Huddersfield via Dewsbury?
   (b) Which is shorter: Huddersfield to Halifax via Brighouse or Huddersfield to Halifax via Sowerby Bridge.
   (c) What is the length of the shortest route from Morley to Sowerby Bridge?

(d) How far is it by road from Dewsbury to Brighouse?

(e) Give the distance by road from Ripponden to Leeds (i) via Brighouse (ii) via Halifax and Bradford (iii) via Huddersfield and Morley.

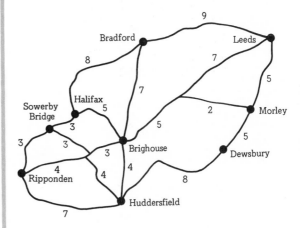

3) The scale on the map overleaf is 1 cm to 0.5 km.

Measure the direct distances and give the number of kilometres between

(a) Cheltenham and Leckhampton
(b) Cheltenham and Charlton Kings
(c) Charlton Kings and Pilley
(d) Andoversford and Charlton Kings
(e) Pilley and Leckhampton
(f) Andoversford and Pilley.

4) 1 cm on the map on the left represents 2 km on the ground.

Estimate how far it is from
(a) Dinard to Pleslin
(b) Châteauneuf to le Vieux Bourg
(c) St Malo to Dinard
(d) St Servan to Pleslin by the shortest route
(e) Châteauneuf to Dinan by the shortest route.

BUS TIMETABLES AND ROUTE MAPS

Use the bus timetable and bus route map shown on the opposite page to answer the following questions.

EXERCISE 2

1) How long does the bus take to travel from Stroud to Cirencester?

STROUD · CIRENCESTER via Chalford

Service 422

Service 422 via Bowbridge, Thrupp, Brimscombe, Chalford, Aston Down Turn, White Horse Inn, Frampton Mansell, Sapperton, Park Corner, Duntisbourne Rouse Turn, Daglingworth, Stratton.

Mondays to Fridays*

STROUD, Bus Station	0855	1055	1255	CIRENCESTER, Bus Station	0950	1150	1450
Thrupp, Brewery Lane	0903	1103	1303	Daglingworth	1000	1200	1500
Bourne Bridge	0907	1107	1307	Sapperton	1010	1210	1510
Chalford, Marle Hill	0912	1112	1312	White Horse Inn	˙1017	1217	1517
White Horse Inn	0917	1117	1317	Chalford, Marle Hill	1022	1222	1522
Sapperton	0924	1124	1324	Bourne Bridge	1027	1227	1527
Daglingworth	0934	1134	1334	Thrupp, Brewery Lane	1031	1231	1531
CIRENCESTER, Bus Station	0944	1144	1344	STROUD, Bus Station	1039	1239	1539

CODE
* — Not Bank Holiday Mondays, Good Friday or Boxing Day.

2) What time must I arrive at Sapperton bus stop in order to catch the bus to Stroud that arrives at 1039?

3) Give the time for the bus to travel between Daglingworth and Cirencester.

4) What time must I arrive at Aston Down Turn in order to make sure of catching the first bus in the morning to Cirencester?

5) What is the number of the bus service from Stroud right into Aston Down?

6) What do you think this sign means ⇌ ?

7) Give the number of the bus service to
(a) Uplands (b) France Lynch.

8) Is there a bus from Cirencester to Stroud at 10 minutes to 3 in the afternoon?

9) Between which stops marked on the time-table is Duntisbourne Rouse Turn?

10) What time is the first bus after 11 a.m. from the White Horse Inn to Stroud?

RAILWAY TIMETABLES

EXERCISE 3

Use the railway timetable overleaf to answer the following questions

1) What is the first train after 9 a.m. on Saturday from Worcester to London?

2) How long does it take the 1046 from Swindon to reach London?

3) What time must I arrive on Kemble Station in order to catch the 0712 from Cheltenham to London on Saturday? How many minutes is this before 8 a.m.?

4) Give the length of the journey in minutes from Worcester to Gloucester on the 1818 on a Sunday.

5) What time does the first train after 11 a.m. on a Friday leave Worcester for London?

WORCESTER · CHELTENHAM · GLOUCESTER · SWINDON · LONDON

Mondays to Fridays

WORCESTER,																	
Shrub Hill		0653	0805	0915	. . .	1107	. . .	1317	. . .	1508	1554	. . .	1757	2022	. . .	. . .	. . .
CHELTENHAM.	0620	0722	0828	0943	1041	1135	1230	1344	1437	1536	1624	1718	1826	2051	2138	. . .	. . .
Gloucester	0633	0741	0847	0956	1055	1148	1244	1358	1451	1550	1638	1732	1843	2105	2152	. . .	. . .
Stonehouse . .	0645	0755	0902	1008	1107	1200	1256	1410	1503	1602	1650	1744	1855	2117	2204	. . .	. . .
Stroud	0650	0802	0909	1013	1112	1206	1302	1415	1508	1607	1656	1749	1900	2123	2209	. . .	. . .
Kemble.	0706	0819	0926	1029	1128	1222	1318	1431	1524	1623	1713	1805	1916	2140	2225	. . .	. . .
SWINDON	0723	0836	0943	1046	1145	1239	1335	1448	1541	1640	1730	1824	1933	2157	2242	. . .	. . .
Reading	*0803*	*0915*	*1017*	*1143*	*1245*	*1353*	*1443*	*1545*	*1643*	*1718*	*1853*	*1908*	*2010*	*2245*		. . .	. . .
LONDON,																	
Paddington. . .	*0834*	*0938*	*1053*	*1216*	*1308*	*1426*	*1517*	*1618*	*1717*	*1747*	*1920*	*1937*	*2039*	*2314*		. . .	. . .

Saturdays

WORCESTER,																	
Shrub Hill	. . .	. . .	. . .	0915	. . .	1114	. . .	1317	. . .	1508	1554	. . .	1757	. . .	. . .	. . .	. . .
CHELTENHAM.	0620	0712	0828	0943	1047	1142	1235	1344	1428	1536	1624	1723	1826	2051	2138	. . .	. . .
Gloucester	0633	0724	0847	0959	1100	1155	1248	1358	1442	1550	1638	1738	1843	2105	2152	. . .	. . .
Stonehouse . .	0645	0737	0902	1012	1112	1208	1300	1410	1454	1602	1650	1750	1855	2117	2204	. . .	. . .
Stroud	0650	0742	0909	1017	1117	1213	1305	1415	1459	1607	1656	1756	1900	2123	2209	. . .	. . .
Kemble.	0706	0758	0926	1033	1133	1229	1321	1431	1515	1623	1713	1813	1916	2140	2225	. . .	. . .
SWINDON	0723	0815	0943	1050	1150	1246	1338	1448	1532	1640	1730	1830	1933	2157	2242	. . .	. . .
Reading	*0803*	*0848*	*1017*	*1143*	*1245*	*1353*	*1443*	*1545*	*1643*	*1718*	*1853*	*1908*	*2010*	*2245*		. . .	. . .
LONDON,																	
Paddington. . .	*0834*	*0917*	*1053*	*1216*	*1308*	*1426*	*1517*	*1618*	*1717*	*1747*	*1920*	*1937*	*2039*	*2314*		. . .	. . .

Sundays

	Up to 3.10.83			11.10.83 to 3.1.84			10.1.84 to 16.5.84			All Sundays				
WORCESTER,														
Shrub Hill	. . .	. . .	1325	. . .	. . .	. . .	. . .	. . .	. . .	1525	. . .	1818	. . .	. . .
CHELTENHAM.	0850	1120	1355	0840	1040	1430	0840	1045	1430	1555	1716	1845	1930	2215
Gloucester	0910	1140	1415	0900	1100	1448	0910	1112	1448	1615	1735	1900	1949	2230
Stonehouse . . .	0930	1200	1427	0920	1120	1500	0922	1124	1500	1627	1749	1912	. . .	2242
Stroud	0940	1210	1432	0930	1130	1505	0927	1129	1505	1632	1756	1917	2007	2247
Kemble.	1005	1235	1448	0955	1155	1521	0943	1145	1521	1648	1812	1933	2023	2303
SWINDON	1035	1305	1507	1025	1225	1540	1000	1202	1540	1705	1830	1950	2041	2320
Reading	*1124*	*1351*	*1551*	*1201*	*1401*	*1620*	*1051*	*1251*	*1620*	*1738*	*1926*	*2032*	*2120*	. . .
LONDON,														
Paddington. . .	*1250*	*1428*	*1628*	*1242*	*1438*	*1657*	*1128*	*1333*	*1657*	*1808*	1933	2108	2144	. . .

CODE
Connecting services in italics.

---

6) What train must I catch from Kemble on a Monday if I want to be sure of arriving in Reading by 4 p.m.?

7) If I am travelling on Sunday 15.10.83 (15 October 1983) what time is the first train from Cheltenham to London? How long does it take to get there?

8) Give the time of the last train from Worcester to London on (a) Monday to Friday, (b) Saturday, (c) Sunday, and the length in hours and minutes of each of these journeys.

THE CALENDAR

EXERCISE 4

1) How many days are there altogether in April, May and June?

2) On which day does 1 June fall in 1983?

3) How many Sundays are there in August 1983?

4) Shrove Tuesday is 40 days before Palm Sunday. If Palm Sunday was 27 March, what day was Shrove Tuesday?

1983 Calendar

JANUARY

Mon	.	3	10	17	24	31
Tue	.	4	11	18	25	.
Wed	.	5	12	19	26	.
Thu	.	6	13	20	27	.
Fri	.	7	14	21	28	.
Sat	1	8	15	22	29	.
Sun	2	9	16	23	30	.

FEBRUARY

Mon	.	7	14	21	28	.
Tue	1	8	15	22	.	.
Wed	2	9	16	23	.	.
Thu	3	10	17	24	.	.
Fri	4	11	18	25	.	.
Sat	5	12	19	26	.	.
Sun	6	13	20	27	.	.

MARCH

Mon	.	7	14	21	28	.
Tue	1	8	15	22	29	.
Wed	2	9	16	23	30	.
Thu	3	10	17	24	31	.
Fri	4	11	18	25	.	.
Sat	5	12	19	26	.	.
Sun	6	13	20	27	.	.

APRIL

Mon	.	4	11	18	25	.
Tue	.	5	12	19	26	.
Wed	.	6	13	20	27	.
Thu	.	7	14	21	28	.
Fri	1	8	15	22	29	.
Sat	2	9	16	23	30	.
Sun	3	10	17	24	.	.

MAY

Mon	.	2	9	16	23	30
Tue	.	3	10	17	24	31
Wed	.	4	11	18	25	.
Thu	.	5	12	19	26	.
Fri	.	6	13	20	27	.
Sat	.	7	14	21	28	.
Sun	1	8	15	22	29	.

JUNE

Mon	.	6	13	20	27	.
Tue	.	7	14	21	28	.
Wed	1	8	15	22	29	.
Thu	2	9	16	23	30	.
Fri	3	10	17	24	.	.
Sat	4	11	18	25	.	.
Sun	5	12	19	26	.	.

JULY

Mon	.	4	11	18	25	.
Tue	.	5	12	19	26	.
Wed	.	6	13	20	27	.
Thu	.	7	14	21	28	.
Fri	1	8	15	22	29	.
Sat	2	9	16	23	30	.
Sun	3	10	17	24	31	.

AUGUST

Mon	1	8	15	22	29	.
Tue	2	9	16	23	30	.
Wed	3	10	17	24	31	.
Thu	4	11	18	25	.	.
Fri	5	12	19	26	.	.
Sat	6	13	20	27	.	.
Sun	7	14	21	28	.	.

SEPTEMBER

Mon	.	5	12	19	26	.
Tue	.	6	13	20	27	.
Wed	.	7	14	21	28	.
Thu	1	8	15	22	29	.
Fri	2	9	16	23	30	.
Sat	3	10	17	24	.	.
Sun	4	11	18	25	.	.

OCTOBER

Mon	.	3	10	17	24	31
Tue	.	4	11	18	25	.
Wed	.	5	12	19	26	.
Thu	.	6	13	20	27	.
Fri	.	7	14	21	28	.
Sat	1	8	15	22	29	.
Sun	2	9	16	23	30	.

NOVEMBER

Mon	.	7	14	21	28	.
Tue	1	8	15	22	29	.
Wed	2	9	16	23	30	.
Thu	3	10	17	24	.	.
Fri	4	11	18	25	.	.
Sat	5	12	19	26	.	.
Sun	6	13	20	27	.	.

DECEMBER

Mon	.	5	12	19	26	.
Tue	.	6	13	20	27	.
Wed	.	7	14	21	28	.
Thu	1	8	15	22	29	.
Fri	2	9	16	23	30	.
Sat	3	10	17	24	31	.
Sun	4	11	18	25	.	.

5) How many months are 30 days long?

6) A school holiday lasts 6 weeks. School breaks up on a Friday and reopens on a Monday. If school breaks up on July 15th, what day does it reopen?

7) How many days are there between but not including 1 February and 8 March in 1983?

8) How many weekdays (Monday to Friday but not Saturday or Sunday) fall between 2 July and 7 August?

9) Give the date of the first Thursday in October in 1983.

10) If December 31st 1983 falls on a Saturday what day will 8 January 1984 be?

THE 24 HOUR CLOCK

The time on this clock could be read as showing 0300 hours or 1500 hours in 24 hour clock notation.

The first two figures show the hours and the second two the minutes.

0300 = 3 a.m.
(three o'clock in the morning)

1500 = 3 p.m.
(three o'clock in the afternoon)

EXERCISE 5

Give these times in 24 hour clock notation

1) 2 p.m.
2) 7 p.m.
3) noon
4) 6.30 a.m.
5) midnight

6) 4.25 p.m.
7) eleven o'clock in the morning
8) quarter past two in the afternoon
9) five past six in the evening
10) quarter to eight in the morning
11) twenty-five past eleven at night
12) two o'clock in the morning

How many minutes are there between

13) 1300 and 1325
14) 0820 and 0950

15) 1715 and 1755
16) 1917 and 2108?

Give these 24 hour clock times in terms of a.m. or p.m. times

17) 0715
18) 1935
19) 2314
20) 0648

17

Basic Algebra

SIMPLE EQUATIONS

Letters are used in place of numbers in algebra, for example:

$x + 4 = 6$

This means some number plus 4 equals 6. Since 2 is the only number which, when added to 4 gives 6, then x must equal 2.

In algebra we would write:

if $x + 4 = 6$

then $x = 2$

$x + 4 = 6$ is an example of an *equation*
$x = 2$ is the *solution* to this equation.

EXAMPLE

Solve the equation $x + 5 = 8$.

If $x + 5 = 8$

then $x = 3$

EXAMPLE

Solve the equation $x - 3 = 7$.

The *only* number that gives 7 when 3 is taken from it is 10.

If $x - 3 = 7$

then $x = 10$

EXERCISE 1

By using common sense solve these equations in the same way as above

1) $x + 6 = 8$
2) $x + 2 = 5$
3) $x + 3 = 10$
4) $x + 4 = 11$
5) $x + 1 = 9$
6) $x + 8 = 15$
7) $x + 7 = 14$
8) $x + 7 = 10$
9) $x - 2 = 5$
10) $x - 1 = 9$
11) $x + 4 = 8$
12) $x + 9 = 12$
13) $x + 7 = 8$
14) $x - 4 = 8$
15) $x - 3 = 6$
16) $x - 5 = 9$
17) $x - 1 = 7$
18) $x + 3 = 5$
19) $x - 7 = 9$
20) $x - 3 = 10$

$x + x + x + x + x$ is written as $5x$ in algebra. It means 5 times x.

$y + y + y$ would be written as $3y$.

EXERCISE 2

In the same way write these numbers algebraically

1) $z + z + z$
2) $y + y$
3) $t + t$
4) $p + p + p + p + p + p$
5) $q + q + q + q$
6) $r + r + r$
7) $n + n + n + n$
8) $t + t + t + t + t$
9) $m + m$
10) $s + s + s$
11) $p + p + p$
12) $w + w + w$

Algebra is used to solve problems. The following problem is easy to solve in your head but it shows how letters can be used for lengths or quantities whose values are not known directly.

EXAMPLE

A square has a perimeter of length 36 cm. How long is each side?

(The perimeter is the distance all the way round the edge.)

First we draw a sketch:

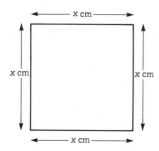

and then say:

let the length of each side be x cm.

Then the perimeter $= x + x + x + x$ cm

$$= 4x \text{ cm}$$

$$= 36 \text{ cm}$$

Since 9 is the only number which, when multiplied by 4 gives 36 then:

$$x = 9$$

The length of each side is 9 cm.

--- **EXERCISE 3** ---

Solve these equations using common sense

1) $5x = 20$	7) $6z = 42$
2) $9p = 27$	8) $3t = 24$
3) $3w = 12$	9) $7z = 21$
4) $5h = 25$	10) $2t = 24$
5) $3y = 18$	11) $5y = 60$
6) $3m = 12$	12) $5s = 35$

COLLECTING LIKE AND UNLIKE TERMS

Put 7 carrots together with 8 carrots and you get 15 carrots.

In the same way in algebra:

$$7c + 8c = 15c$$

If you take 7 carrots away from 8 carrots only 1 carrot is left.

In algebra:

$$8c - 7c = c$$

(Notice that $1 \times c$ or $1c$ is written c in algebra.)

The sum of 3 donkeys and 7 carrots cannot be made any simpler! In the same way $3d + 7c$ cannot be simplified. If, however, there are 3 donkeys and 7 carrots already in a field and another 2 donkeys and 8 carrots were put into the field as well, then we could say there are now 5 donkeys plus 15 carrots, and in the same way, in algebra:

$$3d + 7c + 2d + 8c = 5d + 15c$$

the ds have been collected together and the cs have been collected together.

(7c and 8c are known as *like terms* and 3d and 7c are known as *unlike terms*.)

EXAMPLE

Simplify $4c - 5c + 3c$.

($4c$ and $3c$ are positive terms whereas $-5c$ is a negative term. Group the positive terms first and then group the negative terms.)

$$4c - 5c + 3c = 4c + 3c - 5c$$
$$= 7c - 5c$$
$$= 2c$$

EXAMPLE

Simplify $7t - 3 - 3t + 9$.

$$7t - 3 - 3t + 9 = 7t - 3t + 9 - 3$$
$$= 4t + 6$$

EXAMPLE

Simplify $a - 3b - 2a + 3c + 5a + 6b$.

$$a - 3b - 2a + 3c + 5a + 6b$$
$$= a + 5a - 2a + 6b - 3b + 3c$$
$$= 6a - 2a + 3b + 3c$$
$$= 4a + 3b + 3c$$

─────────── **EXERCISE 4** ───────────

Simplify if possible

1) $3x + 6x$
2) $6d + 2d$
3) $5c - c$
4) $5y + 11y$
5) $3h + 9h$
6) $c + 6c$
7) $11z - 5z$
8) $3s + 2s + s$

9) $3t - 2t + 6t$
10) $14j - 6j$
11) $4c + 3d$
12) $8n - 5n$
13) $4p - p + 3p$
14) $5z - 11z + 6z$
15) $9e + 5e - 6e$
16) $3c + 5d + 2c + d$
17) $8m + 3n + m + 2n$
18) $13w + 2v + 2w + 3v$
19) $15z - 11z + 4q + 3q$
20) $a - 2b + 4a + 5b$
21) $7a + 5b - 2a - 3b$
22) $5x + 3 + 2x + 6$
23) $17y + 11 - 12y - 2$
24) $8p - 2q + 3p + 8q$
25) $2a + 3b + 3c + a + b + c$
26) $7a + 5 + 3b - 4 + a$
27) $3a + 4b + 5c$
28) $13c + 5d - 11c - 5d$
29) $2x - 2x + 3y - 3y + 6$

─────────── **SUBSTITUTION** ───────────

$V = l \times w \times h$ is an example of an algebraic formula. It is, in fact, the formula for the volume (or space), V, taken up by a box with length l, width w and height h.

If the length is 5 cm, the width 4 cm and the height 2 cm then the volume will be $5 \times 4 \times 2$ cm^3 (volume is measured in cubic centimetres, written cm^3)

$$= 20 \times 2 \text{ cm}^3$$
$$= 40 \text{ cm}^3$$

In algebra we would write:

Find V if

$V = l \times w \times h$ and

$l = 5$, $w = 4$ and $h = 2$

$V = 5 \times 4 \times 2$

$\quad = 20 \times 2$

$\quad = 40$

substituting values for the letters. (Substituting means putting numbers in place of the letters.)

EXAMPLE

Find $x + 3$ if $x = 4$.

$x + 3 = 4 + 3$

$\quad = 7$

EXAMPLE

Find $5y$ if $y = 3$.

$5y = 5 \times 3$ (5y means 5 times y and the

$\quad = 15$ $\times$ sign reappears when
numbers are put in
place of the letters.)

EXAMPLE

Find $5a + 3$ if $a = 4$.

$5a + 3 = 5 \times 4 + 3$ (since 5a means 5 times a)

$\quad = 20 + 3$ (multiplication must be
done before addition)

$\quad = 23$

EXAMPLE

Find $3p + 4q$ if $p = 8$ and $q = 2$.

$3p + 4q = 3 \times 8 + 4 \times 2$

$\quad = 24 + 8$

$\quad = 32$

EXAMPLE

Find $\dfrac{s+t}{v}$ if $s = 6$, $t = 8$ and $v = 2$.

$$\frac{s+t}{v} = \frac{6+8}{2} = \frac{14}{2} = 7$$

─────────── **EXERCISE 5** ───────────

Find

1) $x + 3$ if $x = 11$
2) $5z$ if $z = 3$
3) $3w + 2$ if $w = 4$
4) $5s - 3$ if $s = 6$
5) $c - 2$ if $c = 8$
6) $6 - x$ if $x = 1$
7) $4p + 7q$ if $p = 2$ and $q = 3$
8) $3a - 2b$ if $a = 7$ and $b = 4$
9) $7a + 4$ if $a = 10$
10) $7t - 5$ if $t = 6$
11) $\dfrac{p+q}{3}$ if $p = 9$ and $q = 6$
12) $\dfrac{6s}{5}$ if $s = 10$
13) $\dfrac{4+3p}{2}$ if $p = 8$
14) $\dfrac{3m+2n}{5}$ if $m = 6$ and $n = 6$
15) $\dfrac{f+g}{h}$ if $f = 15$, $g = 11$ and $h = 2$
16) $\dfrac{9p+11q}{r}$ if $p = 2$, $q = 10$ and $r = 8$
17) $\dfrac{12s+16t}{8}$ if $s = 2$ and $t = 3$
18) $\dfrac{15p+30q}{10}$ if $p = 4$ and $q = 3$
19) $28a + 20b$ if $a = 2$ and $b = 4$
20) $12x - 11$ if $x = 3$

In algebra $a \times a \times a$ is written a^3 (we say "a cubed") and $r \times r$ is written r^2 (we say "r squared").

Notice carefully that r^2 is not the same as 2r.

$$\boxed{r^2 = r \times r} \quad \text{whereas} \quad \boxed{2r = 2 \times r}$$

If $r = 10$ then $r^2 = r \times r = 10 \times 10 = 100$ but $2r = 2 \times r = 2 \times 10 = 20$.

Writing $r \times r$ as r^2 is known as using *index form*.

EXAMPLE

Write $b \times b \times b \times b \times b$ in index form.

$b \times b \times b \times b \times b = b^5$ in index form

(we say "b to the fifth")

──────── **EXERCISE 6** ────────

Write the following using index form

1) $b \times b \times b$
2) $m \times m \times m \times m$
3) $n \times n$
4) $p \times p \times p$
5) $s \times s$
6) $q \times q \times q \times q \times q \times q$
7) $r \times r \times r$
8) $w \times w \times w \times w \times w$
9) $z \times z \times z$

If $p = 2$, $q = 4$, $r = 10$, $s = 9$ and $t = 11$ find the following. (In questions 16 to 19 square before adding or subtracting.)

10) p^2 15) q^3
11) q^2 16) $p^2 + q^2$
12) s^2 17) $t^2 - r^2$
13) t^2 18) $s^2 + t^2$
14) r^3 19) $s^2 - p^2$

The multiplication sign is often left out when using algebra, for example:

$u \times v \times w$ is written uvw and

$3 \times a \times b$ is written $3ab$

──────── **EXERCISE 7** ────────

Write these leaving out the multiplication signs

1) $p \times q \times r$ 7) $14 \times a \times b$
2) $5 \times s \times t$ 8) $12 \times p \times q \times r$
3) $m \times n$ 9) $3 \times p \times q \times r$
4) $a \times b \times c$ 10) $11 \times a \times b$
5) $8 \times x \times y \times z$ 11) $3 \times a \times b \times c$
6) $8 \times p \times q \times r$ 12) $2 \times p \times q$

If $a = 3$, $b = 5$, and $c = 8$ find the values of

13) ab 19) abc
14) bc 20) bac
15) ac 21) bca
16) $3ab$ 22) $4abc$
17) $5bc$ 23) $4bca$
18) $7ca$ 24) $4cab$

If $p = 4$, $q = 5$ and $r = 6$ find the values of these expressions, remembering that multiplication and division must always be done before addition and subtraction

25) $pq + r$ 34) $pq - r$
26) $6pr + 2pq$ 35) $6pq \div r$
27) $pqr + 4$ 36) $2pq - 3r$
28) $p^2 + qr$ 37) $(3pq \div r) - (2r \div 4)$
29) $2pr^2$
30) $4q^3$ 38) $\dfrac{3pq}{r}$
31) $pr + 2rqp$
32) $qr + pq$
33) $5q + 3p + 2r$ 39) $\dfrac{8q}{p} + \dfrac{qr}{10}$

177

HARDER EQUATIONS

Suppose we wanted to solve the equation:

$7x + 5 = 26$

we could, by trial and error, find the solution:

$x = 3$

but it is much better to use a proper method to find the answer. First we show the method and then the explanation.

Method: $7x + 5 = 26$

$7x = 26 - 5$ (taking 5 from both sides)

$7x = 21$

$x = 21 \div 7$ (dividing both sides by 7)

$x = 3$

An equation is like a balance.

If we take 5 units away from both sides of the scales the scales will still balance.

If we divide each side into 7 equal parts and only take 1 part the scales will still balance.

The scales will still balance (and the equation will still be correct) if we:

1) add or subtract the same quantity from both sides

2) multiply or divide both sides by the same quantity.

EXAMPLE

Solve $2x - 3 = 17$.

When we add 3 to both sides we get:

$2x - 3 + 3 = 17 + 3$

and the -3 and the $+3$ "cancel each other out" leaving $2x$ on the left hand side.

So:

$2x - 3 = 17$

$2x = 17 + 3$ (adding 3 to both sides)

$2x = 20$

$x = 20 \div 2$ (dividing both sides by 2)

$x = 10$

EXERCISE 8

Solve

1) $4x - 1 = 3$ 7) $4x - 5 = 11$

2) $7x - 5 = 16$ 8) $5x - 5 = 35$

3) $8x - 3 = 21$ 9) $2x - 4 = 20$

4) $9x - 4 = 23$ 10) $3x - 7 = 17$

5) $6x - 1 = 35$ 11) $9x - 7 = 20$

6) $8x - 11 = 5$ 12) $6x - 2 = 40$

EXAMPLE

Solve $3x + 5 = 11$.

$3x = 11 - 5$ (taking 5 from both sides)

$3x = 6$

$x = 6 \div 3$ (dividing both sides by 3)

$x = 2$

Solve

1) $3x + 2 = 8$
2) $5x + 7 = 17$
3) $6x + 3 = 51$
4) $2x + 1 = 19$
5) $7x + 5 = 40$
6) $4x + 1 = 13$
7) $7x + 8 = 36$
8) $9x + 2 = 20$
9) $11x + 2 = 35$
10) $6x + 9 = 39$
11) $5x + 4 = 39$
12) $2x + 11 = 17$

We may also:

1) change sides completely
2) square the quantities on both sides.

EXAMPLE

Solve $5 = 3 + x$.

$5 - 3 = x$ (taking 3 from both sides)

$2 = x$

$x = 2$ (changing sides)

It is possible to change sides at the beginning (or indeed at any stage in the working).

EXAMPLE

Solve $12 = 4x$.

$4x = 12$ (changing sides)

$x = 12 \div 4$ (dividing both sides by 4)

$x = 3$

EXAMPLE

Solve $\sqrt{x} = 8$.

$\sqrt{x} \times \sqrt{x} = 8 \times 8$ (squaring both sides)

$x = 64$

Solve

1) $8 = 5 + x$
2) $10 = 4 + x$
3) $14 = 8 + x$
4) $21 = 7 + x$
5) $11 = 2 + x$
6) $20 = 5x$
7) $25 = 5x$
8) $14 = 2x$
9) $15 = 5x$
10) $\sqrt{x} = 5$
11) $\sqrt{x} = 11$
12) $\sqrt{x} = \frac{1}{2}$

EXAMPLE

Solve $5x + 3 = 3x + 7$.

We need to get the xs on one side and the numbers on the other.

Subtract $3x$ from both sides:

$2x + 3 = 7$

Subtract 3 from both sides:

$2x = 4$

Divide both sides by 2:

$x = 2$

EXAMPLE

Solve $4x - 5 = 2x + 3$.

Subtract $2x$ from both sides:

$2x - 5 = 3$

Add 5 to both sides:

$2x = 8$

Divide both sides by 2:

$x = 4$

Solve

1) $7x + 5 = 5x + 7$
2) $8x + 2 = 3x + 12$

3) $5x + 4 = 2x + 13$

4) $11x + 2 = 9x + 4$

5) $8x + 3 = 6x + 13$

6) $8x + 1 = 2x + 7$

7) $7x + 5 = 5x + 15$

8) $10x + 2 = 7x + 14$

9) $11x + 3 = 2x + 39$

10) $5x + 1 = x + 49$

11) $3x - 2 = x + 8$

12) $7x - 3 = 4x + 12$

13) $9x - 7 = 5x + 9$

14) $11x - 9 = 5x + 27$

15) $17x - 11 = 10x + 3$

16) $6x - 1 = x + 14$

17) $20x - 9 = 14x + 3$

18) $9x - 9 = 3x + 9$

19) $5x - 10 = 2x + 20$

20) $6x - 1 = 2x + 3$

FORMULAE

In physics and mathematics, formulae are often used when one quantity is related to other measurements in a definite way.

EXAMPLE

Find v if $v = u + at$ and $u = 2$, $a = 10$ and $t = 4$.

This is one of the most frequently used formulae in physics relating final velocity of a moving object to the initial velocity, constant acceleration and time.

$v = u + at$

$\therefore v = 2 + 10 \times 4$ (multiplication must be done before addition)

$\quad = 2 + 40$

$\quad = 42$

($\therefore$ means "therefore".)

The Greek symbol π is often used in connection with measurements of the circle as will be explained in the next chapter. It is usually given the approximate value of 3.14 or $3\frac{1}{7}$ which as a top-heavy fraction is $\frac{22}{7}$. The formulae in the next exercise are all in common use.

--- **EXERCISE 12** ---

1) Find A if $A = l \times b$ and $l = 7$ and $b = 9$.

2) Find C if $C = 2\pi r$ and $\pi = 3.14$ and $r = 10$.

3) Find A if $A = \pi r^2$ and $\pi = 3.14$ and $r = 10$.

4) Find v if $v = \sqrt{2gh}$ and $g = 10$ and $h = 20$.

5) Find f if $\dfrac{1}{f} = \dfrac{1}{v} + \dfrac{1}{u}$ and $v = 12$ and $u = 6$.

6) Find s if $s = ut + \dfrac{1}{2}at^2$ and $u = 2$, $t = 4$ and $a = 10$.

7) Find s if $s = \dfrac{v^2 - u^2}{2a}$ and $v = 5$, $u = 1$, and $a = 4$.

8) Find V if $V = \dfrac{1}{3}\pi r^2 h$ and $\pi = 3.14$, $r = 10$ and $h = 6$.

9) Using the formula $I = \dfrac{PRT}{100}$, find I if $P = 500$, $R = 5$ and $T = 4$.

10) If $A = P\left(1 + \dfrac{R}{100}\right)^n$ find A when $P = 200$, $R = 10$ and $n = 2$.

PLOTTING EQUATIONS ON A GRAPH

The equation $y = 5x + 1$ can be plotted on a graph.

A table of values is constructed by substituting different values of x into the equation. It is easier to choose simple values such as 0, 1, 2, 3, etc.

$y = 5x + 1$ which means y is 5 times the value of x plus 1

when $x = 0$ $y = 1$
   (since $5 \times 0 + 1 = 0 + 1 = 1$)

when $x = 1$ $y = 6$
   (since $5 \times 1 + 1 = 5 + 1 = 6$, etc.)

when $x = 2$ $y = 11$

when $x = 3$ $y = 16$

when $x = 4$ $y = 21$

The table of values is thus:

x	0	1	2	3	4
y	1	6	11	16	21

These values can be plotted on a graph:

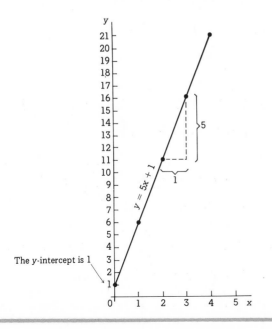

The y-intercept is 1

Gradient = Distance up ÷ Distance along

   $= 5 \div 1$

   $= 5$ (see Chapter 15 on graphs and charts)

Notice that:

   The equation of the graph is $y = 5x + 1$.

   The gradient (slope) of the graph is 5.

   The line cuts the y-axis at $y = 1$ (this is called the y-intercept).

The equation of a straight line graph is

   $y = (\text{gradient})x + (y\text{-intercept})$

EXAMPLE

Plot the equation $y = 4x + 1$ on a graph.
(a) What is the gradient?
(b) What is the value of the y-intercept?
(c) What is the value of y when $x = -1$?

The table of values will be:

x	0	1	2	3	4
y	1	5	9	13	17

Because of question (c) we will have to include negative values on the x and y-axes:

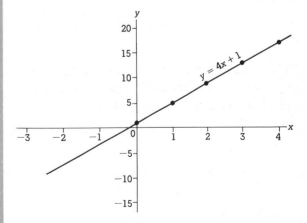

(a) the gradient is 4
(b) the y-intercept is 1
(c) when $x = -1$ then $y = -3$.

1) Plot the equation $y = 2x + 7$ on a graph. Label the x and y-axes and label the straight line with the equation.
   (a) What is the gradient of the straight line?
   (b) What is the value of the y-intercept?

2) Plot the equation $y = 3x + 5$ on a graph.
   (a) State the gradient (slope) of the graph.
   (b) Where does the line cut the y-axis?

3) Plot these values on a graph, choosing a suitable scale and draw a straight line through them:

x	0	1	2	3	4	5
y	3	5	7	9	11	13

   (a) What is the gradient of the straight line?
   (b) What is the y-intercept?
   (c) What is the equation of the straight line?

4) $y = 3x - 7$.

x	0	1	2	3	4	5
y	-7	-4	-1	2	5	8

   Plot these points on a graph and write down
   (a) the value of the gradient
   (b) the value of y when $x = 0$. Draw a straight line through the points.

5) Plot these values on a graph and draw a straight line through them:

x	-3	-2	-1	0	1	2	3
y	3	4	5	6	7	8	9

   (a) What is the gradient of the straight line?
   (b) Where does the line cut the y-axis?
   (c) What is the equation of the straight line?

18

── Plane Shapes and Solid Figures ──

── PLANE SHAPES ──

A "plane" shape is made from lines, known as the *sides* of the shape. It is flat. Here are some of the more familiar plane shapes:

The Triangle (Three Sides)

An *angle* is formed where the sides meet. It is a measure of the amount of opening between the lines.

A triangle with three sides of equal length and with three equal angles is known as an *equilateral* triangle.

The Square (Four Sides)

All the angles are equal. The sides are of equal length.

The Quadrilateral (Four Sides)

Any plane shape with four sides is called a "quadrilateral". The square and the rectangle are quadrilaterals.

The Rectangle (Four Sides)

All the angles are equal. Two pairs of opposite sides are of equal length.

The Circle

The length across the centre of a circle is called the *diameter*. The length round the edge is known as the *circumference*.

A shape is *regular* if all the sides are of equal length and all the angles are equal. The equilateral triangle and the square are regular. The pentagon (a five-sided figure), hexagon (a six-sided figure) and the octagon (an eight-sided figure) as drawn below are all regular:

Regular Pentagon (Five Sides)

Regular Hexagon (Six Sides)

Regular Octagon (Eight Sides)

The length all the way round the edge of a plane shape is called the *perimeter*.

───── SOLID FIGURES ─────

Sphere

A ball bearing and a cricket ball are examples of spheres.

Cube

A lump of sugar is some-times called a sugar cube.

It has six faces, eight corners (or *vertices*) and twelve edges.

Prisms

A prism has the same shape all the way along its length.

Cube

All the sides are of equal length and each face is a square.

Cuboid

Each face is a rectangle. The cuboid is a box shape.

Cylinder

Most tins are cylindrical.

The cuboid could be called a rectangular prism and the cylinder could be called a circular prism.

Triangular prism

The front face is a triangle.

Hexagonal prism

The front face is a hexagon.

An *irregular prism* has a front face with no particularly well-known shape. The front face is sometimes called the "cross-section".

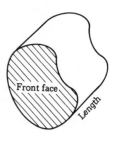

Pyramids

Pyramids sit on a flat base and come up to a point. The shape of the base gives the name to the type of pyramid:

Triangular based pyramid

Square based pyramid

Circular pyramid (cone)

A triangular pyramid with all its faces equilateral triangles (triangles with three equal sides) is known as a *tetrahedron*.

A tetrahedron has all its sides of equal length.

A *net* is the shape you would cut from a piece of cardboard in order to make a model of a solid figure. This is the net of a cuboid:

You could fold this

to make this

Different nets can make the same shape:

This net would also make the same cuboid shape:

──── **EXERCISE 1** ────

1) Write down the number of sides of these plane shapes
   (a) triangle (b) hexagon (c) quadrilateral
   (d) pentagon (e) rectangle (f) octagon
   (g) square.

2) Work out the perimeter (length all the way round the edge) of these shapes

(a)
3 cm
3 cm

(b)
3.5 cm 4.6 cm
7.7 cm

(c)
7.5 mm
3.5 mm

(d)
1.25 cm

3) Write down the number of faces of these solid figures
   (a) cuboid (b) triangular prism (c) square based pyramid (d) hexagonal prism
   (e) tetrahedron.

4) How many edges are there on (a) a square based pyramid (b) a cuboid (c) a triangular prism (d) a tetrahedron?

5) How many vertices do these solid figures have
   (a) a cuboid (b) a square based pyramid
   (c) a triangular prism (d) an octagonal prism?

185

6) Draw a suitable net for (a) a cube (b) a triangular prism (c) a square based pyramid.

7) Which of these nets would make a cube and which would not?

(a)

(b)

(c)

(d)

(e)

(f)

(g)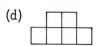

8) Draw three different types of prism and three different types of pyramid and label each carefully.

If you face in a certain direction and then turn completely round so that you face the same way again, we can say you have turned through 360 degrees, written 360° with the small symbol ° standing for the word "degrees".

Half a complete turn is 180°

and a quarter turn is 90°, called a *right angle*.

A right angle is often shown like this:

or

There are *two right angles in 180°* and *four right angles in 360°*.

Angles less than 90° are called *acute*, e.g. 15°, 60°, 76°.

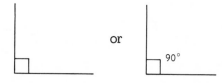

— MEASUREMENT OF ANGLES —

An angle is the amount of opening between two lines. *It does not depend on the lengths of the lines.*

An angle can also be regarded as a measure of *turning*.

AO and OB are called the *arms* of the angle. If the line AO is turned about O until it is in the same position as OB, then it has "turned through the angle AÔB" (compare the turning of the hands of a clock).

Second 'arm' of the angle

First 'arm' of the angle

Angles more than 90° but less than 180° are called *obtuse*, e.g. 110°, 150°, 138°.

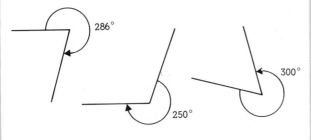

110°   150°   138°

Reflex angles are those angles which are bigger than 180°, e.g. 286°, 250°, 300°.

286°   300°   250°

─────────── **EXERCISE 2** ───────────

Draw up a table with three headings: acute, obtuse and reflex, and put these angles in the correct columns

17°, 190°, 240°, 173°, 65°, 230°, 185°,
54°, 135°, 270°, 155°, 72°, 85°, 169°,
315°, 198°, 32°, 88°, 350°, 120°, 12°,
110°, 51°, 95°, 103°, 114°, 63°, 210°

─────────────────────────────

Angles are measured using an instrument called a *protractor.*

There are 180° in a semi-circle (half a circle).

How to Measure an Angle

Place the protractor so that its centre lies on the point where the arms of the angle meet and the bottom line of the protractor lies along one of the arms as shown.

43° or 137°

Then read off the measurement of the angles as shown by the arrow. Care must be taken to choose the correct number. This angle is obviously less than 90° so we choose 43° rather than 137°.

There are 60 minutes in a degree but these are too small to be shown on a protractor. We write 60 minutes as 60′.

How to Draw a Given Angle

Draw a straight line with a pencil and ruler leaving enough space for the angle to be drawn and mark a small fine line across it to make a small cross. Place the protractor so that the bottom line lies along the line you have drawn and the centre of the protractor lies on the cross. Mark off the required angle with a sharp pencil and join the cross and marked line with a pencil and ruler.

EXAMPLE

Draw an angle of 60°.

60°   Put a small line at the 60° mark and join it to the cross using a ruler

Draw this line first

Mark a small cross

187

J

EXERCISE 3

(a) Measure these angles using a protractor.
(b) On a separate piece of paper draw them (with a protractor) as accurately as possible.

1)

5)

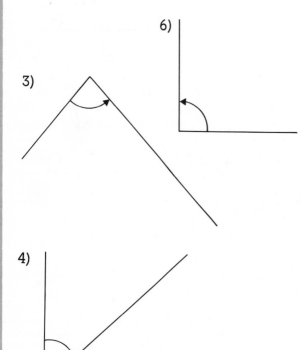

2)

3)

4)

6)

NAMING OF ANGLES

Angles are named either with one small letter, for example, a

or with three capital letters, letters, for example, $B\hat{A}C$

A sign like this $\frown$ is put over the middle letter to show that an angle is being denoted.

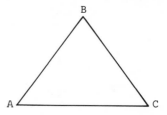

If the angles are in a triangle, to find which angle is meant by $A\hat{C}B$, say, the angle can be traced out in the order of the letters.

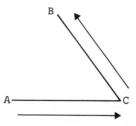

The angles $A\hat{C}B$ and $B\hat{C}A$ are considered to be the same, the ordering of the "outside" letters making no difference.

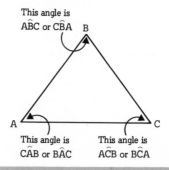

This angle is $A\hat{B}C$ or $C\hat{B}A$

This angle is $C\hat{A}B$ or $B\hat{A}C$

This angle is $A\hat{C}B$ or $B\hat{C}A$

If small letters are used to label angles the usual labelling for triangle AB̂C is as shown here:

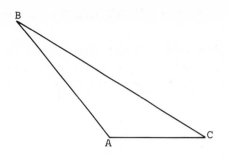
2)

EXERCISE 4

Rename the angles $a, b, c, d, e, f, g, p, q$ and r using capital letters.

3)

4)

5)

EXERCISE 5

(a) Measure these angles using a protractor.
(b) For each triangle copy a table similar to this one:

CÂB	
AB̂C	
BĈA	
Sum	

Put your results into the table.

(c) In each case find the sum of the angles.

1)

6)

7)
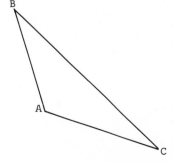

– SIMPLE ANGLE PROPERTIES –

This is a pair of *parallel lines*:

Parallel lines never meet. They are always the same distance apart and are in the same direction. Railway lines are parallel.

In geometry a pair of parallel lines is shown by a pair of single or double arrows:

or

A four-sided shape with one pair of parallel sides is called a *trapezium*:

This shape formed by two sets of parallel lines is called a *parallelogram*:

A line drawn across a pair of parallel lines is called a *transverse line* and it forms eight angles. Some of these angles are equal in size to each other and have special names.

Alternate Angles

Angles *c* and *f* are equal. They are called alternate angles. The two angles which are formed by the letter Z are alternate angles.

A special geometrical property of angles is that:

Alternate angles are equal

Angles *d* and *e* are also a pair of equal alternate angles.

Corresponding Angles

Angles *c* and *g* are equal. They are called corresponding angles.

Corresponding angles are equal

d and *h* are another pair of corresponding angles, as are *a* and *e*. Angles *f* and *b* also form a pair of corresponding angles.

Angles on a Straight Line

Angles *a* and *b* lie on a straight line. Therefore the sum of these two angles must be 180°.

Angles on a straight line add up to 180°

Vertically Opposite Angles

Angles b and c lie opposite to each other and are equal. Such angles as b and c are called vertically opposite angles.

Vertically opposite angles are equal

Angles f and g are also vertically opposite and thus equal to each other. The obtuse angles a and d are vertically opposite to each other as are the obtuse angles e and h.

In the diagram below angles q and s are equal (alternate angles) and angles p and t are equal (corresponding angles)

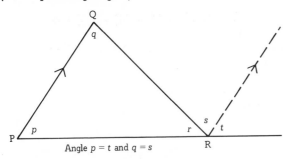

Angle $p = t$ and $q = s$

$$\therefore p + q + r = t + s + r = 180°$$

(since r, s and t lie on a straight line).

Angle Sum of a Triangle

It can be shown (by a method similar to that indicated in the last example) that:

The angle sum of a triangle is $180°$

EXAMPLE

Find angle x.

The angle sum of a triangle is $180°$

$$\therefore x + 52 + 83 = 180$$
$$x + 135 = 180$$
$$x = 180 - 135$$
$$x = 45$$

The unknown angle is $45°$.

Similarly, using the angle properties just described, other unknown angles can be worked out.

EXAMPLE

Find angles a, b, c, d and e in this diagram:

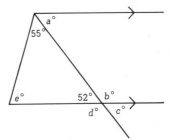

$a = 52$ (alternate angles)

$b = 180 - 52 = 128$ (angles on a straight line add up to $180°$)

$c = 52$ (vertically opposite angles)

$d = 128$ (vertically opposite to b)

$e = 180 - (55 + 52) = 73$ (angle sum of a triangle is $180°$)

Note that $b + c + d + 52 = 360$.
Angles at a point add up to $360°$.

––––––––––––– **EXERCISE 6** –––––––––––––

Give reasons for your answers in this exercise.

1) Find x.

2) Find *a* and *b*.

3) Find *x*, *y* and *z*.

4) Find *x*.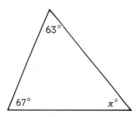

5) Find *x* and *y*.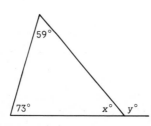

6) Find *a*, *b* and *c*.

7) Find *x*.

8) Find *x* and *y*.

9) Find *x* and *y*.

10) Find *x*, *y*, *z*, *w* and *t*.

11) Find *x*, *w* and *t*.

12) Find *y*.

13) Find *w*, *x*, *y* and *z*.

TRIANGLES

A triangle which has every angle less than 90° is called *acute-angled* or *scalene*.

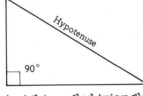

Every angle is less than 90°

A scalene triangle

A right-angled triangle has one of its angles equal to 90°.

The longest side is opposite the right angle and is called the *hypotenuse*.

Hypotenuse

90°

A right-angled triangle

A triangle with one angle greater than 90° is called an obtuse-angled triangle.

Height

Angle x is greater than 90°

x

Base

An obtuse-angled triangle

An isosceles triangle has two equal sides and two angles equal. The equal angles are opposite the equal sides.

A

Angle x = angle y
Side AB = side AC

B x   y C

An isosceles triangle

An equilateral triangle has all its sides and all its angles equal. Each angle is 60°.

60°

60°   60°

An equilateral triangle

A small line drawn across the sides of a triangle shows that the lengths of those sides are equal. In this triangle sides AC and BC are equal.

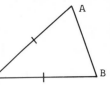

A

C   B

Sometimes a pair of lines is drawn to show equal sides:

A

C   B

The Right-angled Triangle

In a right-angled triangle the square of the length of the hypotenuse is equal to the sum of the squares of the lengths of the other two sides. This is known as Pythagoras' theorem:

A

AC is the hypotenuse

90°

B   C

$$AC^2 = AB^2 + BC^2$$

We think the Egyptians may have used Pythagoras' theorem to build tools to help them construct the Pyramids. There is actually no known record of Pythagoras having written anything about the rule which bears his name!

EXAMPLE

Triangle ABC has a right angle at B. The length of AB is 6 cm and the length of BC is 8 cm. Find the length of AC.

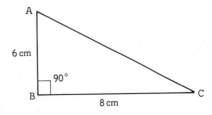

A

6 cm

90°

B   8 cm   C

$$AC^2 = AB^2 + BC^2$$
$$= 6^2 + 8^2$$
$$= 36 + 64$$
$$= 100$$
$$AC = \sqrt{100} = 10$$

The length of side AC is 10 cm.

EXAMPLE

A rectangle is 9 cm long and 5 cm wide. What is the length of the diagonal of the rectangle?

The *diagonal* of the rectangle is the distance from one corner to the opposite corner, so it can be seen that it is the hypotenuse of the right-angled triangle.

If we label the rectangle ABCD as shown then we have to find the length of AC:

$$AC^2 = AB^2 + BC^2 = 5^2 + 9^2 = 25 + 81 = 106$$
$$AC = \sqrt{106} = 10.3 \text{ cm} \quad \text{(using square root tables)}$$

When the length of the hypotenuse (the longest side) and the length of one other side are given, then we rearrange the equation before finding the third side.

EXAMPLE

In a right-angled triangle the length of the hypotenuse, AC, is 10 mm and the length of side BC is 5 mm. Find the length of the third side.

$$AC^2 = AB^2 + BC^2$$

Rearranging this equation:
$$AB^2 = AC^2 - BC^2 = 10^2 - 5^2 = 100 - 25$$
$$= 75$$
$$AB = \sqrt{75} = 8.66 \text{ mm (using square root tables)}$$

EXERCISE 7

Square root tables will be needed.

1) Find the length of side AC.

2) Find the length of the hypotenuse.

3) Find the lengths of the sides marked x.

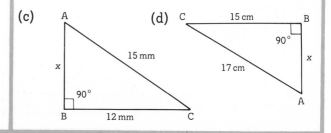

194

4) Find the length of the diagonal of a rectangle with width 10 cm and length 24 cm.

5) Find the length of the diagonal of a square of side 5 cm.

6) In a right-angled triangle the lengths of the two shorter sides are 2 cm and 1 cm. Find the length of the longest side.

The Isosceles Triangle

Triangle ABC is isosceles with length AB = length AC. D is the middle point of the line BC.

Angle $B\hat{A}D$ = Angle $D\hat{A}C$

Length BD = Length DC

Angle $B\hat{D}A$ = Angle $A\hat{D}C$ = 90°

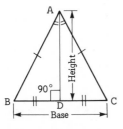

A line from A to D (the middle point of BC) forms two right-angled triangles. The triangles are BDA and CDA and both have a right angle at D. This fact is frequently used to find the height of an isosceles triangle.

EXAMPLE

Find the height of this isosceles triangle:

The height is the length AD

$$BC = 10\,\text{cm} \quad \text{so} \quad BD = \frac{1}{2} \times 10 = 5\,\text{cm}$$

Using Pythagoras' theorem

$$AB^2 = AD^2 + BD^2 \quad \text{so}$$

$$AD^2 = AB^2 - BD^2 = 8^2 - 5^2$$

$$= 64 - 25 = 39$$

$$AD = \sqrt{39} = 6.24\,\text{cm} \quad \text{(using square root tables)}$$

Find the heights of these isosceles triangles

1)

4)

2)

5)

3)

6)

7) Find the height of an isosceles triangle with two equal sides of length 11 cm and base 12 cm.

8) Find the height of an equilateral triangle with sides of length 8 cm.

195

CIRCLES

The *radius* of a circle is the distance from the centre to the edge of the circle.

The *diameter* of a circle is the distance across the centre from edge to edge.

The diameter = 2 × The radius

The distance round the edge of a circle is called the *circumference* and, for *any* circle you care to draw, the *circumference is just over three times the length of the diameter.* (It is difficult to measure round the edge of a circle but you could try with a piece of cotton and then measure the length of the cotton to verify that this is so.)

A better approximation is to say that:

Circumference = 3.14 × Diameter

The exact value of circumference ÷ diameter can never be worked out but it is so important that it has been given the special symbol π (the Greek letter "pi"). We generally take π as being 3.14 or $\frac{22}{7}$ when working in fractions.

Using an algebraic formula:

$$C = \pi \times d$$

where C is the circumference, π is 3.14 or $\frac{22}{7}$ and d is the diameter.

Since the diameter is twice the length of the radius, an alternative form is:

$$C = 2 \times \pi \times r \quad \text{or} \quad 2\pi r$$

where C is the circumference, π is 3.14 or $\frac{22}{7}$ and r is the radius.

EXAMPLE

The diameter of a circle is 10 cm. Find the length of the circumference of the circle.

$$C = \pi \times d$$
$$= 3.14 \times 10$$
$$= 31.4 \, \text{cm}$$

The circumference is 31.4 cm.

Circumference = ?

EXAMPLE

The radius of a circle is 14 cm. What is its circumference?

$$C = 2 \times \pi \times r$$
$$= 2 \times \frac{22}{7} \times 14$$
$$= 88 \, \text{cm}$$

(it is easier to use $= \frac{22}{7}$ when the radius is a multiple of 7 since the numbers cancel)

EXERCISE 9

Find the circumferences of the following circles
1) Diameter 2 cm
2) Diameter 5 cm
3) Diameter 7 mm
4) Diameter 21 cm
5) Radius 3 cm
6) Radius 7 m
7) Radius 10 mm
8) Radius $3\frac{1}{2}$ cm.
9) A wheel has a diameter of 70 cm. What is the length around the rim?
10) A circular flowerbed measures 4 m across the centre. How far is it round the edge?

SCALE DRAWINGS

Architects use scale drawings when submitting plans of a house or building to the Local Authority for planning permission.

On a scale drawing every measurement is in proportion to the actual or real measurement. Above is a scale drawing of a room with 1 cm on the drawing representing 1 m in the actual room.

From this drawing we could tell that the lounge is 4 m wide by 5 m long and that the hall is 2 m square.

EXERCISE 10

1) This is a sketch of the plan of a boat. Make an accurate scale drawing with 1 cm representing 1 m. You will need a ruler and a pair of compasses.

2) Draw quarter size an equilateral triangle which has sides 24 cm long, using a protractor and a ruler. Measure the height on your drawing. What would be the height of the original triangle?

3) Using a pair of compasses and a ruler make a scale drawing of this clock tower.

Use a scale of 1 cm to 1 metre. Measure the perimeter of the scale drawing.

4) Make a full size drawing of these nets, cut them out and decide which will fold to make the net of a cuboid.

(a)

(b)

(c)

(d)

5) Using a protractor, make a full size or half size scale drawing of the net of this tetrahedron and fold it to make the solid figure as shown.

10 cm 10 cm
10 cm
60°
All angles are 60°
The length of each side is 10 cm

Tetrahedron

BEARINGS

The more familiar points of the compass are shown on this diagram.

North
NW NE
West East
SW SE
South

The four main points are north, south, west and east with the intermediate points, north-east (NE), north-west (NW), south-east (SE), and south-west (SW) as shown.

Directions can also be expressed in degrees measured from north. Usually three figures are used, so 45° would be written 045°.

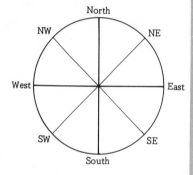

This is a sketch of a ship steaming in a direction of 045° (which is the same as NE).

North would be 000°, east 090°, south 180° and west 270°.

Bearings are always measured clockwise:

EXERCISE 11

1) Give three-figure bearings for the directions (a) south-west (b) north-west.

2) Draw four separate diagrams to show the directions of these bearings
(a) 030° (b) 125° (c) 240° (d) 300°.

3) Using a protractor and *measuring the angle clockwise* express these directions using a three-figure bearing

(a) N   (b) N   (c) N

4) An aircraft leaves an aerodrome A and flies on a bearing of 080° for a distance of 90 km to a point P. It then changes direction and flies due west for a distance of 60 km until it reaches a point Q. Draw a scale diagram to represent this flight using a scale of 1 cm to 10 km. Hence find the distance from A to Q and write down the bearing of Q from A.

5) As shown in the diagram opposite, a boat sails from a port P to a point X. It then sails to a second point Y. The diagram has been drawn to scale. Use it to find

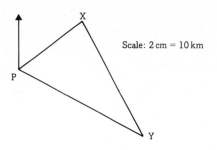

Scale: 2 cm = 10 km

(a) the distance of X from P, (b) the bearing of X from P, (c) the distance of Y from P, (d) the bearing of Y from P.

19

Area

Area is the space taken up by a flat surface such as a table top:

or a curved surface such as the outside of a tin:

It is measured in *square units*.

This is a unit square of side 1 cm:

It is called a "1 cm square" and it has an *area* of 1 square centimetre (1 cm²).

UNITS OF AREA

The *metric* units of area are:

square millimetres	(mm²)
square centimetres	(cm²)
square metres	(m²)
or square kilometres	(km²)

A square metre is the amount of space taken up by a square of side 1 metre.

The *imperial* units of area are:

square inches	(sq. in)
square feet	(sq. ft)
square yards	(sq. yd)
or square miles	(sq. miles)

A square inch is the amount of space taken up by a square of side 1 inch.

Land is measured in *hectares* (1 hectare is 10 000 m²) or *acres* (1 acre is 4840 sq. yd):

1 hectare is about $2\frac{1}{2}$ acres

Carpets and vinyl flooring are generally sold by the square metre (metric) or square yard (imperial).

AREAS OF RECTANGLES AND SHAPES MADE FROM THEM

Twenty 1 cm squares would fit inside this rectangle:

We say its area is 20 cm².

The area of a rectangle is defined as length × width (even when the length and width are not whole numbers).

EXAMPLE

Find the areas of these rectangles

Area = Length × Width
= 10 × 4 cm²
= 40 cm²

Area = Length × Width
$$= 1\frac{1}{2} \times 1\frac{1}{3} \text{ cm}^2$$
$$= \frac{\overset{1}{\cancel{3}}}{\underset{1}{\cancel{2}}} \times \frac{\overset{2}{\cancel{4}}}{\underset{1}{\cancel{3}}}$$
= 2 cm²

Area = Length × Width
= 8.5 × 4 cm²
= 34.0 cm²

EXAMPLE

Find the area of this rectangle (a) exactly (b) to the nearest square metre.

It is **essential to** make both measurements of **the** *same type.*

Change centimetres to metres:

50 cm = 0.5 m

Area = Length × Width
= 1.5 × 0.5 m²
= 0.75 m² **exactly**
= 1 m² (to the nearest square metre)

Working:

1.5
0.5 ×
―――
0.75

1 d.p. plus 1 d.p. gives 2 d.p. in answer.

───────── **EXERCISE 1** ─────────

Find the areas of these rectangles

1)

2)

3)

4)

5)

6)

7)

8)

9)

10)

11)

12)

13)

14)

15)

Find the areas of these rectangles

16) Length 10 mm width 8 mm
17) Length 3 m width 50 cm
18) Length 5 cm width 28 mm
19) Length 4.5 cm width 2.3 cm
20) Length 13.5 cm width 8.6 cm.

21) Find the area of a carpet which is 2 m wide and 350 cm long.

22) What is the area of a 15 cm square tile?

23) Calculate the area in square feet of a pane of glass which is 3'6" by 8'.

24) A piece of vinyl flooring is 2 m wide and 2.8 m long. What is its area to the nearest square metre? If it costs £2.25 per square metre how much will it cost? (Assume that you are charged for a whole number of square metres.)

25) Sheet metal is sold at £4.50 per square yard. What is the cost of a piece 6 feet long and 3 feet wide?

26) What is the area of a wall consisting of 150 tiles which are each 10 cm by 10 cm?

27) How many 6 inch square tiles will be needed to tile two walls of a shower unit, each wall being 7 ft 6 in high and 2 ft 6 in wide? What will be the cost if tiles are £6 a square yard?

EXAMPLE

Find the area of the side of the L-shaped piece of wood shown:

This shape can be divided into two rectangles. Call one rectangle A and the other B.

The area of A = Length × Width

$$= 5 \times 3.2 = 16.0 \text{ cm}^2$$

The area of B = Length × Width

$$= 2.4 \times 2 = 4.8 \text{ cm}^2$$

Total area = 20.8 cm²

───────────── **EXERCISE 2** ─────────────

By dividing these shapes into rectangles find their total areas. (All measurements are in cm.)

1)

7)

2)

8)

3)

9)

4)

10)

5)

11)

6)

12)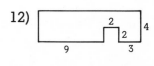

202

AREAS OF BORDERS

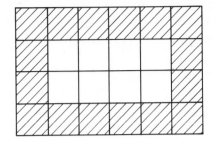

There are $6 \times 4 = 24$ squares altogether in this rectangle.

There are $4 \times 2 = 8$ white squares.

There are 16 shaded squares (count them!)

The number of shaded squares = total number of squares − white squares.

The shaded squares form a *border* round the edge of the white squares.

To find the area of a border:

Calculate the total area (by multiplying length × width of the outside rectangle)

and *take away* the area of the central rectangle.

EXAMPLE

A lawn is 6 m by 3 m and has a 1 m wide path all the way round the edge. Find the area of the path.

Total area = length × width of outer rectangle.

The length of the outer rectangle is 8 m and the width 5 m.

Total area $= 8 \times 5 = 40 \, m^2$

Area of central rectangle $= 6 \times 3 = 18 \, m^2$

Area of border $= 40 - 18 \, m^2 = 22 \, m^2$
(check by counting the shaded squares)

EXAMPLE

Find the area of the shaded border of the rectangle below which is 0.5 cm wide all the way round.

First we must find the length and width of the inner rectangle.

Length of inner rectangle $= 8.0 - (2 \times 0.5)$
$$= 8.0 - 1.0$$
$$= 7.0 \, cm$$

Width of inner rectangle $= 4.5 - (2 \times 0.5)$
$$= 4.5 - 1.0$$
$$= 3.5 \, cm$$

Total area = Length × Width of outer rectangle
$$= 8.0 \times 4.5 \, cm^2$$
$$= 36.0 \, cm^2$$

Area of inner rectangle $= 7.0 \times 3.5 \, cm^2$
$$= 24.5 \, cm^2$$

Area of border = Total area − Area of central rectangle
$$= 36.0 - 24.5 \, cm^2 = 11.5 \, cm^2$$

EXERCISE 3

Find the areas of the borders. (It might be helpful to draw these on squared paper and to check your answers by counting the squares.)

1)

4)

2)

5)

3)

6)

7) This is a sketch of the top of an iron pillar. Find the area of the iron.

8) A lawn which is 7 m by 10 m has a path which is 1 m wide all round it. Draw a sketch of the lawn and path and mark the length and width of (i) the lawn and (ii) the lawn plus the path on your diagram. Find (a) the total area of lawn plus path (b) the area of the lawn (c) the area of the path (d) the cost of putting weedkiller on the path if it costs 2 p per square metre.

9) A picture measures 1.5 m by 1 m. It has a wooden frame around it which is 0.25 m wide. Draw a diagram of the picture and mark the length and width on it. Draw the frame round the picture and work out the length and width of the frame and mark them on your sketch. Calculate (a) the total area of picture plus frame (b) the area of the picture alone (c) the area of the frame (d) the cost of buying the wood for the frame if the wood was sold at £2 per square metre.

AREAS OF CIRCLES

It can be shown that the area of a circle = $\pi \times$ radius $\times$ radius where π is about 3.14 or $\frac{22}{7}$.

The *radius* is the distance from the centre to the edge. The *area* is the space taken up by the inside of the circle.

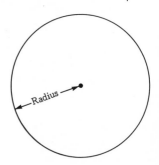

EXAMPLE

Find the area of a circle of radius 2 cm.

$$\text{Area} = \pi \times \text{Radius} \times \text{Radius}$$
$$= 3.14 \times 2 \times 2 \text{ cm}^2$$
$$= 6.28 \times 2 \text{ cm}^2$$
$$= 12.56 \text{ cm}^2$$

It is easier when using a calculator to take π as 3.14. However, if the radius is 7 or 14 or another multiple of 7 it is sometimes easier to take π as $\frac{22}{7}$. When working with *fractions* it is often best to take $\pi = \frac{22}{7}$.

EXAMPLE

Find the area of a circle of radius 7 cm.

$$\text{Area} = \pi \times \text{Radius} \times \text{Radius}$$

$$= \frac{22}{7} \times 7 \times 7 \text{ cm}^2 \quad \text{(make the whole numbers into top-heavy fractions and } \textit{cancel} \text{ by 7)}$$

$$= \frac{22}{\cancel{7}} \times \frac{\cancel{7}}{1} \times \frac{7}{1} \text{ cm}^2$$

$$= 22 \times 7 \text{ cm}^2$$

$$= 154 \text{ cm}^2$$

You may *choose* whichever value of π is most convenient. Some people prefer always to take the value of π as about 3.14 because they find working with decimals easier than working with fractions. In this case all fractions must be changed to decimals first.

─────────── **EXERCISE 4** ───────────

Find the areas of these circles. The answers will vary slightly according to whether you use $\pi = 3.14$ or $\pi = \frac{22}{7}$.

1) Radius 3 cm
2) Radius 5 cm
3) Radius 10 cm
4) Radius 14 cm
5) Radius $3\frac{1}{2}$ cm
6) Radius $1\frac{3}{4}$ cm

───────────────────────────

Sometimes the diameter is given instead of the radius:

EXAMPLE

Find the area of a circle of diameter 8 cm.

$$\text{Diameter} = 2 \times \text{Radius}$$

$$\therefore \text{ Radius} = 4 \text{ cm}$$

$$\text{Area of the circle} = \pi \times \text{Radius} \times \text{Radius}$$

$$= 3.14 \times 4 \times 4 \text{ cm}^2$$

$$= 12.56 \times 4 \text{ cm}^2$$

$$= 50.24 \text{ cm}^2$$

A *composite* figure is made up of several simpler shapes. The shape in the example below is made up of a square and half a circle (a semi-circle). To find the total area we find the areas of the separate shapes and *add them together*.

EXAMPLE

Find the area of this composite figure:

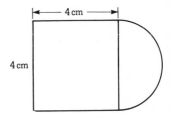

The area of the square is $4 \times 4 \text{ cm}^2 = 16 \text{ cm}^2$

The circle has diameter 4 cm.

$$\text{Diameter} = 2 \times \text{Radius}$$

$\therefore$ Radius is 2 cm

The area of a whole circle with radius 2 cm is given by

$$\pi \times \text{Radius} \times \text{Radius} = 3.14 \times 2 \times 2 \text{ cm}^2$$

$$= 6.28 \times 2 \text{ cm}^2$$

$$= 12.56 \text{ cm}^2$$

The area of half such a circle $= 12.56 \div 2$

$$= 6.28 \text{ cm}^2$$

The total area of the shape = The area of the square + The area of the semi-circle

$$= 16 + 6.28 \text{ cm}^2$$

$$= 22.28 \text{ cm}^2$$

─────────── **EXERCISE 5** ───────────

These are harder questions. Take care with the units. Give your answers correct to 3 significant figures.

1) Find the area of a circle with diameter 12 cm.

2) Find the area of a circle with diameter 16 mm.

3) Find the area of a circle with diameter 40 m.

4) Find the area of a circle with diameter 1.4 m.

Find the areas of these shapes (they are all made from rectangles or squares and circles or semi-circles).

5)

8)

6)

9)

7)

10)

In the next six questions find the area of (a) the square, (b) the circle or part of a circle and (c) the shaded area by *taking away the area of the circle, or part of a circle, from the area of the square.*

11)
10 cm

10 cm

12)
0.5 cm

0.5 cm

13)

4 cm

4 cm

15)
4 cm ⟶⟵ 4 cm

8 cm

14)

14 cm

14 cm

16)
7 cm

7 cm

AREAS OF TRIANGLES

It is easy to see that the area of a right-angled triangle is *half* the area of a rectangle with the same height and base. (Imagine a piece of paper folded in half.)

Height

Base

This is also true for *any* triangle:

Height

Base

Area of a triangle $= \dfrac{1}{2}$ Base $\times$ Height

Height

Base

It is not so easy to see that this is true for a triangle that "leans over". However, such a triangle can be shown to have an area half that of a parallelogram (which looks like a pushed over rectangle) with the same base and height. In turn, the parallelogram has the same area as a rectangle with the same base and height as shown by this diagram (by transferring the triangle on the end to the shaded area):

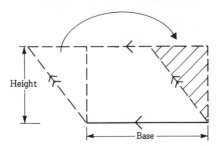

Reminder: Area is the space taken up by a flat (or curved) surface.

The *area of a triangle* is the amount of space inside the triangle.

EXAMPLE

Find the areas of these triangles:

(a)

10 cm
8 cm

(b)

$1\frac{1}{2}$ m
4 m

(c)

3 mm
5.6 mm

$$\text{Area of a triangle} = \frac{1}{2}\text{Base} \times \text{Height}$$

(Care must be taken with the units.)

(a) $\text{Area} = \frac{1}{2} \times 8 \times 10 \text{ cm}^2$

$= 4 \times 10 \text{ cm}^2$

$= 40 \text{ cm}^2$

(b) $\text{Area} = \frac{1}{2} \times 1\frac{1}{2} \times 4 \text{ m}^2$

$= \frac{1}{\underset{1}{2}} \times \frac{3}{\underset{1}{2}} \times \frac{\overset{2}{\overset{\cancel{4}}{1}}}{1} \text{ m}^2$

$= 3 \text{ m}^2$

(c) $\text{Area} = \frac{1}{2} \times 5.6 \times 3 \text{ mm}^2$

$= 2.8 \times 3 \text{ mm}^2$

$= 8.4 \text{ mm}^2$

EXERCISE 6

Find the areas of these triangles

1)

6 cm
10 cm

5)

8 cm
9 cm

2)

5 cm
6 cm

6)

5 cm
12 cm

3)

7 cm
5 cm

7)

5 cm
8.6 cm

4)

4.2 cm
10 cm

8)

5.6 cm
10 cm

9)

11)

10)

12)

Find the areas of these triangles

13) Base 16 mm height 7 mm
14) Base 3.2 m height 4 m
15) Base 26 mm height 8 mm
16) Base 12.5 cm height 6 cm
17) Base 24 m height 5 m
18) Base $4\frac{1}{2}$ cm height $1\frac{1}{3}$ cm
19) Base 50 mm height 9 mm
20) Base 46 mm height 8 mm

— THE AREA OF A TRAPEZIUM —

The area of a trapezium may be found by dividing the shape into two triangles.

EXAMPLE

Find the area of this shape:

First divide the shape into two triangles, labelling them A and B:

Area of triangle A $= \frac{1}{2} \times 3 \times 8 = 12\,\text{cm}^2$

Area of triangle B $= \frac{1}{2} \times 9 \times 8 = 36\,\text{cm}^2$

Total area of trapezium $= 12 + 36 = 48\,\text{cm}^2$

EXERCISE 7

Find the areas of these shapes

1)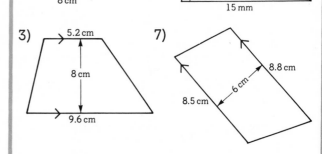

5)

2)

6)

3)

7)

4)

8) Find the area of a trapezium with two parallel sides of length 5 cm and 7 cm and height 8 cm.

9) The distance between the two parallel sides of a trapezium is 10 cm. The lengths of the parallel sides are 8 cm and 9 cm. What is the area of the trapezium?

10) Calculate the area of a trapezium with parallel sides 3 m and 5 m and distance between them 12 m.

— REARRANGING FORMULAE —

If we are given the *area* of a shape and need to find the *height* or *length* it is often useful to use the algebraic formula for the area and *rearrange* it to find the unknown height or length.

$$\text{Area of a rectangle} = \text{Length} \times \text{Width}$$

$$A = l \times w$$

$$\therefore l = A \div w \quad \text{and} \quad w = A \div l$$

EXAMPLE

Find the width of this rectangle:

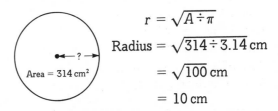

$$w = A \div l$$
$$\text{width} = 132 \div 12$$
$$= 11 \text{ cm}$$

$$\text{Area of a triangle} = \frac{1}{2} \text{ Base} \times \text{Height}$$

$$A = \frac{1}{2} \times b \times h$$

$$\therefore b = 2 \times A \div h \quad \text{and} \quad h = 2 \times A \div b$$

EXAMPLE

Find the height of this triangle:

$$h = 2 \times A \div b$$
$$\text{height} = 2 \times 56 \div 7$$
$$= 112 \div 7$$
$$= 16 \text{ cm}$$

$$\text{Area of a circle} = \pi \times \text{Radius} \times \text{Radius}$$

$$A = \pi \times r \times r \quad (\text{or } A = \pi r^2)$$

$$\therefore r \times r = A \div \pi$$

$$\text{and} \quad r = \sqrt{A \div \pi}$$

EXAMPLE

Find the radius of this circle:

$$r = \sqrt{A \div \pi}$$
$$\text{Radius} = \sqrt{314 \div 3.14} \text{ cm}$$
$$= \sqrt{100} \text{ cm}$$
$$= 10 \text{ cm}$$

(For more difficult numbers the use of a calculator is recommended.)

— EXERCISE 8 —

1) Find the length of this rectangle

2) Find the width of this rectangle

9 m

Area = 54 m²   ?

209

3) (a) Find the height of this triangle

(b) Find the height of this triangle

4) Find the length of the base of this triangle

5) Find the radius of this circle

6) Find the length of a rectangle with area 56 cm² and width 4 cm.

7) Find the width of a rectangle with length 9 mm and area 45 mm².

8) Find the height of a triangle with base 100 cm and area 300 cm².

9) Find the height of a triangle with area 60 mm² and base 5 mm.

10) Find the base of a triangle with area 84 cm² and height 12 cm.

1) Find the areas of these rectangles

2) Find the area of a rectangle with length 26 cm and width 5 cm.

3) By dividing these shapes into rectangles find their total areas

4)

(a) Write down the number of white squares.

(b) Write down the number of shaded squares.

(c) Write down the total number of squares.

5) Find the area of a rectangular lawn measuring 2.5 m by 3 m. There is a path 0.5 m wide all round such a lawn. Sketch the lawn plus path and put on the measurements of the larger rectangle. What is the total area of lawn plus path?

Find the area of the path and calculate the cost of putting on weedkiller at 3 p per square metre.

6) What is the area of a circle of radius (a) 2 cm (b) 35 cm?

7) Give the areas of these triangles
(a) base 16 cm height 9 cm
(b) base 1.8 m height 10 m.

8) Find the areas of these shapes

(a)

3 cm

6 cm

(b)

10 cm

6 cm

6 cm

9) Find the shaded areas of these shapes

(a)

4 cm

2 cm

4 cm

(b)

10 cm

8 cm

5 cm

5 cm

10) Find (a) the length of a rectangle area 81 cm² and width 8.1 cm (b) the height of a triangle area 20 mm² and base 10 mm.

K

20

Volume

Volume is the space taken up by a solid object such as a cardboard carton or a football:

It is measured in *cubic units*.

This is a unit cube of side 1 cm:

It is called a "1 cm cube" and has a *volume* of 1 cubic centimetre (1 cm³).

— UNITS OF VOLUME —

The *metric* units of volume are:

	cubic millimetres	(mm³)
	cubic centimetres	(cm³)
	cubic metres	(m³)
or	cubic kilometres	(km³)

The *imperial* units of volume are:

	cubic inches	(cu. in)
	cubic feet	(cu. ft)
	cubic yards	(cu. yds)
or	cubic miles	(cu. miles)

A cubic metre is the amount of space contained in a cube whose edge is 1 metre. Similarly a cubic foot is the amount of space contained in a cube whose edge is 1 foot long.

The volume of liquids is sometimes measured in litres and

   1 litre = 1000 cm³

In imperial measure, pints, quarts and gallons are used as was described in Chapter 5.

VOLUMES OF CUBOIDS AND — SHAPES MADE FROM THEM —

Thirty 1 cm cubes would fit inside this shape:

We say its volume is 30 cm³.

*The volume of a cuboid is defined as length ×
width × height* (even when the length, width and height are not whole numbers).

EXAMPLE

Find the volumes of these cuboids

(a)

$$\text{Volume} = \text{Length} \times \text{Width} \times \text{Height}$$
$$= 10 \times 8 \times 5 \text{ cm}^3$$
$$= 80 \times 5 \text{ cm}^3$$
$$= 400 \text{ cm}^3$$

(b)

$$\text{Volume} = \text{Length} \times \text{Width} \times \text{Height}$$

All measurements must be in the *same units* so changing 250 cm to metres

$$250 \text{ cm} = 2.5 \text{ m}$$
$$\text{Volume} = 3 \times 2 \times 2.5 \text{ m}^3$$
$$= 6 \times 2.5 \text{ m}^3$$
$$= 15.0 \text{ m}^3$$

———————— **EXERCISE 1** ————————

Find the volumes of these shapes

1)

3)

2)

4)

5)

6)

Find the volumes of these cuboids

7) Length 3 m width 2 m height 1.5 m
8) Length 500 cm width 250 cm height 4 m
9) Length 6 mm width 4 mm height 12 mm
10) Length 15 cm width 6 cm height 4 cm
11) Length 35 mm width 1 cm height 5 cm
12) Length 13 cm width 7 cm height 10 cm.
13) Find the volume of a cardboard box measuring 30 cm by 20 cm by 15 cm.
14) The length, width and height of a tin are 15 cm, 10 cm and 8 cm respectively. What is its volume?
15) Calculate the volume of a box with length 35 cm, width 10 cm and height 8 cm.

————————————————————

EXAMPLE

Find the volume of this podium:

Divide the shape into 3 cuboids (boxes) and label them A, B and C:

A has length 1 m, width 0.8 m and height 0.75 m

B has length 1 m, width 0.8 m and height 1 m

C has length 1 m, width 0.8 m and height 0.5 m

The volume of A $= 1 \times 0.8 \times 0.75 \text{ m}^3$

$$= 0.6 \text{ m}^3$$

The volume of B $= 1 \times 0.8 \times 1\,\text{m}^3$

$\qquad = 0.8\,\text{m}^3$

The volume of C $= 1 \times 0.8 \times 0.5\,\text{m}^3$

$\qquad = 0.4\,\text{m}^3$

The total volume of the podium is $1.8\,\text{m}^3$

EXERCISE 2

By dividing these shapes into cuboids (boxes) find their total volumes

1)

2)

3)

4)

5)

6)

7) A block of wood 10 cm by 10 cm by 9 cm has a square hole drilled into it measuring 8 cm by 8 cm by 9 cm.

(a) Find the volume of the wood before the hole is drilled.

(b) Find the volume of air in the square hole drilled through the centre of the wood.

(c) By subtracting your answer to (b) from your answer to (a) find the volume of wood remaining after the hole has been drilled.

VOLUMES OF PRISMS

A *prism* has the same shape all the way along its length.

It can be shown that:

214

Volume of a prism = Area of the front face
$$\times Length$$

$$V = A \times l$$

where V is the volume, A is the area of the front face and l is the length.

A new pencil is an example of a *hexagonal prism*. The front face is a hexagon. (It has six sides.)

A *rectangular prism* is another name for a *cuboid* (or box shape)

and a *cylinder* is a special name for a *circular prism*. Most tins are made in the shape of a cylinder.

This piece of cheese is in the shape of a *triangular prism*. The front face is a triangle and the cheese has the same shape all the way along its length.

This lean-to greenhouse has the shape of a prism. Its front face is made up from a rectangle plus a triangle.

EXAMPLE

Find the volume of the triangular prism shown below:

Volume of a prism = Area of front face
$$\times Length$$

Area of triangle $= \dfrac{1}{2}$ Base $\times$ Height

$\therefore$ Area of front face $= \dfrac{1}{2} \times 6 \times 8\, m^2 = 3 \times 8\, m^2$

$$= 24\, m^2$$

Volume $= 24 \times 10\, m^3 = 240\, m^3$

EXAMPLE

Find the volume of this tin:

Volume = Area of front face $\times$ Length

(If the tin were laid on its side the front face would be a circle, radius 4 cm, and the length of the tin would be 5 cm.)

Area of a circle $= \pi \times$ Radius $\times$ Radius

$\therefore$ Area of front face $= 3.14 \times 4 \times 4\, cm^2$

$$= 12.56 \times 4\, cm^2$$

$$= 50.24\, cm^2$$

Volume $= 50.24 \times 5\, cm^3 = 251.20\, cm^3$

───────────────── **EXERCISE 3** ─────────────────

By finding the area of the front face and multiplying by the length find the volumes of these prisms

1)

2)

3)

4)

5)

6)

7)

8)

9) Find the volume of a cylinder of length 10 cm and radius 2 cm.

10) Find the volume of a triangular prism with base 10 cm, height 8 cm and length 12 cm.

VOLUMES OF PYRAMIDS

It can be shown that:

The volume of a pyramid $= \dfrac{1}{3}$ *Area of the base* $\times$ *Height*

$$V = \dfrac{1}{3} \times A \times h$$

where V is the volume, A is the area of the base and h is the height.

EXAMPLE

Find the volume of this square based pyramid:

Area of the base $= 4 \times 4 \, \text{cm}^2 = 16 \, \text{cm}^2$

Volume $= \dfrac{1}{3} \times 16 \times 9 \, \text{cm}^3$

$= 16 \times 3 \, \text{cm}^3$

$= 48 \, \text{cm}^3$

A *cone* is a special kind of pyramid with a circular base:

The volume of a cone $= \dfrac{1}{3}$ Area of the base $\times$ Height

$$= \dfrac{1}{3} \times \pi \times \text{Radius} \times \text{Radius} \times \text{Height}$$

$$V = \dfrac{1}{3}\pi r^2 h$$

where V is the volume, r is the radius of the base and h is the height.

EXAMPLE

Find the volume of this cone:

6 cm

10 cm

$$\text{Volume} = \dfrac{1}{3} \times \pi \times \text{Radius} \times \text{Radius} \times \text{Height}$$

$$= \dfrac{1}{3} \times 3.14 \times 10 \times 10 \times 6 \text{ cm}^3$$

$$= \dfrac{1}{3} \times 314 \times 6 \text{ cm}^3$$

$$= 314 \times 2 \text{ cm}^3$$

$$= 628 \text{ cm}^3$$

To find the volume of a pyramid find the area of the base, multiply by the height and divide by 3.

Using the formula *volume of a pyramid* $= \dfrac{1}{3}$ *area of the base* $\times$ *height* find the volume of these solid figures

1)

3 cm
2 cm
2 cm

4)

2.5 m
3 m
3 m

2)

10 cm
3 cm

5)

5 cm
6 cm
6 cm

3)

10 mm
5 mm
5 mm

6)

6 cm
10 cm

———— **EXERCISE 5** ————

1) Find the volumes of these boxes

(a)

8 cm
5 cm
2 cm

(b)
1 cm
6 cm
2 cm

(c)
4 mm
4 mm
5 mm

(d)

1.5 m
4.5 m
2 m

217

(e) 8 mm, 8 mm, 8 mm

(f) 8 m, 5 m, 5.5 m

2) The measurements of these pieces of wood are as shown. Find their volumes

(a)

5 m, 3 m, 3 m, 3 m, 1 m, 4 m

(b)

3 m, 2 m, 5.5 m, 2 m, 4 m

3) Find the volumes of these triangular prisms

(a)

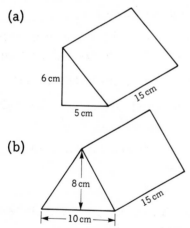

6 cm, 15 cm, 5 cm

(b)

8 cm, 15 cm, 10 cm

4) Using the fact that the volume of a cylinder = area of circle × depth find the volume of this gas holder

7 m, 5 m

5) The volume of a pyramid is $\frac{1}{3}$ area of the base × height. Use this fact to determine the volume of the pyramid with measurements as shown on this diagram

(The base of this pyramid is a square.)

200 m, 150 m, 150 m

Harder questions:

6) The formula for the volume of a cone is $\frac{1}{3}\pi r^2 h$ where r is the radius of the base and h is the height of the cone. Use this formula to find the volume of a cone with base radius 7 cm and height 10 cm.

7) The formula for the volume of a sphere is $\frac{4}{3}\pi r^3$ where r is the radius of the sphere. Use this formula to find the volume of a sphere with radius 2 cm.

8) Another formula for the volume of a cylinder is $\frac{1}{4}\pi d^2 h$ where d is the diameter of the circle and h is the height of the cylinder. Use this formula to find the volume of a cylinder with diameter 10 cm and height 7 cm.

9) The volume of a cuboid is given by $V = l \times w \times h$ where V is the volume, l is the length, w is the width and h is the height. If this formula is rearranged then $h = V \div (l \times w)$. Use this fact to find the height of a box with volume 150 cm³, length 10 cm and width 3 cm.

10) Rearrange the formula $V = l \times w \times h$ to find the width of a box with volume 96 m³, height 8 m and length 4 m.

218

21

Similarity

Similar figures have the *same* shape.

These two toys are similar in shape:

However, these two trucks are *not* similar in shape:

The larger truck is wider and longer but it is not taller. For shapes to be similar they must be wider, longer *and* taller in the *same* proportion.

You might say the larger brick is 3 times bigger than the smaller brick and indeed all the *lengths* are 3 times bigger. However, 9 small bricks would sit on top of the larger brick. It would take 27 small bricks to make a shape as big as the larger brick.

If both bricks were made of the same type of wood, the larger brick would be 27 times heavier than the smaller brick.

Notice that the *length* is 3 times bigger.

The *area* is 3×3 times bigger.

The *volume* and the *weight* (if they were made of the same material) are $3 \times 3 \times 3$ times bigger.

The areas vary as the *square* of the lengths.

The volumes (weights) vary as the *cube* of the lengths.

This property applies to all similar figures.

EXAMPLE

The model of a bronze sculpture is 10 times smaller than the actual figure

Model   Sculpture

I need $\frac{1}{2}$ tin of paint for the model. How many tins will I need to paint the actual figure?

If the model weighs 2 kg how much will the actual figure weigh?

> Lengths are 10 times larger.
> Areas are 10×10 times larger.
> Volume and weight are $10 \times 10 \times 10$ times larger.

Painting depends on the area of the figure. The area of the actual figure is 100 times the area of the model.

I will need $100 \times \frac{1}{2}$ tins of paint = 50 tins of paint.

The weight of the sculpture will be 1000 times the weight of the model. The sculpture weighs 1000×2 kg = 2000 kg.

EXERCISE 1

1)

The two tins of beans are similar in shape and content. If the second tin is twice as tall as the first, how much heavier will it be?

2) How many 5 cm tiles will fit on a section of wall measuring 25 cm by 25 cm?

25 cm

Wall

25 cm

5 cm 5 cm

3)

20 cm

20 cm   20 cm

The length of the side of the brick is 5 cm. How many of these bricks will fit inside the box shown?

4) The diagrams show the area of the front of two tunnels. They are similar in shape.

$7\frac{1}{2}$ ft

$2\frac{1}{2}$ ft

If the area of the front of the smaller tunnel is 5 square feet, what is the area of the front of the larger tunnel?

5) How many 1 cm sugar cubes will fit (a) on the first layer, (b) inside a box measuring 6 cm by 6 cm by 6 cm?

6)

The larger bottle of shampoo is similar in shape to the smaller but twice as high. How much more liquid is there in the larger bottle? The price of the smaller is 52 p. The price of the larger is £4.56. Is the larger bottle a good buy?

7)

The two cubes are made of the same metal. The larger one is 8 times heavier than the smaller. The length of the side of the smaller cube is 5 cm. What is the length of the side of the larger?

8)

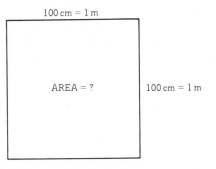

100 cm = 1 m

AREA = ?   100 cm = 1 m

What is the area of a square which is 1 m long and 1 m wide (a) in m^2, (b) in cm^2?

How many square centimetres are there in 1 square metre? (Note carefully that the number of *square centimetres* in one *square metre* is not the same as the number of *centimetres* in one *metre*.)

9)

1 cm

1 cm = 10 mm

This square has an area of 1 mm^2 This square has an area of 1 cm^2

How many mm^2 make 1 cm^2?

10)

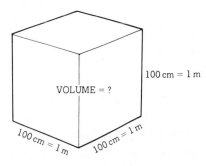

100 cm = 1 m

VOLUME = ?

100 cm = 1 m   100 cm = 1 m

Using the picture above, state how many cm^3 there are in 1 m^3.

11)

Costs double!

Why is this diagram misleading?

22

Further Topics

In this chapter we look at some of the aspects of mathematics that have been developed relatively recently and are obviously going to continue to be of tremendous importance in the future.

PROBABILITY

This work has great importance in the field of genetics (the study of how human characteristics are passed on from generation to generation), pure science, insurance (the risks have to be carefully calculated before premiums are set), investment in business, and so on.

We measure probability on a scale between 0 and 1.

A probability of 0 means *absolute impossibility* (for example, the probability that we will live to be 200 years old).

A probability of 1 means *absolute certainty* (for example, the probability that all the people alive today were born in either the nineteenth or the twentieth century).

Throwing a 7 on a normal die with six faces is impossible:

probability = 0

We are certain to throw a 1, 2, 3, 4, 5 or 6:

probability = 1

All other probabilities have a value between 0 and 1 which we write as a fraction or a decimal.

We talk of a chance being, say, 1 in 3. As a fraction we would write 1 in 3 as $\frac{1}{3}$.

Two words that often occur with probability are "event" and "random".

An *event* is a particular happening or occurrence that we are interested in. For example, an insurance company may be interested in the number of people unable to work through illness. "Unable to work through illness" would be the event. Another example might be winning the pools. We may say the chance of winning the pools is 1 in 50 000 or $\frac{1}{50\,000}$. The event is "winning the pools".

Random means purely by chance in an unbiased way. For example, if we pick a card from a pack at random, then all cards are equally likely to be picked and there is an equal chance of picking any particular card. Winning Premium bonds are selected at random. Every bond has an equal chance of being picked for a prize.

$$\text{Probability of an event} = \frac{\text{Number of ways the event can occur}}{\text{Total possibilities}}$$

222

Probability is an extremely complicated subject, so it is usually introduced by considering simple (but fairly artificial) events such as "throwing a 5 on a die", or "drawing a queen from a pack of cards" or "picking a green marble at random from a bag".

EXAMPLE

What is the probability of drawing a picture card from a normal pack of cards?

A normal pack of cards has 4 suits of 13 cards each. The suits are hearts, clubs, diamonds and spades with ace, 2 to 10, and the picture cards — Jack, Queen and King — in each suit. Hearts and diamonds are red, spades and clubs are black.

There are 52 cards in a normal pack. 12 of these are picture cards.

The probability of drawing a picture card is $\frac{12}{52} = \frac{3}{13}$ in its lowest terms.

—— TOTAL PROBABILITY ——

The total probability is always 1.

This is useful when we wish to calculate the probability of something *not* happening.

EXAMPLE

What is the probability of drawing a card *other* than a picture card from a normal pack of cards?

The probability of drawing a card other than a picture card is $1 - \frac{3}{13} = \frac{10}{13}$.

EXPERIMENTAL PROBABILITY

When we cannot work out the probability by reason alone, then we have to carry out an experiment on a sample of whatever is involved. We might want to check some light-bulbs made in a factory to see how many of them are faulty. The bigger the sample the more accurate the value for the probability of a light-bulb being faulty. However, if the machine breaks down, it may start to produce all faulty light-bulbs. It is always important to be aware that circumstances may change. Tests should continue to be taken at regular intervals.

EXAMPLE

Tests showed that out of 5000 light-bulbs made in a factory, 25 were found to be faulty. If I pick a light-bulb at random, what is the chance that it is faulty?

Since 25 in 5000 were found to be faulty the chance of picking a faulty light-bulb at random is 25 in 5000 or $\frac{25}{5000}$ which equals $\frac{1}{200}$ in its lowest terms.

—————— EXERCISE 1 ——————

1) In a family with two children it is possible to have two girls, two boys, a boy then a

girl, or a girl then a boy. This is shown as

GG,   BB,   BG,   GB

with B standing for boy and G for girl.
If the chance of having a boy or a girl is
the same, write down the probability of
having (a) two boys, (b) two girls, (c) a boy
and a girl in a family of two children.

2) It is known that there are 3 winning raffle
tickets and that 150 tickets have been
sold. What is the chance of winning with
1 raffle ticket (a) first prize, (b) any prize?

3) It is my turn to throw the die and I need
a 6 or a 1 to be able to move. What is the
chance that I can move on my next turn?

4) Three boys bet on the colour of marbles
which are drawn at random from a bag
without looking. There are 6 green marbles,
4 yellow marbles and 2 red marbles.
Calculate the probability that the first one
drawn will be (a) green, (b) yellow, (c) not
red.

5) In a game a coin is placed at random on
one of the squares on the board shown
below. What is the probability that it is
placed on (a) a black square, (b) a shaded
square, (c) a white square?

6) A card is drawn at random from a pack of
52 cards. Find the probability that it will
be (a) red, (b) a spade, (c) a jack.

7) The probability of a particular couple
having a blue-eyed child is $\frac{1}{4}$. What is the
probability that the child's eyes will not be
blue?

8) 100 ball-bearings are checked in a factory
and 15 are found to be defective. If one is
picked at random, what is the chance that
it will be a good one?

9) A letter is chosen at random from the
word   POSSESSES.   What is the
probability that it will be (a) P, (b) S,
(c) not E?

10) I have signed 6 letters on my desk but I
still have 8 more to sign. If I pick up a
letter at random from my desk, what is
the chance that it is unsigned?

11) Two dice are thrown together. What is the
probability that their total will be (a) 6,
(b) less than 6, (c) more than 6?

12) In a survey it is found that 5 out of 150
light-bulbs are faulty. I buy a pack of 10
light-bulbs. What is the chance that the
first light-bulb I try is faulty?

13) At a village fête on the tin and bottle stall
a prize is won if a raffle ticket ending in
0 or 5 is picked out of a box. If raffle
tickets numbered 1 to 200 are placed in
the box, what is the initial chance of
winning a prize? Describe in words why
the chance of winning a prize may vary
as the draw proceeds.

14) A hand of cards consists of the king of
hearts, the queen of clubs, the ace of
spades, the king of diamonds and the 10 of
hearts. What is the probability, if I draw a
card at random from the hand, of choosing
(a) a heart, (b) a spade, (c) a king, (d) a
card which is not an ace?

15) The leaves on a certain type of plant may
be either striped, variegated or plain. If the
chance of their being striped is $\frac{1}{8}$ and the
chance of their being variegated is $\frac{1}{4}$, what
is the chance of their being plain?

16) I take the four aces, the four kings and
the four queens from a pack of cards,
shuffle them, and deal three cards to four
players. The first player turns up one of

his cards. It is a queen. What is the probability that if he turns up another of his cards it will also be a queen?

FLOW CHARTS

Flow charts are used in business and computing. Sometimes certain actions have to be carried out in a particular order. Flow charts can show this particularly clearly. A simple example is shown below.

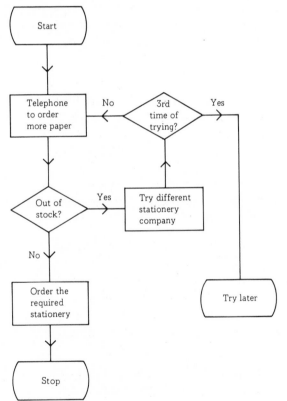

Start and stop boxes are usually shaped like

this (⬭). Instruction boxes may be shaped

like this [▭]. A diamond-shaped decision

box ◇ has two exits, one for "yes" and

one for "no". They allow different paths to be taken through the flow chart. There are usually *loops* which permit certain instructions to be repeated. In the flow chart above, the caller would go round the loop 3 times if three different stationery companies were out of stock.

Quite complicated flow charts might be seen on the wall of an office or on a manager's desk.

A computer programmer would draw a flow chart before writing a program for a computer.

EXAMPLE

The maximum and the minimum measurements of the diameter of a steel rod are entered into a computer. We want the computer to print the larger number but we do not know which is which. If the two measurements are the same we want a message to be printed. Draw a suitable flow chart.

Flow chart to print the larger of two numbers:

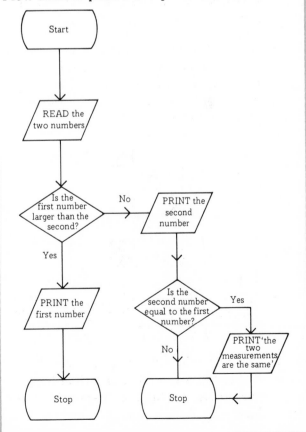

READ and PRINT are called *input* and *output* instructions and are in a box shaped like this

.

This flow chart could be drawn in a shorter way by letting A and B represent the two numbers and by using symbols such as $<$ (less than), $>$ (greater than), or $=$ (equals):

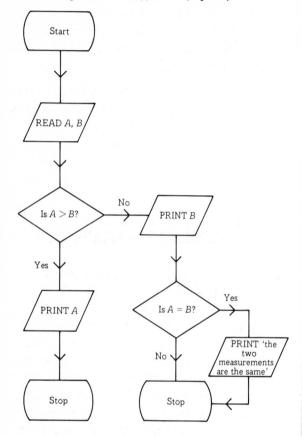

──────── **EXERCISE 2** ────────

Draw a flow chart showing

1) How to make toast and a boiled egg.

2) What to check before going on a holiday which entails a long journey in the car (petrol, water, luggage, map, coffee and sandwiches, etc.).

3) The actions needed to bath a baby (test temperature of water, too hot? too cold? fetch soap, clothes, etc.).

4) Two numbers representing the maximum and minimum age for a particular job are fed into a computer but we do not know which is which. Draw a flow chart to read the two numbers and print the smaller number first and then the larger. Use the signs $<$ or $>$ and letters to represent the numbers.

5) The wages of three people are entered into a computer. Draw a flow chart to print them in ascending order.

─────────────────────

USING A FLOW CHART METHOD FOR CALCULATORS WITH NO ─── MEMORY ───

In Chapter 2 we showed that multiplication and division must be done before addition and subtraction so that

$$3 + 4 \times 5 = 23 \ (not \ 35)$$
$$\text{and} \quad 15 + 48 \div 12 = 19 \ (not \ 5.25)$$

Some calculators and all computers will do this for you automatically but sometimes, if your calculator is a very simple one without a memory, you have to take steps yourself to make sure you get the right answer. (This is very important as it easily leads to errors in calculator work.)

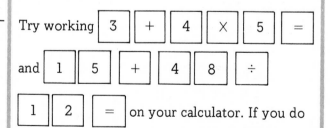

on your calculator. If you do not get the correct answers 23 and 19, then your calculator is one which does not perform arithmetic operations automatically in the correct order. For sums of this type you have to work out the answers by *doing the multi-*

plication and division first yourself. A flow chart can help you to decide the correct order.

If you work out | 4 | × | 5 | = | and

then | + | 3 | = | you should get the

right answer 23. The second example is done by

pressing the buttons | 4 | 8 | ÷ |

| 1 | 2 | = | and then | + | 1 | 5 |

| = | to give the answer 19.

These could be shown on flow charts like this

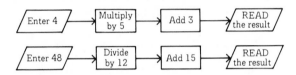

(We have written the flow charts across the page to save space.)

─────────── **EXERCISE 3** ───────────

Suppose you are borrowing a simple calculator with no memory. Draw flow charts to show how you would calculate

1) $16 + 84 \times 12$

2) $35 + 112 \div 7$

3) $7 + \dfrac{5}{8}$ as a decimal

4) $5\dfrac{3}{16}''$ in decimal form

5) the price of an electricity bill with fixed charge £6.50 and 415 units at 5.23 p per unit

6) the length of a piece of cloth 1.5 m plus 17 times 0.32 m long

7) the change received from £10 for a tie at £1.25 and 3 pairs of socks at 72 p per pair (you will have to write down an inter-

mediate result or use the | +/− | button to

change the sign in the display)

8) the cost of 4 items at £12.50 each, 17 items at £15.95 each and 9 items at £3.50 each (you will have to write down intermediate results and re-enter them into the calculator for the final total).

9) Use any calculator and the methods shown on your flow charts to work out the correct answers to questions 1) to 8).

─────────────────────────────

FLOW CHART METHOD FOR ── ALGEBRAIC EQUATIONS ──

Flow charts can be used to show algebraic equations. Suppose we wish to flow chart $y = 3x + 5$. We start with x, the unknown letter on the right-hand side of the equation and look to see what is happening to it. Since multiplication is done before addition the first thing is "multiply by 3". We write this in an instruction box and show $3x$ on the exit line. The next thing we do is "add 5" so we write "add 5" in the next instruction box and show $3x + 5$ on the next exit line.

If we want to rearrange the equation so that x is on the left-hand side, then we work back again from right to left replacing "add" by "subtract" and "multiply" by "divide".

The flow chart overleaf shows the algebraic equation $y = 3x + 5$. To save space we draw the flow chart across the page and leave out the start and stop boxes.

To find what x is in terms of y, we merely reverse the process (working from right to left and starting with y).

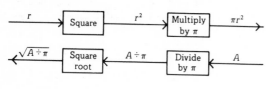

So $x = \dfrac{y-5}{3}$

This method can be useful for rearranging simple formulae.

EXAMPLE

$A = \pi r^2$

Show this on a flow chart and rearrange to find r in terms of A and π.

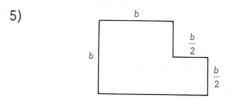

$r = \sqrt{A \div \pi}$

────────── EXERCISE 4 ──────────

1) Draw a flow chart to show $y = 7x + 4$ and then draw a second flow chart working from right to left to find x in terms of y.

2) $m = 8n - 6$. Use the flow chart method to find n in terms of m.

3) $C = 2\pi r$. First find r in terms of C and then, using a calculator, find the value of r when $C = 100$.

4) The surface area of a cube is given by $A = 6x^2$ where x is the length of one side. Use the flow chart method to find x in terms of A. What is x when $A = 714$? (Use a calculator.)

5)

![shape with dimensions b, b/2, b, b/2]

The area of this shape is given by $A = \dfrac{5b^2}{4}$.

Find b in terms of A and work out the value of b when $A = 18.75$. (Use a calculator.)

6) Draw a flow chart of $v = u + at$ with t the unknown letter and then reverse it to find t in terms of v, u and a.

7) Show the flow chart of $A = \frac{1}{2}b \times h$ with b the unknown letter. Draw a second flow chart from right to left to find b in terms of A and h. Find b if $h = 10.4$ and $A = 200$. (Use a calculator.) (*Reminder:* multiplying by $\frac{1}{2}$ is the same as dividing by 2.)

Mental Test

The questions should be read *twice* slowly.

Allow 30 seconds for each of these questions including reading time.

1) Add together sixty-three and forty-seven.
2) Take seventeen away from thirty.
3) Multiply seven by nine.
4) What is the cost of five articles at forty-five pence each?
5) Write three point one four correct to one decimal place.
6) From six times eight take away nine.
7) Multiply six point two by ten.
8) Write the fraction four-fifths as a decimal.
9) Multiply seven point six by one hundred.
10) Write the number eight thousand, five hundred and forty to the nearest hundred.
11) How many centimetres are there in two and a half metres?
12) How many quarters are there in two and three-quarters?
13) Write in figures the number seventy thousand.
14) Express forty marks out of fifty as a percentage.
15) A rectangle has an area of fifteen square centimetres. How wide is it if the length is five centimetres?
16) How many minutes are there in one and a half hours?
17) Twenty-five per cent of a class are boys. What percentage are girls?
18) What is the time eighteen minutes after eight fifty-five?
19) Divide sixteen point eight by four.
20) What is one-fifth of two pounds fifty.
21) Multiply nought point three by five.
22) Using the twenty-four hour clock write down the time seven minutes after fourteen fifty-eight.
23) What is the area of a triangle of base three metres and height six metres?
24) Write down the average of nine, eleven and sixteen.
25) How much change is left from a pound note after buying three articles at twelve pence each?
26) What is the perimeter of a square whose sides are each two and a half feet long?
27) A motorist travels fifty miles in two hours. What is his average speed?
28) Multiply nought point four by nought point three.
29) How many feet are there in three yards?
30) Give the cost of ten fifteen-and-a-half pence stamps.

Miscellaneous Questions

1) (a) 3020×407
   (b) 47×38
   (c) $250 \div 8$ (to the nearest whole number)
   (d) Give the remainder when 250 is divided by 8.

2) (a) 250 g of pepper are shared equally into 8 boxes. What is the weight in each box? (Give the answer first as a whole number and a fraction and then as a whole number and a decimal.)
   (b) The surface temperature of a pond changes from $-3°$ to $5°$ from one day to the next. By how many degrees has the temperature risen?
   (c) A man has £35 in his bank account. He writes a cheque for £50. By how much will he be overdrawn?

3) (a) $145 - (24 + 92)$
   (b) $15 + 4 \times 3$
   (c) $2 \times 9 + 3 \times 5$
   (d) $10 - 36 \div 6$
   (e) $84 \div 12 - 49 \div 7$

4) (a) A woman saves £25 in order to redecorate a room. If the wallpaper costs £15.96 and the paint £5.25 how much has she left over for other items?
   (b) A carton contains 840 g of soap powder when full. If 2460 g of powder are shared equally between 3 cartons how much more must be added to each carton to fill it?

5) Work out
   (a) 9^2
   (b) the square root of 64
   (c) 4^3
   (d) $3^2 + 4^2$
   (e) $10^2 - 5^2$

6) What is the value of 3 in
   (a) 22 103   (b) 30.6   (c) 1.3
   (d) 2.035?

7) Write in standard form
   (a) 150 000   (b) 0.000 15.

8) Express as single numbers
   (a) 2.4×10^5 (b) 2.4×10^{-2}.

9) Which is larger 1.5×10^4 or 16×10^3?

10) (a) 2.8×0.3 (b) 0.5×0.1
    (c) $307.2 \div 4$ (d) $6.4 \div 0.8$
    (e) $2.1 \times 3.6 + 0.83 \times 1.2$

11) (a) How many pieces of wool for rug-making can be cut from a piece of wool 1.56 m long if each piece of wool must be 7.8 cm long?
    (b) Find the total cost of 1.2 kg bacon at £2.50 per kg and 0.5 kg sausages at £1.28 per kg.

12) (a) $\dfrac{3}{16} + \dfrac{1}{4}$ (b) $2\dfrac{5}{6} + 3\dfrac{7}{12}$

    (c) $3\dfrac{5}{16} - 2\dfrac{9}{16}$ (d) $3\dfrac{1}{2} \times 1\dfrac{1}{7}$

    (e) $5\dfrac{1}{3} \times 3$ (f) $\dfrac{7}{16} \div 2\dfrac{5}{8}$

    (g) $3\dfrac{3}{4} \div \dfrac{1}{2}$

13) (a) Find the cost of $3\frac{1}{2}$ dozen eggs at 42 p per $\frac{1}{2}$ dozen.

(b) If a piece of wood $4\frac{1}{4}$ m long is divided into 17 equal lengths, how long is each piece?

(c) Three people share a flat. One pays $\frac{1}{3}$ of the rent, the second $\frac{5}{12}$ and the third the rest. If the rent is £60 a week how much does each pay?

(d) Basic wages are £60 a week. How much is this per hour if a basic week is 40 hours?

(e) Overtime is paid at time and a quarter. How much is paid for 3 hours overtime if the basic wage is £8 per hour?

14) VAT is charged at 15% on a £50 coat. What is the price of the coat plus VAT?

15) A salesman earns 2% commission on a sale worth £2500. How much commission does he get?

16) A girl earns 14 marks out of 25. What percentage is this?

17) Using square root tables find (a) $\sqrt{0.52}$ (b) $\sqrt{520}$.

18)

Temperature		Temperature	
°C	°F	°C	°F
0°	32°	50°	122°
10°	50°	60°	140°
20°	68°	70°	158°
30°	86°	80°	176°
40°	104°	90°	194°
		100°	212°

Use the above table to convert
(a) 15°C to °F
(b) 140°F to °C.

19) Use the 24 hour clock to convert
(a) 9.00 a.m.
(b) 4.15 p.m.
to 24 hour clock time.

20) How many minutes before midnight is 2333 hours?

21) Give the fares from
(a) Linden Avenue to the Bus Station
(b) Princess Avenue to High Street
(c) Queen Street to The Bullring.

Linden Avenue

10	The Bullring					
15	10	High Street				
15	15	10	Weston Road			
17	15	15	10	Knight Lane		
20	17	17	15	10	Princess Av.	
25	20	17	17	15	10	Queen Street
30	25	20	17	15	15	10	Bus Station

All fares in this chart are in pence.

22) Plot these points on a graph, choosing a suitable scale.

x	0	1	2	3	4	5
y	2	5	8	11	14	17

Draw a line through the points.
(a) Give the value of y when $x = 2.5$.
(b) Give the value of x when $y = 15.5$.
(c) Write down the equation of the straight line.

23) Change to fractions
    (a) 0.75   (b) 0.35   (c) 1.75
    (d) 60%   (e) 36%   (f) 125%.

24) Change to decimals
    (a) $\dfrac{1}{10}$ (b) $\dfrac{5}{8}$ (c) $2\dfrac{4}{5}$

    (d) 80%   (e) $12\dfrac{1}{2}\%$ (f) 175%.

25) Change to percentages
    (a) $\dfrac{1}{5}$ (b) $\dfrac{1}{3}$ (c) $2\dfrac{5}{8}$
    (d) 0.5   (e) 0.6̇6̇   (f) 1.625.

26) (a) What fraction of 400 is 25?
    (b) What percentage of 400 is 25?

27) Which is greater, 0.3 or $\dfrac{1}{3}$?

28) Write down in the correct order the buttons that you would press on a calculator to add
    $£1.25 + 12\dfrac{1}{2}p + £12.50$

    What answer should you expect to see in the display and what would this mean in pounds and pence?

29) Approximately how many centimetres are there in 1 foot?

30) Two swimming pools have shallow ends of depth 3 ft 6 in and 1 metre respectively. Which is deeper?

31) A boy in Britain buys 4 oz sweets while on the same day his French penfriend buys 100 g sweets. Who has more?

32) The marks obtained in 10 different tests are
       2, 4, 6, 2, 3, 5, 5, 2, 3 and 4
    (a) find the mean, mode and median
    (b) give the range.

33) The cricket scores for 5 different innings are 30, 110, 0, 50 and 70
    (a) What is the average score?
    (b) What must the batsman score in the next innings to improve his average by 3 runs?

34) A motorist travels 60 miles at an average speed of 40 mph and 30 miles at an average speed of 60 mph. Give the total time, the total distance and the overall average speed.

35) The curved surface area of a cylinder is $2\pi rl$ where r is the radius and l is the length. Find the area when $r = 5$ cm and $l = 21$ cm. Take π as $\frac{22}{7}$.

36) The volume of a sphere is given by $V = \dfrac{4}{3}\pi r^3$ where r is the radius. Find the volume, V, when $r = 10$ cm. Take π as 3.14. Give your answer correct to 3 significant figures.

37) The radius of a cylindrical piece of wood is given by $r = \sqrt{V \div (\pi \times h)}$ where V is the volume and h is the height. Find r when $h = 7$ cm and $V = 88$ cm^3. Take π as $\frac{22}{7}$.

38) How many right angles are there in 270°?

39) Find (a) x (b) y (c) z.

40) There are 60 minutes in 1 degree, so 6 minutes = 0.1°. (60 minutes may be written as 60′.)
    (a) Express 23.5° in degrees and minutes.
    (b) Write 54°12′ in decimal form.

41) Following is a sketch of a small picture in a frame.
    (a) What is the total area of the picture and frame?
    (b) What is the area of the picture only?
    (c) What is the area of the frame alone?
    (d) If the frame cost 5p per cm^2 what is the cost of the frame?

1.5 cm

1.5 cm

Picture

8 cm

Frame

5 cm

42) A ladder 13 ft long leans against a vertical wall so that it reaches to a height of 12 ft. How far from the wall is the base of the ladder?

43) The cardboard pieces in a game are made in the shape of a triangle and a semi-circle as shown. Find the area of cardboard in each shape and the total area of six such pieces.

16 mm

14 mm

44) What is the reading on (a) the scales and (b) the gas-meter dials?

(a)

(b)

45) Plot these points, choosing a suitable scale and draw a smooth curve through them.

Temperature in °C	Time in minutes
86°	0
68°	1
54°	$2\frac{1}{2}$
44°	4
38°	$5\frac{1}{2}$
32°	8
30°	10

(a) From your graph estimate the time at which the temperature is 50°.
(b) What is the probable temperature after 5 minutes?

46)

Inches	Millimetres
1	25.4
2	50.8
3	76.2
4	101.6
5	127.0
10	254.0
50	1270.0
100	2540.0

Using this conversion table change

(a) 3   (b) 8

(c) 14   (d) 56

(e) 98

inches to millimetres.

47) The chart below shows how index numbers have changed. -2 means down 2, $+7$ means up 7. One of the numbers in the right-hand column is wrong. Which one is it and what should the correct number be?

Index	1st week	2nd week	Overall change	Final value
500	-2	-4	-6	494
512	$+4$	$+3$	$+7$	519
511	-6	$+5$	-1	510
514	$+7$	-4	$+3$	517
517	-7	$+6$	-1	516
520	-2	-5	-7	513
519	$+3$	-2	-1	518
516	$+5$	-1	$+4$	520

48) (a) Profit (P) is worked out by taking the cost price (C) from the selling price (S). Write an equation for calculating profit.

(b) A motorist travels s miles at an average speed of u miles/hour. He takes t hours. Write an equation for s using u and t.

(c) An electricity bill is worked out by multiplying the number of units used (N) by the cost per unit (Q) and adding the fixed charge (F). Write an equation for the cost of electricity (C) in terms of N, Q and F.

Multiple Choice Revision Exercise

Write down the letter corresponding to the correct answer for each question.

1) The fraction of the circle which has been shaded in the diagram is

$A \dfrac{5}{18}$ $B \dfrac{1}{2}$ $C \dfrac{5}{8}$

$D \dfrac{13}{18}$

2) What is the median of the numbers: 8, 9, 8, 12, 10, 7, 6, 9, 10 and 8?
   A 9   B 8.5   C 8   D 7.5

3) $78.75 \div 0.35$ is
   A 2.25   B 22.5   C 225   D 2250

4) $\dfrac{7}{40}$ as a percentage is

   A 7% $B\ 17\dfrac{1}{2}\%$ C 40%   D 70%

5) During a sale a shop reduced the price of everything by 10%. What was the sale price of an article originally priced at £12.90?
   A £1.29   B £11.61   C £11.91   D £14.19

6) $2\dfrac{1}{4} \times 3\dfrac{1}{2}$ is

   $A\ 6\dfrac{1}{8}$ $B\ 6\dfrac{7}{8}$ $C\ 7\dfrac{1}{8}$ $D\ 7\dfrac{7}{8}$

7) 350×60 is
   $A\ 2.1 \times 10^5$ $B\ 2.1 \times 10^4$ $C\ 2.1 \times 10^3$
   $D\ 2.1 \times 10^2$

8) A boy scored 60% in a test. If the maximum mark was 50, then the boy's score was
   A 5   B 15   C 30   D 35

9) A girl obtains 60 marks out of 75 in a test. This is equivalent to a percentage of
   A 30%   B 60%   C 80%   D 90%

10) The perimeter of the triangle ABC shown in the diagram is
    A 70 cm
    B 80 cm
    C 82 cm
    D 90 cm

11) If the exchange rate for French francs is 10 francs for £1, then 2876 francs changed into pounds would be
    A £28.76   B £287.60   C £2876
    D £28 760

12) A transistor radio can be bought for £37.90 or on hire purchase for 9 monthly payments of £4.74 each. How much more does the hire purchase method cost?
    A £4.76   B £5.90   C £6.62   D £7.42

13) $10 - 0.005$ equals
    A 0.005   B 9.005   C 9.995   D 10.005

14) What is $\dfrac{1}{2} + \left(\dfrac{1}{2} \times \dfrac{1}{2}\right)$?

    $A\ \dfrac{1}{8}$ $B\ \dfrac{1}{2}$ $C\ \dfrac{3}{4}$ $D\ 1$

15) The number 0.075 538 correct to two decimal places is
    A 0.07   B 0.075   C 0.076   D 0.08

235

L

16) Which of the following does *not* equal $\frac{1}{2}xy$?

   A $\frac{xy}{2}$ B $x \times \frac{y}{2}$ C $\frac{1}{2}xy$ D $\frac{1}{2x} \times y$

17)
Hockey	⅃⃥⃥⃥⃥⃥
Baseball	⅃⃥⃥⃥⃥⃥ ||
Rugby	⅃⃥⃥⃥⃥⃥ |||
Cricket	⅃⃥⃥⃥⃥⃥ |||
Football	⅃⃥⃥⃥⃥⃥ ⅃⃥⃥⃥⃥⃥ ||

(⅃⃥⃥⃥⃥⃥ equals 5)

The tally marks above show the distribution in the sports preferred by a sample of schoolboys. What fraction of the sample preferred rugby?

   A $\frac{1}{8}$ B $\frac{7}{40}$ C $\frac{1}{5}$ D $\frac{1}{4}$

18) What is 0.0089 correct to two decimal places?
   A 0.008   B 0.009   C 0.01   D 0.09

19) £189 is divided into two parts so that the first part is $\frac{3}{4}$ of the second. What is the value of the larger part?
   £108   B £84   C £81   D £72

20) In an examination, 240 candidates out of 720 results were awarded Grade C. On a pie chart showing all the grades, the angle at the centre for Grade C would be
   A 135°   B 120°   C 105°   D 90°

21) The value of 0.7×0.05 is
   A 0.035   B 0.35   C 0.75   D 3.5

22) In the number 350.47, the actual value represented by the digit 7 is
   A 70   B 7   C $\frac{7}{10}$ D $\frac{7}{100}$

23) If £240 is divided in the ratio 2 to 3 then the smaller share is
   A £80   B £96   C £120   D £144

24) If 20% of a sum of money is £200 then the whole sum of money is
   A £20   B £40   C £400   D £1000

25) If $4M = 20$, then the value of M is
   A 80   B 24   C 16   D 5

26) The total surface area of a cube of edge 2 cm is
   A 8 cm²   B 8 cm³   C 24 cm   D 24 cm²

27) Calculate the mean of 1, 2, 5, 7 and 15.
   A 4   B 6   C 7   D 30

28) Find the value of $13^2 - 12^2$.
   A 1^2 B 5   C 25   D 125

29) The pie chart in the diagram illustrates the subjects taken by a group of pupils in the sixth form of a school. What percentage take French?
   A 20%   B 25%   C 30%   D 50%

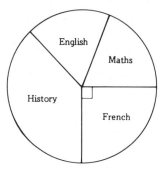

30) Find the value of x in the equation $5x + 1 = 61$.
   A 10   B 12   C 50   D 62

31) Find the size of the angle marked Q in the diagram.
   A 63°
   B 107°
   C 117°
   D 127°

32) Find the area of a triangle whose sides are 3 cm, 4 cm and 5 cm.
   A 6 cm²   B 10 cm²   C 12 cm²   D 15 cm²

33) The sum of eleven thousand and eleven hundred is
   A 11 100   B 11 110   C 11 111   D 12 100

34) $8 + 5 \times (4 - 2)$ is equal to
   A 2   B 18   C 22   D 50

35) Which is the largest of the following fractions?
   A $\frac{1}{2}$ B $\frac{2}{3}$ C $\frac{5}{6}$ D $\frac{7}{10}$

36) $0.1 \times 0.2 \times 0.3$ equals
A 0.006   B 0.06   C 0.6   D 6

37) Which of the following is the largest?
A 0.22   B 2.20   C 2.02   D 0.022

38) The cost of 2 metres of material at £2.40 per metre and 6 metres at £1.50 per metre is
A £5.40   B £13.20   C £13.80   D £14.20

39) 0.9 as a percentage is
A 0.9%   B 9%   C 90%   D 99%

40) For her holidays a woman saved 10% of her weekly wage of £150 for 40 weeks in the year. How much did she save for her holiday?
A £150   B £300   C £450   D £600

41) The perimeter of a square is 36 cm. Its area, in square centimetres, is
A 6   B 9   C 36   D 81

42) 42 600 m expressed in kilometres is
A 4.26   B 42.6   C 426   D 4260

43) Four packets have weights of 2 kg, 250 g, $3\frac{1}{2}$ kg and 500 g. Their total weight in kilograms is
A 5.25   B 6   C 6.25   D 6.5

44) The number 63 700 written in standard form is
A 637×10^2 B 63.7×10^3 C 6.37×10^4 D 0.637×10^5

45) If $2q = 8$ then the value of q is
A $\frac{1}{4}$ B 4   C 6   D 16

46) The square of 0.12 is
A 0.0144   B 0.14   C 0.144   D 0.24

47) $2\frac{1}{5}$ when written in decimal form is
A 2.01   B 2.02   C 2.1   D 2.2

48) $6\frac{1}{5} - 2\frac{3}{4} + 1\frac{1}{6}$ equals
A $2\frac{17}{60}$ B $4\frac{17}{60}$ C $4\frac{37}{60}$ D $5\frac{22}{60}$

49) Correct to 2 significant figures, 3.0394 is equal to
A 3.0   B 3.03   C 3.039   D 3.4

50) A man's taxable income is £1800. If tax is levied at 30% how much does he pay in income tax?
A £48.60   B £486   C £540   D £1620

Answers

CHAPTER 1

Exercise 1

1) (a) (i) 35 (ii) XXXV
   (b) (i) 305 (ii) CCCV
   (c) (i) 350 (ii) CCCL
2) (a) (i) 79
      (ii) LXXVIIII or LXXIX
   (b) (i) 709
      (ii) DCCVIIII or DCCIX
   (c) (i) 790
      (ii) DCCLXXXX (or DCCXC)
3) (a) (i) 65 (ii) LXV
   (b) (i) 605 (ii) DCV
   (c) (i) 650 (ii) DCL
4) (a) nine hundred and eighty
   (b) ninety-eight
   (c) nine hundred and eight
5) (a) eight hundred (b) eighty
   (c) eight
6) (a) eighty-nine
   (b) eight hundred and ninety
   (c) eight hundred and nine
7) (a) one hundred and ten
   (b) one hundred and one
   (c) eleven
8) (a) seventy-eight
   (b) seven hundred and eight
   (c) seven hundred and eighty
9) (a) one hundred and thirty
   (b) one hundred and three
   (c) thirteen
10) (a) fourteen
    (b) one hundred and forty
    (c) one hundred and four
11) (a) 26 (b) 206 (c) 260
12) (a) 55 (b) 550 (c) 505
13) (a) 12 (b) 120 (c) 102
14) (a) 21 (b) 210 (c) 201

15) (a) 700 (b) 70 (c) 7
16)

Number in words	figures H T U
twenty-four	2 4
nineteen	1 9
seventy-six	7 6
eight	8
one hundred and sixty-four	1 6 4
seven hundred and eight	7 0 8
three	3
sixty-one	6 1
two hundred and fifty-four	2 5 4
fifty-eight	5 8

17) 5 hundreds 4 tens 2 units
18) 9 hundreds 0 tens 2 units
19) (a) 5 hundreds (b) 5 tens
    (c) 5 units (d) 5 tens
20) (a) 3 units (b) 3 hundreds
    (c) 3 tens (d) 3 units
21) (a) 9 tens (b) 9 tens
    (c) 9 units (d) 9 hundreds
22) (c) and (d)
23) (b) and (d)
24) (b) and (c)
25) 123, 132, 321
26) 35, 53, 305, 350, 503, 530
27) 13, 31, 103, 130, 301, 310
28) 510, 501, 150, 105, 51, 15
29) 321, 312, 231, 213, 132, 123

Exercise 2

1) 2451
2) 5311
3) 6112
4) 1014

5) 6009
6) 5300
7) 14 000
8) 24 000
9) 70 000
10) 16 208
11) 75 142
12) 40 064
13) 300 000
14) 195 580
15) 114 613
16) 351 645
17) 712 201
18) five thousand, seven hundred and sixty-three
19) six thousand, seven hundred and twenty-one
20) nine thousand, eight hundred and eighty-four
21) sixteen thousand
22) sixty-five thousand
23) eight hundred and nine thousand
24) seventy-two thousand and fifty
25) seven thousand and nine
26) eight thousand and two
27) seven thousand and eighty
28) eight thousand and ninety
29) six thousand and fifty
30) eight thousand nine hundred
31) seven thousand eight hundred
32) sixty-five thousand, three hundred and thirty-two
33) fourteen thousand five hundred
34) one hundred and sixty-three thousand, four hundred and four
35) nine hundred thousand and nine
36) four hundred and fifty-two thousand, nine hundred and eighty-six

37) three hundred and four
thousand and twenty-one
38) . . . .
```
        5  0 0 0
      6 2  0 0 0
    3 0 0  0 0 0
      7 4  0 0 9
    6 0 0  2 0 0
      7 0  0 5 0
    9 9 0  0 0
        6  0 0 0
```

Exercise 3

1) 8 000 000
2) 19 000 000
3) 600 000 000
4) 324 000 567
5) 3 700 030
6) 4 000 040
7) 64 300 666
8) 999 000 000
9) 464 330 206
10) seven million
11) fifty-seven million
12) one hundred and eighty-nine million
13) seven million, twelve thousand, five hundred and six
14) five million, eight hundred and sixty-nine thousand and fourteen
15) one hundred and sixty-seven million, one hundred and eighty-nine thousand, one hundred and twelve
16) nine hundred million, three thousand and forty
17) . . . .
```
    1 610 000 000
        8 030 050
      706 000 000
```

Exercise 4

1) (a) yes   (b) yes   (c) no
   (d) no   (e) yes   (f) yes
   (g) yes   (h) no
2) (a) no   (b) yes   (c) yes
   (d) no   (e) yes   (f) no
   (g) no   (h) yes
3) (a) yes   (b) no   (c) no
   (d) no   (e) yes   (f) yes
   (g) yes   (h) no

4) (a) yes   (b) no   (c) yes
   (d) yes   (e) no   (f) yes
   (g) yes   (h) no
5) (a) no   (b) yes   (c) no
   (d) yes   (e) no   (f) yes
   (g) no   (h) yes
6) (b) and (c)
7) (a), (b), (e) and (h)
8) (a), (c), (d) and (e)
9) (a) and (b)

Exercise 5

1) (a) 1, 2, 5, 10
   (b) 1, 2, 7, 14
   (c) 1, 3, 5, 15
   (d) 1, 2, 4, 8, 16
   (e) 1, 2, 4, 5, 10, 20
   (f) 1, 5, 25
   (g) 1, 2, 3, 4, 6, 9, 12, 18, 36
   (h) 1, 2, 3, 6, 7, 14, 21, 42

Exercise 6

1) (a), (b), (e), (h), (i), (k), (l), (n) and (o)

Exercise 7

1) (a) 8   (b) 7   (c) 7   (d) 6
2) (a) 2   (b) 5   (c) 4   (d) 2
3) (a) 1   (b) 3   (c) 9   (d) 1
4) (a) 6   (b) 9   (c) 6   (d) 3

Exercise 8

1) (b) and (d)
2) (b) and (d)
3) (b) and (c)
4) (a), (b) and (d)
5) (c)
6) (a), (b) and (c)
7) (a) and (c)

Exercise 9

1) (b)
2) (a), (b) and (c)
3) (c)
4) (a) and (c)

Exercise 10

1) (a), (b) and (c)
2) (a), (b) and (c)
3) (a) and (c)
4) (a) and (b)
5) (a), (b) and (c)

Exercise 11

1) (a), (b), (d), (f), (g), (i), (k), (m) and (n)
2) (i) (b), (f), (h), (j), (k), (l) and (o)
   (ii) (b), (h), (j) and (o)
3)

(i)	(ii)	(iii)	(iv)
4	9	25	7
8	33	35	19
16	321	215	
34			
104			
206			

Exercise 12

1) (c), (d), (f) and (h)
2) (a), (c) and (e)

Exercise 13

1) (b), (c), (d) and (e)
2) (b), (c), (d) and (e)
3) (b)

Exercise 14

1) negative whole number
2) positive fraction
3) positive decimal
4) positive whole number
5) negative fraction
6) negative decimal
7) positive whole number
8) negative decimal
9) positive fraction

Exercise 15

1) (a) $6\frac{1}{2}$ (b) $13\frac{1}{2}$ (c) $509\frac{1}{2}$
2) (a) $\underline{4}.1$ (b) $\underline{45}.2$ (c) $\underline{390}.12$

Exercise 16

1) 240
2) six hundred and five
3) six thousands
4) no

6) fifty thousand and twenty
7) yes
8) no
9) yes
10) yes
11) yes
12) yes
13) yes
14) (a) 1, 3, 9   (b) 1, 3, 7, 21
15) no
16) no
17) yes
18) yes
19) yes
20) yes
21) 12, 14, 16, 18, 20
22) 6, 9, 12, 15, 18, 21, 24
23) yes
24) yes
25) yes
26) yes
27) $2\frac{1}{2}$, 12.5
28) yes
29) yes
30) sixty thousand and fifty
31) 3 hundreds 1 ten 2 units
32) 3 thousands 2 units
33) (a) 8   (b) 1
34) (a) and (b)

CHAPTER 2

Exercise 1

1) 136
2) 209
3) 363
4) 160
5) 3977
6) 8701
7) 2012
8) 9956
9) 9113
10) 25 976
11) 221
12) 7798
13) 54 772
14) 89 043
15) 93 972
16) 31 368
17) 138 103
18) 902 028
19) 18 538
20) 10 972
21) 1 109 676
22) 1 900 716
23) 10 777
24) 469
25) 666 679
26) 9099
27) 1 683 830
28) 98 199
29) 581 587
30) 2 124 689
31) 133 036
32) 1 362 951
33) 523 745
34) 58 330
35) 197 135
36) 915 997

37) 2180
38) 4498
39) 298
40) 397
41) 1834
42) 10 713
43) 5071
44) 630
45) 5458
46) 152
47) 959
48) 148
49) 85
50) 169
51) 5656
52) 17 210
53) 1 015 021
54) 104 813
55) 27 751
56) 4 110 286
57) 279 639 414
58) 14 008
59) 31 987
60) 224 851

Exercise 2

1) 32
2) 13
3) 33
4) 33
5) 33
6) 43
7) 18
8) 66
9) 26
10) 46
11) 114
12) 151
13) 233
14) 171
15) 68
16) 471
17) 749
18) 6918
19) 4943
20) 2939
21) 7911
22) 4937
23) 1465
24) 4020
25) 1451
26) 977
27) 5957
28) 9646
29) 2609
30) 5278
31) 4337
32) 6551
33) 493
34) 8202
35) 9862
36) 1598
37) 2483
38) 2889
39) 1070
40) 53 625
41) 4094
42) 9421
43) 75 096
44) 1921
45) 41 931
46) 2
47) 24 992
48) 50 902

Exercise 3

1) 235
2) 183
3) 178
4) 379
5) 4558
6) 501
7) 473
8) 175
9) 2023
10) 4780
11) 2919
12) 3708

Exercise 4

1) 8
2) 7
3) 6
4) 23
5) 4
6) 12

7) 9
8) 13
9) 16
10) 6
11) 5
12) 13
13) 8
14) 4
15) 11

Exercise 5

1) 56
2) 30
3) 21
4) 63
5) 32
6) 48
7) 42
8) 45
9) 24
10) 36
11) 40
12) 30
13) 16
14) 81
15) 49
16) (a) (i) 4   (ii) 6   (iii) 8   (iv) 12
    (b) (i) 6   (ii) 9   (iii) 12 (iv) 18
    (c) (i) 8   (ii) 12   (iii) 16 (iv) 24
    (d) (i) 10 (ii) 15   (iii) 20 (iv) 30
17) (a) (i) 30 (ii) 36   (iii) 54
    (b) (i) 35 (ii) 42   (iii) 63
    (c) (i) 40 (ii) 48   (iii) 72
    (d) (i) 45 (ii) 54   (iii) 81

Exercise 6

1) 70
2) 69
3) 144
4) 260
5) 448
6) 729
7) 296
8) 415
9) 324
10) 392

Exercise 7

1) 4536
2) 1215
3) 2233
4) 3372
5) 3400
6) 1356
7) 792
8) 8334
9) 2149
10) 2736
11) 675
12) 5306
13) 5376
14) 5418
15) 7016
16) 2169
17) 4208
18) 3012
19) 4182
20) 4672

Exercise 8

1) (i) 80   (ii) 800
2) (i) 650   (ii) 6500
3) (i) 170   (ii) 1700
4) (i) 3310   (ii) 33 100
5) (i) 1510   (ii) 15 100
6) (i) 40 000   (ii) 400 000
7) (i) 49 900   (ii) 499 000
8) (i) 511 990   (ii) 5 119 900

Exercise 9

1) (i) 680   (ii) 1020
   (iii) 1700   (iv) 2720
2) (i) 1440   (ii) 2160
   (iii) 3600   (iv) 5760
3) (i) 3020   (ii) 4530
   (iii) 7550   (iv) 12 080
4) (i) 15 780   (ii) 23 670
   (iii) 39 450   (iv) 63 120
5) (i) 900   (ii) 1350
   (iii) 2250   (iv) 3600
6) (i) 1200   (ii) 1800
   (iii) 3000   (iv) 4800
7) (i) 6020   (ii) 9030
   (iii) 15 050   (iv) 24 080
8) (i) 131 060   (ii) 196 590
   (iii) 327 650   (iv) 524 240
9) (i) 1120   (ii) 1680
   (iii) 2800   (iv) 4480
10) (i) 620   (ii) 930
   (iii) 1550   (iv) 2480
11) (i) 13 620   (ii) 20 430
   (iii) 34 050   (iv) 54 480
12) (i) 40 160   (ii) 60 240
   (iii) 100 400   (iv) 160 640

Exercise 10

1) 11 352   11) 2730
2) 17 608   12) 7222
3) 13 468   13) 22 824
4) 8192   14) 17 950
5) 56 238   15) 15 570
6) 11 046   16) 25 912
7) 8730   17) 35 168
8) 9975   18) 28 350
9) 19 965   19) 10 710
10) 21 975   20) 28 728

Exercise 11

1) 46 008   6) 158 080
2) 127 484   7) 226 171
3) 370 230   8) 722 160
4) 316 050   9) 404 670
5) 128 512   10) 27 468

Exercise 12

1) 3564   17) 427 r 2
2) 158   18) 1365
3) 128   19) 697 r 5
4) 61 r 2   20) 715 r 3
5) 130 r 3   21) 1135 r 7
6) 49   22) 2050 r 1
7) 43   23) 565 r 6
8) 101 r 4   24) 610
9) 125   25) 101 r 1
10) 35   26) 1129 r 1
11) 91   27) 320
12) 61   28) 1049
13) 29   29) 469
14) 25   30) 432
15) 93 r 2   31) 257 r 6
16) 112 r 3   32) 241 r 5

Exercise 13

1) 27   8) 19
2) 16   9) 1500
3) 23   10) 2600
4) 13 r 24   11) 750
5) 11   12) 130 r 3
6) 48 r 2   13) 210
7) 33   14) 371

Exercise 14

1) 32   13) 13
2) 40   14) 16
3) 36   15) 20
4) 49   16) 31
5) 42   17) 10
6) 63   18) 31
7) 72   19) 40
8) 45   20) 17
9) 27   21) 11
10) 32   22) 10
11) 88   23) 10
12) 96   24) 12

25) 17   47) 12
26) 19   48) 13
27) 15   49) 81
28) 36   50) 9
29) 27   51) 8
30) 77   52) 32
31) 53   53) 7
32) 45   54) 7
33) 23   55) 35
34) 43   56) 2
35) 61   57) 14
36) 72   58) 52
37) 10   59) 5
38) 6   60) 22
39) 11   61) 13
40) 15   62) 45
41) 13   63) 18
42) 17   64) 32
43) 11   65) 14
44) 14   66) 12
45) 17   67) 5
46) 10   68) 24

Exercise 15

1) should be 10 099
2) correct
3) correct
4) should be 27 292
5) should be 1171
6) should be 70
7) should be 9004
8) should be 9002

Exercise 16

1) 11 067   7) 6732
2) 3666   8) 20 532
3) 4680   9) 17 884
4) 11 937   10) 6562
5) 3468   11) 263 504
6) 11 152   12) 397 350

Exercise 17

1) 19   11) 9
2) 26   12) 540
3) 82   13) 31
4) 102   14) 400
5) 33   15) 31
6) 28   16) 42
7) 9   17) yes
8) 60   18) 32
9) 432   19) 4
10) 5   20) 1420

Exercise 18

1) 9340, 15 458, 1990
2) (a) 344   (b) 277
   (c) 5778   (d) 4348
   (e) 492   (f) 1725
3) (a) 4578   (b) 1152
   (c) 4128   (d) 2409
   (e) 5334
4) (a) 49   (b) 91
   (c) 36   (d) 170
5) (a) 2560   (b) 17 700
   (c) 30 458   (d) 7665
   (e) 376 012
6) (a) 22   (b) 11
   (c) 18   (d) 96
   (e) 23
7) 22
8) 7
9) 6
10) 10
11) 9
12) 40
13) 26
14) 10

Exercise 19

1) 382 mm
2) 3104 ohms
3) 154 mm
4) 759 litres
5) 4950 grams
6) 129 kilograms
7) 30 mm
8) 15 000 grams
9) 109 metres
10) 612 millimetres
11) 18 millimetres
12) £13
13) 355 grams
14) 83 kilograms
15) £1339
16) 29 remainder 8 millimetres
17) 78 patterns
18) 203
19) 422
20) 582 millimetres
21) (a) 267   (b) 148
   (c) 435
22) 10 hours
23) 100 pages
24) 36 litres
25) 7866

CHAPTER 3

Exercise 1

1) $\frac{3}{5}$
2) (a)

$\frac{3}{8}$

(b)

$\frac{1}{5}$

(c)

$\frac{1}{12}$

(d)

$\frac{4}{5}$

(e)

$\frac{5}{12}$

(f)

$\frac{5}{8}$

3) (a)

     (b)

$\frac{1}{3}$ $\frac{2}{3}$

(c)

$\frac{5}{6}$

Exercise 2

1)

$\frac{4}{5}$ $\frac{8}{10}$

2)

$\frac{1}{3}$ $\frac{3}{9}$

3)

$\frac{2}{3}$ $\frac{4}{6}$

4)

$\frac{1}{5}$ $\frac{2}{10}$

5)

$\frac{3}{4}$ $\frac{9}{12}$

6)

$\frac{1}{3}$ $\frac{4}{12}$

7)

$\frac{3}{5}$ $\frac{6}{10}$

8)

$\frac{1}{3}$ $\frac{2}{6}$

9)

$\frac{2}{3}$ $\frac{8}{12}$

10) (a) $\frac{1}{8}$ (b) $\frac{5}{6}$ (c) $\frac{6}{12}$ or $\frac{1}{2}$
    (d) $\frac{2}{3}$

Exercise 3

1) (a) $\frac{1}{4} = \frac{5}{20}$ (b) $\frac{2}{3} = \frac{4}{6}$
   (c) $\frac{5}{6} = \frac{10}{12}$ (d) $\frac{4}{5} = \frac{16}{20}$
2) (a) $\frac{3}{4} = \frac{12}{16}$ (b) $\frac{1}{2} = \frac{5}{10}$
   (c) $\frac{3}{8} = \frac{9}{24}$ (d) $\frac{3}{5} = \frac{6}{10}$
3) (a) $\frac{5}{6} = \frac{15}{18}$ (b) $\frac{1}{4} = \frac{6}{24}$
   (c) $\frac{6}{7} = \frac{36}{42}$ (d) $\frac{9}{11} = \frac{72}{88}$
4) (a) $\frac{4}{9} = \frac{12}{27}$ (b) $\frac{6}{11} = \frac{12}{22}$
   (c) $\frac{5}{8} = \frac{35}{56}$ (d) $\frac{3}{4} = \frac{15}{20}$
5) (a) $\frac{5}{6} = \frac{30}{36}$ (b) $\frac{6}{7} = \frac{18}{21}$
   (c) $\frac{3}{5} = \frac{15}{25}$ (d) $\frac{7}{8} = \frac{28}{32}$
6) (a) $\frac{3}{8} = \frac{15}{40}$ (b) $\frac{2}{3} = \frac{12}{18}$
   (c) $\frac{5}{9} = \frac{25}{45}$ (d) $\frac{3}{5} = \frac{18}{30}$
7) (a) $\frac{5}{11} = \frac{15}{33}$ (b) $\frac{3}{8} = \frac{24}{64}$
   (c) $\frac{1}{2} = \frac{20}{40}$ (d) $\frac{2}{3} = \frac{18}{27}$
8) (a) $\frac{4}{5} = \frac{20}{25}$ (b) $\frac{7}{8} = \frac{49}{56}$
   (c) $\frac{3}{7} = \frac{21}{49}$ (d) $\frac{5}{12} = \frac{25}{60}$

Exercise 4

1) (a)

$\frac{6}{9}$ $\frac{2}{3}$

(b)

$\frac{6}{8}$ $\frac{3}{4}$

(c)

$\frac{4}{12}$ $\frac{1}{3}$

2) $\frac{1}{3}$ 6) $\frac{1}{2}$
3) $\frac{1}{4}$ 7) $\frac{1}{3}$
4) $\frac{3}{5}$ 8) $\frac{6}{7}$
5) $\frac{1}{3}$ 9) $\frac{6}{7}$

10) $\frac{3}{4}$
11) $\frac{7}{8}$
12) $\frac{3}{5}$
13) $\frac{1}{4}$
14) $\frac{4}{5}$
15) $\frac{1}{2}$
16) $\frac{3}{4}$
17) $\frac{2}{3}$
18) $\frac{3}{4}$

19) $\frac{3}{5}$
20) $\frac{3}{5}$
21) $\frac{1}{6}$
22) $\frac{1}{7}$
23) $\frac{1}{3}$
24) $\frac{1}{2}$
25) $\frac{2}{3}$
26) $\frac{1}{2}$

Exercise 5

1) $2\frac{1}{4}$
2) $3\frac{2}{3}$
3) $2\frac{1}{7}$
4) $2\frac{1}{8}$
5) $2\frac{6}{7}$
6) $6\frac{3}{8}$
7) $2\frac{1}{2}$
8) $2\frac{1}{3}$
9) $2\frac{3}{4}$
10) $2\frac{5}{6}$
11) $6\frac{2}{5}$
12) $6\frac{1}{4}$
13) $2\frac{1}{9}$
14) $5\frac{5}{6}$
15) $6\frac{3}{4}$
16) $5\frac{3}{8}$
17) $2\frac{7}{11}$
18) $7\frac{1}{8}$

19) $3\frac{1}{4}$
20) $3\frac{3}{5}$
21) $9\frac{1}{9}$
22) $11\frac{2}{5}$
23) $9\frac{1}{4}$
24) $4\frac{5}{12}$
25) $1\frac{7}{8}$
26) $2\frac{1}{5}$
27) $8\frac{3}{5}$
28) $3\frac{2}{7}$
29) $5\frac{1}{4}$
30) $4\frac{1}{4}$
31) $5\frac{1}{5}$
32) $8\frac{3}{4}$
33) $6\frac{1}{2}$
34) $4\frac{4}{5}$
35) $1\frac{1}{2}$
36) $4\frac{1}{8}$

Exercise 6

1) $\frac{7}{2}$
2) $\frac{23}{4}$
3) $\frac{19}{3}$
4) $\frac{14}{3}$
5) $\frac{15}{2}$
6) $\frac{5}{2}$
7) $\frac{11}{3}$
8) $\frac{22}{5}$
9) $\frac{16}{3}$
10) $\frac{53}{6}$
11) $\frac{48}{5}$
12) $\frac{55}{8}$
13) $\frac{44}{7}$
14) $\frac{16}{5}$
15) $\frac{59}{6}$
16) $\frac{60}{7}$
17) $\frac{15}{7}$
18) $\frac{32}{9}$

19) $\frac{29}{9}$
20) $\frac{58}{5}$
21) $\frac{19}{7}$
22) $\frac{31}{8}$
23) $\frac{28}{5}$
24) $\frac{89}{10}$
25) $\frac{31}{7}$
26) $\frac{68}{7}$
27) $\frac{10}{3}$
28) $\frac{62}{7}$
29) $\frac{75}{5}$
30) $\frac{31}{2}$
31) $\frac{13}{5}$
32) $\frac{37}{4}$
33) $\frac{39}{5}$
34) $\frac{22}{5}$
35) $\frac{20}{3}$

Exercise 7

1) 6
2) 15

3) 8
4) 6

5) 10
6) 20
7) 18
8) 10
9) 12
10) 14
11) 30
12) 30
13) 16
14) 30

15) 72
16) 42
17) 20
18) 18
19) 12
20) 24
21) 30
22) 8
23) 12
24) 90

Exercise 8

1) (a) (b) (d) (c)
2) (b) (a) (c) (d)
3) (c) (d) (a) (b)
4) (b) (c) (a) (d) (e)

Exercise 9

1) $1\frac{1}{4}$
2) $\frac{5}{6}$
3) $\frac{7}{8}$
4) $\frac{7}{10}$
5) $1\frac{1}{12}$
6) $1\frac{1}{2}$
7) $\frac{7}{8}$
8) $1\frac{7}{15}$
9) $\frac{17}{21}$
10) $\frac{7}{12}$
11) $\frac{11}{12}$
12) $1\frac{1}{12}$
13) $1\frac{3}{8}$
14) $1\frac{1}{16}$
15) $\frac{11}{15}$
16) $1\frac{1}{8}$
17) $\frac{8}{15}$
18) $\frac{16}{21}$
19) $1\frac{1}{6}$
20) $1\frac{3}{20}$
21) $\frac{5}{8}$
22) $1\frac{11}{20}$
23) $1\frac{1}{30}$
24) $1\frac{1}{9}$

25) $8\frac{1}{4}$
26) $7\frac{7}{8}$
27) $3\frac{9}{20}$
28) $9\frac{5}{8}$
29) $8\frac{7}{10}$
30) $6\frac{14}{15}$
31) $5\frac{5}{8}$
32) $5\frac{17}{20}$
33) $5\frac{1}{2}$
34) 5
35) 5
36) $13\frac{3}{4}$
37) $6\frac{1}{6}$
38) $7\frac{5}{12}$
39) $6\frac{1}{9}$
40) $\frac{15}{56}$
41) $1\frac{8}{63}$
42) $5\frac{1}{2}$
43) $5\frac{6}{7}$
44) $7\frac{7}{8}$
45) $4\frac{1}{2}$
46) $4\frac{7}{15}$
47) $\frac{1}{2}$
48) $4\frac{1}{10}$

Exercise 10

1) $\frac{1}{10}$
2) $\frac{3}{14}$
3) $\frac{1}{8}$
4) $\frac{1}{2}$
5) $\frac{1}{8}$

6) $\frac{5}{22}$
7) $\frac{1}{2}$
8) $\frac{1}{12}$
9) $\frac{3}{10}$
10) $\frac{1}{12}$

Exercise 11

1) $1\frac{1}{2}$
2) $2\frac{1}{2}$
3) $\frac{5}{6}$
4) $3\frac{1}{4}$
5) $1\frac{11}{12}$
6) $\frac{7}{8}$

7) $\frac{5}{6}$
8) $\frac{7}{12}$
9) $\frac{3}{8}$
10) $\frac{5}{12}$
11) $\frac{1}{2}$
12) $2\frac{1}{2}$

Exercise 12

1) $2\frac{5}{8}$
2) 1
3) $\frac{3}{20}$
4) $\frac{11}{12}$
5) $\frac{7}{8}$

6) $1\frac{1}{12}$
7) $\frac{7}{12}$
8) $\frac{5}{12}$
9) $1\frac{5}{8}$

Exercise 13

1) $\frac{1}{2}$
2) $\frac{12}{35}$
3) $\frac{3}{20}$
4) $\frac{1}{3}$
5) 2
6) $\frac{4}{5}$
7) $14\frac{1}{2}$
8) 1
9) $\frac{1}{2}$
10) 3
11) $\frac{1}{6}$
12) $\frac{1}{6}$
13) $\frac{4}{5}$
14) $\frac{1}{4}$

15) 2
16) $\frac{5}{8}$
17) $\frac{2}{15}$
18) $\frac{3}{4}$
19) $\frac{3}{4}$
20) $\frac{1}{32}$
21) $1\frac{1}{3}$
22) $\frac{4}{9}$
23) $\frac{1}{2}$
24) $\frac{3}{10}$
25) 1
26) 6
27) 2
28) $\frac{2}{3}$

Exercise 14

1) $1\frac{1}{2}$
2) $1\frac{1}{4}$
3) $2\frac{4}{5}$
4) $\frac{2}{3}$
5) 2
6) 12
7) 12
8) 2
9) $\frac{5}{6}$
10) 4
11) $\frac{1}{6}$
12) $\frac{2}{3}$

13) $1\frac{1}{2}$
14) $\frac{3}{4}$
15) $2\frac{2}{3}$
16) $3\frac{1}{2}$
17) 5
18) 14
19) $\frac{1}{2}$
20) $1\frac{1}{3}$
21) $\frac{5}{6}$
22) $\frac{1}{4}$
23) 6
24) $1\frac{1}{2}$

Exercise 15

1) $5\frac{1}{3}$
2) 2
3) 9
4) 4

5) $\frac{1}{4}$
6) $\frac{3}{4}$
7) $\frac{2}{9}$
8) $\frac{2}{5}$

Exercise 16

1) 12
2) 12
3) 15
4) 21
5) 60
6) 180
7) 90
8) 120

Exercise 17

1) (a) $\frac{1}{6}$ (b) $\frac{2}{7}$
   (c) $\frac{2}{5}$ (d) $\frac{1}{3}$

2) (a)   (b) $\frac{7}{12}$ $\frac{7}{12}$

   (c) $\frac{3}{8}$ $\frac{3}{8}$

3) (diagram) $\frac{5}{6}$ $\frac{10}{12}$ $\frac{10}{12}$

4) $\frac{5}{7}$

5) (a) $\frac{6}{8}$ (b) $\frac{10}{20}$ (c) $\frac{2}{12}$ (d) $\frac{9}{15}$
6) (a) $\frac{1}{2}$ (b) $\frac{1}{5}$ (c) $\frac{3}{4}$ (d) $\frac{1}{8}$
7) (a) $5\frac{2}{5}$ (b) $3\frac{5}{8}$ (c) $5\frac{1}{6}$ (d) $7\frac{1}{6}$
8) (a) $\frac{5}{3}$ (b) $\frac{20}{3}$ (c) $\frac{59}{8}$ (d) $\frac{23}{2}$
9) 40
10) $\frac{1}{2}, \frac{3}{5}, \frac{5}{8}, \frac{3}{4}$
11) (a) $5\frac{3}{4}$ (b) $1\frac{1}{10}$ (c) $6\frac{11}{12}$
12) (a) $\frac{9}{10}$ (b) $1\frac{11}{12}$ (c) $\frac{7}{16}$ (d) $\frac{3}{20}$
13) $1\frac{1}{8}$
14) $2\frac{3}{4}$
15) (a) $\frac{1}{2}$ (b) $\frac{1}{2}$ (c) 2 (d) $1\frac{1}{2}$
16) (a) $\frac{24}{25}$ (b) $\frac{8}{15}$
17) (a) $\frac{3}{4}$ (b) $1\frac{1}{3}$ (c) $1\frac{1}{8}$ (d) $\frac{1}{6}$
18) (a) 420 (b) 280

Exercise 18

1) £1.80
2) £1400
3) 14 yards
4) 412
5) 160
6) $5\frac{1}{4}$ metres
7) $43\frac{7}{8}$ minutes
8) £69.35
9) $146\frac{1}{2}$ litres
10) 340
11) 630 grams copper,
    162 grams tin, 108 grams zinc
12) $727\frac{1}{2}$ tonnes
13) 38 metres
14) 935
15) £8700

CHAPTER 4

Exercise 1

1) 0 units 2 tenths
2) 3 units 4 tenths
3) 1 ten 0 units 0 tenths
   4 hundredths
4) 1 ten 6 units 0 tenths
   2 hundredths
5) 8 units 2 tenths 4 hundredths
6) 1 ten 5 units 1 tenth
   6 hundredths
7) 3 units 8 tenths 1 hundredth
   7 thousandths
8) 0 units 0 tenths 8 hundredths
   2 thousandths
9) 5 tens 0 units 2 tenths
   0 hundredths 7 thousandths
10) 0 units 3 tenths 0 hundredths
    4 thousandths
11) 6 tenths
12) 2 hundredths
13) 7 tens
14) 5 thousandths

Exercise 2

13) 0.7 is larger
14) 5.8 is larger
15) 7.0 is larger
16) 7.0 is larger
17) 5.2 is larger
18) 2.5 is larger
19) 6.8 is larger
20) 4.4 is larger
21) 2.1 is larger
22) 5.3 is larger

Exercise 3

1) (a) (i) 5.0 (ii) 5.00 (iii) 5.000
   (b) (i) 8.0 (ii) 8.00 (iii) 8.000
   (c) (i) 9.0 (ii) 9.00 (iii) 9.000
2) (a) yes (b) yes (c) yes
   (d) no
3) (a) yes (b) yes (c) yes
   (d) no
4) (a) 2 (b) 56 (c) 342 (d) 15

Exercise 4

1) 48.8
2) 4
3) 6
4) 8
5) 0.8
6) 0.7

7) 0.045
8) 1.103
9) 5070
10) 300
11) 0.272
12) 11
13) 2.02
14) 0.055
15) 6
16) no
17) yes
18) no
19) 6.5

Exercise 5

1) 0.6
2) 0.03
3) 0.004
4) 0.25
5) 0.127
6) 0.3
7) 0.08
8) 0.009
9) 0.14
10) 0.628
11) 0.5
12) 0.07
13) 0.006
14) 0.75
15) 0.954
16) 0.2
17) 0.06
18) 0.003
19) 0.15
20) 0.205
21) 0.011
22) 0.015
23) 0.062
24) 0.058

Exercise 6

1) 103.45
2) 8.6
3) 49.93
4) 236.81
5) 1549.8
6) 13.98
7) 13.55
8) 57.4
9) 34.48
10) 178.1
11) 9.851
12) 28.759
13) 29.508
14) 36.47
15) 45.25
16) 7.99
17) 26.3
18) 20.67
19) 19.706
20) 62.9
21) 92.448
22) 19.054
23) 413.043
24) 48.90
25) 842.23
26) 740.092
27) 189.642
28) 61.985
29) 184.58
30) 386.12
31) 78.013
32) 98.20
33) 29.09
34) 22.26

Exercise 7

1) 4.32
2) 1.39
3) 5.1
4) 56.49
5) 314.82
6) 1.4
7) 0.04
8) 3.8
9) 113.1
10) 5.5
11) 12.88
12) 799.84
13) 35.7
14) 6947.5
15) 5273.6
16) 14.5
17) 194.03
18) 467.492
19) 12.46
20) 153.302

21) 6.34
22) 40.61
23) 132.71
24) 76.06
25) 10.12
26) 298.5
27) 388.88
28) 12.361

29) 0.0054
30) 0.098
31) 12.34
32) 192.4
33) 0.15
34) 8.055
35) 93.1
36) 308.9

Exercise 8

1) 37.17
2) 9.28
3) 12.14
4) 256.017
5) 77.547

6) 137.4
7) 47.51
8) 9.68
9) 30.04
10) 94.11

Exercise 9

1) (i) 57   (ii) 570
   (iii) 5700
2) (i) 62.1   (ii) 621
   (iii) 6210
3) (i) 0.23   (ii) 2.3
   (iii) 23
4) (i) 4.6   (ii) 46
   (iii) 460
5) (i) 2.178   (ii) 21.78
   (iii) 217.8
6) (i) 0.028 54   (ii) 0.2854
   (iii) 2.854
7) (i) 5.823   (ii) 58.23
   (iii) 582.3
8) (i) 0.07   (ii) 0.7
   (iii) 7
9) (i) 1600.7   (ii) 16 007
   (iii) 160 070
10) (i) 1.4729   (ii) 14.729
   (iii) 147.29

Exercise 10

1) 26.8
2) 10.5
3) 33.6
4) 73.2
5) 124.6
6) 318.6
7) 7.5
8) 23.87
9) 46.64
10) 457.5
11) 614.4
12) 51.85
13) 0.0572

14) 0.008
15) 0.3213
16) 2.014
17) 17.4
18) 41.72
19) 0.576
20) 0.813 72
21) 23.3
22) 40.28
23) 16.371
24) 10.881
25) 401.28
26) 15.225

27) 0.072
28) 82.34
29) 11.475
30) 3.914
31) 20.259
32) 0.2416
33) 0.0234

34) 239.4
35) 0.0261
36) 0.732
37) 8.64
38) 79.8
39) 6.351
40) 0.1512

Exercise 11

1) (i) 0.61   (ii) 0.061
   (iii) 0.0061
2) (i) 7.25   (ii) 0.725
   (iii) 0.0725
3) (i) 0.005   (ii) 0.0005
   (iii) 0.000 05
4) (i) 26.005   (ii) 2.6005
   (iii) 0.260 05
5) (i) 0.0469   (ii) 0.004 69
   (iii) 0.000 469
6) (i) 0.128   (ii) 0.0128
   (iii) 0.001 28
7) (i) 0.000 26   (ii) 0.000 026
   (iii) 0.000 002 6
8) (i) 32.55   (ii) 3.255
   (iii) 0.3255
9) (i) 462.89   (ii) 46.289
   (iii) 4.6289
10) (i) 71.3598   (ii) 7.135 98
   (iii) 0.713 598

Exercise 12

1) 17.5
2) 9.7
3) 2.03
4) 0.184
5) 0.51
6) 11.33
7) 8.16
8) 0.223
9) 0.36
10) 0.903
11) 72.1
12) 201.1
13) 178.9
14) 0.478
15) 0.091

16) 0.2
17) 1.544
18) 2.166
19) 1.037
20) 0.357
21) 1.713
22) 0.176
23) 0.21
24) 6.49
25) 10.35
26) 1.844
27) 8.04
28) 2.2
29) 1.744
30) 1.206

Exercise 13

1) 10.6
2) 10.5
3) 69
4) 6900

5) 80
6) 8100
7) 0.21
8) 0.6

9) 13
10) 68 500
11) 70
12) 0.4
13) 8.5
14) 10.3
15) 314 100
16) 172.1
17) 1970
18) 10.24
19) 80
20) 501
21) 1031
22) 112.4

23) 0.223
24) 72
25) 106.8
26) 20.2
27) 40.6
28) 0.9
29) 12.07
30) 14.7
31) 4.08
32) 0.009
33) 0.14
34) 0.17
35) 8.64

Exercise 14

1) 2
2) 4
3) 3
4) 3
5) 8

6) 1
7) 5
8) 3
9) 1
10) 4

Exercise 15

1) 2.2
2) 5.8
3) 9.4
4) 8.1
5) 1.2

6) 2.3
7) 5.7
8) 9.3
9) 8.2
10) 1.3

Exercise 16

1) 0.25
2) 0.36
3) 0.68
4) 0.79
5) 0.11
6) 0.12

7) 0.80
8) 0.79
9) 5.23
10) 5.24
11) 7.22
12) 7.22

Exercise 17

1) 0.86
2) 0.76
3) 0.56
4) 5.66
5) 0.25
6) 0.19
7) 0.39
8) 0.49

9) 3.70
10) 4.60
11) 8.30
12) 11.20
13) 102.18
14) 84.19
15) 15.78
16) 14.29

Exercise 18

1) 0.653
2) 0.652
3) 0.653
4) 0.653
5) 0.652
6) 5.512
7) 5.513
8) 5.512
9) 5.513
10) 5.513
11) 0.780
12) 0.779
13) 0.780
14) 3.000
15) 3.000
16) 2.999
17) 2.999
18) 3.000
19) 3.000
20) 2.999

Exercise 19

1) 1.733
2) 68.889
3) 3.971
4) 7.889
5) 0.729
6) 117.333
7) 13.667
8) 0.093
9) 70.167
10) 77.143
11) 75.167
12) 5.722

Exercise 20

1) 0.25
2) 0.5
3) 0.125
4) 0.875
5) 0.2
6) 0.4
7) 0.6
8) 0.05
9) 0.04
10) 0.15

Exercise 21

1) 3.75
2) 2.5
3) 1.5
4) 1.25
5) 2.75
6) 4.75
7) 5.5
8) 1.375
9) 2.625
10) 3.5
11) 15.5
12) 3.8
13) 2.4
14) 2.125
15) 5.6
16) 2.2
17) 6.25
18) 10.5
19) 11.75
20) 4.875

Exercise 22

1) $\frac{3}{5}$
2) $\frac{7}{10}$
3) $\frac{9}{100}$
4) $\frac{1}{50}$
5) $\frac{1}{25}$
6) $\frac{1}{20}$
7) $\frac{2}{25}$
8) $\frac{17}{100}$
9) $\frac{31}{50}$
10) $\frac{11}{20}$
11) $\frac{3}{20}$
12) $\frac{23}{100}$
13) $\frac{29}{40}$
14) $\frac{123}{1000}$
15) $\frac{513}{1000}$

Exercise 23

1) $2\frac{1}{2}$
2) $3\frac{3}{4}$
3) $5\frac{1}{4}$
4) $6\frac{1}{5}$
5) $18\frac{1}{10}$
6) $27\frac{1}{2}$
7) $3\frac{3}{10}$
8) $5\frac{1}{4}$
9) $14\frac{1}{2}$
10) $22\frac{1}{5}$

Exercise 24

1) $0.\dot{4}$
2) $0.3\dot{4}$
3) $0.4\dot{6}75\dot{3}$
4) $7.\dot{8}$
5) $30.7\dot{8}$
6) $12.503\dot{0}\dot{9}$
7) $0.\dot{2}$
8) $0.1\dot{9}$
9) $2.\dot{3}14\dot{5}$

Exercise 25

1) 31.7
2) 0.26
3) 21
4) 6
5) 4.98
6) 0.06
7) 20
8) 0.8
9) 9.8
10) 21.885
11) 0.03
12) 2.3

Exercise 26

1) (a) 4 tens
   (b) 4 tenths
   (c) 4 hundredths
   (d) 4 units
2) (a) 17.0   (b) 17.000
3) (a) no   (b) yes
4) (a) 72.5   (b) 63.1
   (c) 402.05
5) (a) 0.3   (b) 0.06
   (c) 0.007   (d) 0.35
6) (a) 9.3   (b) 1.12
7) (a) 16.338   (b) 98.04
8) 70.85
9) (a) 7.2   (b) 72
10) (a) 2.6   (b) 10.4
11) (a) 14.85   (b) 0.2412
    (c) 1.548
12) (a) 0.1756   (b) 0.017 56
13) 72.6
14) (a) 5.12   (b) 0.122
15) 51.2
16) 1038
17) 500
18) (a) 4.3   (b) 4.2
19) (a) 14.630   (b) 14.629
20) (a) 59   (b) 59.3
    (c) 59.34   (d) 59.342
    (e) 59.3416

21) 1.667
22) (a) 0.8   (b) 0.7
    (c) 0.$\dot{3}$
23) (a) 2.25   (b) 5.1
    (c) 4.2
24) (a) $\frac{1}{5}$ (b) $\frac{2}{25}$
    (c) $\frac{9}{20}$
25) (a) $6\frac{1}{2}$ (b) $4\frac{1}{4}$
    (c) $9\frac{1}{10}$ (d) $1\frac{3}{4}$
26) (a) $0.\dot{1}$ (b) $0.2\dot{9}$
    (c) $0.\dot{5}01\dot{2}$
27) (a) 2.27   (b) 2.79
    (c) 1.78

Exercise 27

1) 7.1 tonnes
2) 765 tonnes
3) 554.4 litres
4) 147.84 kilograms
5) 85.97 mm
6) 950.4 millimetres
7) 280.46 minutes (2 h 40.46 min)
8) 54.9 ohms per metre
9) 2916
10) 68.15 metres
11) 856.8p (£8.57 to nearest penny)
12) 0.3 millimetres
13) 0.882, by 0.007 or $\frac{7}{1000}$
14) 700

CHAPTER 5

Exercise 1

1) 3 kg
2) 5 kg
3) 9 kg
4) 1.5 kg
5) 6.5 kg
6) 7.5 kg
7) 3.85 kg
8) 5.67 kg
9) 4.5 kg
10) 1.654 kg
11) 3.045 kg
12) 6.723 kg
13) 0.423 kg
14) 0.56 kg
15) 0.305 kg
16) 25 kg
17) 40 kg
18) 50 kg

Exercise 2

1) 5000 g
2) 7000 g
3) 9000 g
4) 2340 g
5) 9160 g
6) 2080 g
7) 500 g
8) 900 g
9) 400 g
10) 5100 g

11) 4150 g
12) 3200 g
13) 25 000 g
14) 50 000 g
15) 60 000 g
16) 150 g
17) 350 g
18) 950 g

Exercise 3

1) 2000
2) 4000
3) 10 000
4) 500
5) 3500
6) 3000
7) 5000
8) 500
9) 8500
10) 250

Exercise 4

1) (a) 4   (b) 40   (c) 80
2) (a) 10   (b) 60   (c) 110
3) (b)
4) more
5) (b)

Exercise 5

1) 20
2) 40
3) 60
4) 90
5) 15
6) 5
7) 55
8) 95
9) 2400
10) 3500
11) 5000

Exercise 6

1) 200
2) 400
3) 700
4) 900
5) 40
6) 60
7) 80
8) 90
9) 4000
10) 5000
11) 8500
12) 9500

Exercise 7

1) 4 cm
2) 2 cm
3) 2.5 cm
4) 3.7 cm
5) 6.5 cm
6) 4.5 cm
7) 2.4 cm
8) 0.9 cm
9) 5.6 cm
10) 5 cm

Exercise 8

1) 2 km
2) 4 km
3) 7 km
4) 9 km
5) 2.5 km
6) 3.55 km
7) 4.5 km
8) 7.5 km
9) 0.5 km
10) 0.65 km
11) 0.7 km
12) 0.9 km

Exercise 9

1) 9
2) 880
3) 42
4) 14 ft
5) less
6) 16
7) longer
8) (a) 4   (b) 2   (c) 8
9) (a) 90   (b) 45   (c) 15
10) (a) 16   (b) 24
11) (b)
12) less

Exercise 10

1) 50
2) 2
3) more
4) (d)
5) less
6) (a) 20   (b) 6
7) 75 cℓ
8) yes
9) 2.5 litres
10) 23
11) 40
12) 5
13) 500
14) 2500
15) (b)

Exercise 11

1) the 1530 train
2) the 1700 train
3) 1 h 55 min
4) 30 min
5) no

Exercise 12

1) 135
2) 210
3) 2 h 30 min
4) 1 h 40 min
5) (a) 31   (b) 30   (c) 29
6) 26
7) £500

Exercise 13

1) £5.74
2) £3.97
3) £57.40
4) £4.83
5) £2.05$\frac{1}{2}$
6) £1.13
7) £30.08$\frac{1}{2}$
8) £49.47
9) £30.54
10) £342

Exercise 14

1) £72.31
2) £334.18
3) £201.90
4) £59.50
5) £20.11
6) £541.65
7) £29.94$\frac{1}{2}$
8) £0.75$\frac{1}{2}$
9) £20.47$\frac{1}{2}$
10) £33.50

Exercise 15

1) £9
2) £9.90
3) £22.88
4) £5.25
5) £83
6) £68.21
7) £30.16$\frac{1}{2}$
8) £105
9) £1084
10) £4.05
11) £280
12) £169.05
13) £125
14) £248.50
15) £4.04
16) £13.50

Exercise 16

1) £1.12
2) £1.20
3) £2.03
4) £3.12
5) £1.20
6) £3.35
7) £3.55
8) £0.27
9) £1.04
10) £1.50
11) £0.55
12) £2.04
13) £1.67
14) £1.13
15) £3.50
16) £6.75
17) £15.50
18) £5.10
19) £5.11
20) £1.07$\frac{1}{2}$

Exercise 17

1) 2.2 kg
2) 1.05 km
3) 1.7 litres
4) 12.7 kg
5) 2.1 m
6) 1.25 kg
7) 500 m
8) 7.5 litres
9) 1250 g
10) 5 cm

Exercise 18

1) 2250 g
2) 670 cm
3) 3550 g
4) 38 mm
5) 6.7 km
6) 600 m
7) 3450 g
8) 100 cm
9) 750 g
10) 30 mm

Exercise 19

1) 800 g
2) 1 km
3) 150 mm
4) 17.5 kg
5) 0.5 litres
6) 150 km
7) 1500 g
8) 15 cm
9) 4 kg
10) 50 cm
11) 750 g
12) 50 g
13) 3.5 litres
14) 500 m
15) 6 km
16) 7 mm
17) 10.5 kg
18) 80 cm
19) 28 m
20) 30 cℓ

Exercise 20

1) 56 p
2) (a) 14   (b) 35   (c) 49
   (d) 63
3) £10
4) £17.50
5) £1.95
6) £1.26
7) £1.70
8) (a) 8   (b) 20   (c) 28
9) £8
10) £4
11) £30, £20 and £10
12) £3.07
13) £2.04
14) £16.50
15) £12.25
16) £3.84
17) 2200 hours, 10 p.m.
18) £2.80
19) £2.82
20) 110 litres
21) $13\frac{1}{2}$ min

CHAPTER 6

Exercise 1

1) £3
2) 4 cm
3) 2 p
4) 6 min
5) 55 p
6) 7.5 km
7) 9 m
8) 32 p

Exercise 2

1) $\frac{1}{5}$
2) $\frac{3}{10}$
3) $\frac{2}{5}$
4) $\frac{1}{2}$
5) $\frac{3}{5}$
6) $\frac{7}{10}$
7) $\frac{4}{5}$
8) $\frac{9}{10}$

9) $\frac{11}{20}$
10) $\frac{7}{20}$
11) $\frac{3}{20}$
12) $\frac{3}{4}$
13) $\frac{17}{20}$
14) $\frac{1}{25}$
15) $\frac{1}{50}$
16) $\frac{1}{100}$
17) $\frac{1}{40}$
18) $\frac{1}{200}$
19) $\frac{3}{8}$
20) $\frac{5}{8}$
21) $1\frac{1}{2}$

Exercise 3

1) £9
2) 9 cm
3) 2 km
4) 1 p
5) 6 mm
6) 15 m
7) £20
8) £2
9) £9
10) 9 kg
11) £18.28
12) £60
13) £60
14) 38 p
15) £1

Exercise 4

1) £18
2) £20
3) £40
4) £110
5) £35
6) £58.50
7) £1.60
8) £7.50
9) £28
10) £4.57
11) £52.50
12) £450
13) £30
14) £12
15) £30
16) £5

Exercise 5

1) £363
2) £532.40
3) £665.50
4) £726
5) £661.50
6) £1058

Exercise 6

1) 20%
2) 80%
3) 25%
4) 50%
5) 75%
6) $33\frac{1}{3}$%
7) $66\frac{2}{3}$%
8) $12\frac{1}{2}$%
9) $37\frac{1}{2}$%
10) $62\frac{1}{2}$%
11) 40%
12) $87\frac{1}{2}$%
13) 5%
14) $2\frac{1}{2}$%
15) 70%
16) 90%
17) 10%
18) 1%
19) 3%
20) 2%

Exercise 7

Percentage	Fraction	Decimal
50%	$\frac{1}{2}$	—
75%	—	0.75
—	$\frac{1}{3}$	$0.3\dot{3}$
$66\frac{2}{3}$	—	$0.6\dot{6}$
$12\frac{1}{2}$	$\frac{1}{8}$	—
—	$\frac{1}{4}$	0.25
10%	$\frac{1}{10}$	—
—	$\frac{1}{5}$	0.2
30%	$\frac{3}{10}$	—
—	$\frac{5}{8}$	0.625

Exercise 8

1) 20%
2) 60%
3) 10%
4) 16%
5) 30%
6) 50%
7) 80%
8) $16\frac{2}{3}$%
9) 20%
10) 40%
11) 15%
12) $12\frac{1}{2}$%, $52\frac{1}{2}$%, $47\frac{1}{2}$%
13) 75%, $62\frac{1}{2}$%
14) 4%
15) 65%

Exercise 9

1) 0.4, $\frac{1}{2}$, 60%
2) $\frac{1}{5}$, 0.22, 25%
3) 45%, 0.54, $\frac{4}{5}$
4) 66%, $\frac{2}{3}$, 0.67
5) all the same
6) $12\frac{1}{2}$%, $\frac{3}{20}$, 0.2
7) 9%, $\frac{1}{9}$, 0.9
8) 0.33, 35%, $\frac{3}{8}$
9) $\frac{5}{6}$, 85%, 0.875
10) $1\frac{1}{4}$, 150%, 1.75

Exercise 10

1) £345
2) £900
3) £4.86
4) £18, £102
5) £10
6) £21
7) 13%
8) $33\frac{1}{3}\%$
9) $12\frac{1}{2}\%$
10) 528
11) 10 500
12) 46%
13) least 9.8 mm, most 10.2 mm
14) 60%

Exercise 11

1) (a) £4 (b) £20
   (c) £3.65 (d) £1.82$\frac{1}{2}$
   (e) 40 g
   (f) 0.25 kg (or 250 g)
   (g) 34 m (h) 2 s
2) (a) $\frac{1}{8}$ (b) 0.125
3) (a) £2 (b) £4
4) (a) $\frac{1}{3}$ (b) 0.33
5) (a) £2 (b) £5
6) (a) $\frac{19}{20}$ (b) 0.95
7) (a) £6 (b) £66.50
8) £181.50
9) (a) £82.75 (b) £332.75
10) (a) 17% (b) 95%
11) (a) 0.3 (b) 30%
12) £51.75
13) £1500
14) £84
15) £518.75
16) £24
17) 30
18) 59 400
19) 80%, 88% and 96%
20) maximum 2.04 cm, minimum 1.96 cm
21) 80%
22) 10%

CHAPTER 7

Exercise 1

1) 4 4) 49
2) 25 5) 64
3) 36 6) 81

Exercise 2

1) 169 7) 5184
2) 676 8) 5776
3) 1225 9) 5929
4) 2304 10) 6561
5) 3249 11) 7744
6) 4761 12) 9025

Exercise 3

1) $\frac{1}{16}$ 9) $2\frac{7}{9}$
2) $\frac{25}{49}$ 10) $1\frac{7}{9}$
3) $\frac{16}{81}$ 11) $6\frac{1}{4}$
4) $\frac{4}{25}$ 12) $5\frac{1}{16}$
5) $\frac{25}{64}$ 13) $20\frac{1}{4}$
6) $\frac{9}{49}$ 14) $30\frac{1}{4}$
7) $\frac{16}{121}$ 15) $11\frac{1}{9}$
8) $\frac{49}{144}$

Exercise 4

1) 2.25 6) 30.25
2) 12.25 7) 33.64
3) 17.64 8) 39.69
4) 24.01 9) 0.25
5) 26.01 10) 0.49

Exercise 5

1) 8 5) 4
2) 7 6) 5
3) 9 7) 10
4) 3 8) 6

Exercise 6

1) $\frac{3}{5}$ 6) $\frac{5}{6}$
2) $\frac{4}{7}$ 7) $\frac{5}{9}$
3) $\frac{7}{8}$ 8) $\frac{3}{10}$
4) $\frac{6}{11}$ 9) $\frac{4}{5}$
5) $\frac{7}{10}$

Exercise 7

1) 3.2 7) 9.2
2) 5.5 8) 9.3
3) 6.7 9) 9.5
4) 7.1 10) 5.9
5) 7.9 11) 5.4
6) 8.7 12) 7.7

Exercise 8

1) 1.44 7) 10.2
2) 7.29 8) 95.1
3) 12.3 9) 4.75
4) 17.6 10) 18.9
5) 26.0 11) 39.2
6) 62.4 12) 67.1

Exercise 9

1) 361 17) 31 400 000
2) 729 18) 12 300 000
3) 1230 19) 16 000 000
4) 2030 20) 32 100 000
5) 22 500 21) 0.0967
6) 78 400 22) 0.207
7) 608 000 23) 0.262
8) 270 000 24) 0.454
9) 0.0784 25) 19 000
10) 0.137 26) 159 000
11) 0.325 27) 317 000
12) 0.0625 28) 569 000
13) 0.314 29) 441
14) 0.203 30) 1370
15) 0.04 31) 2700
16) 0.81 32) 7740

Exercise 10

1) 1.95 10) 2.13
2) 2.07 11) 2.3
3) 2.28 12) 7.27
4) 3.46 13) 5.92
5) 3.90 14) 9.11
6) 5.79 15) 2.65
7) 1.79 16) 2.61
8) 5.66 17) 4.68
9) 6.73 18) 6.65

Exercise 11

1) 152
2) 15.2 12) 158
3) 0.048 13) 0.253
4) 228 14) 80
5) 22.8 15) 25.3
6) 0.721 16) 22.1
7) 132 17) 0.7
8) 13.2 18) 70
9) 0.132 19) 24.5
10) 0.5 20) 0.775
11) 15.8 21) 77.5

Exercise 12

1) (a) 9   (b) 100
2) 49, 64, 81, 100, 121, 144
3) (a) 196   (b) 400
   (c) 22 500
4) (a) $\frac{1}{4}$ (b) $\frac{9}{25}$
   (c) $2\frac{1}{4}$
5) (a) 0.04   (b) 1.21
   (c) 0.0016
6) (a) 25   (b) 40
7) (a) 11   (b) 12
8) (a) 3.5   (b) 5.3
9) (a) $\frac{2}{3}$ (b) $\frac{5}{8}$
10) (a) 5   (b) 4
11) (a) 6.25   (b) 0.0361
    (c) 203 000
12) (a) 29.4   (b) 294 000
    (c) 0.294
13) (a) 1.84   (b) 18.4
    (c) 0.583
14) (a) 7.34   (b) 23.2
    (c) 73.4   (d) 0.734

CHAPTER 8

Exercise 1

1) £600   12) £15 600
2) £600   13) £80
3) £700   14) £180
4) £900   15) £180
5) £1500   16) £290
6) £23 900   17) £480
7) £50   18) £46
8) £150   19) £73
9) £200   20) £31
10) £250   21) £174
11) £800   22) 274

Exercise 2

1) 20 m, 17.1 m
2) £2, £1.89
3) 4 kg, 3.978 kg
4) 80 cm, 89 cm
5) £9, £8.95$\frac{1}{2}$
6) £25, £25.02
7) 40, each child has 44 sweets and 3 are left over
8) 800 kg, 842.1 kg
9) 3 m, 2.871 m
10) 30 g, 29 g

Exercise 3

1) 30, 33   7) 20, 23.2
2) 1500, 1341   8) 110, 108
3) 100, 90   9) 2, 2.31
4) 7, 7.2   10) 21, 21.1702
5) 10, 9.45   11) 100, 104$\frac{1}{2}$
6) 90, 81.7   12) 4, 4.455

Exercise 4

1) 3^2
2) 4^3
3) 6^4
4) 5^6
5) 10^2
6) 9^{10}
7) 11^3
8) $3 \times 3 \times 3 \times 3$
9) 7×7
10) $8 \times 8 \times 8$
11) $10 \times 10 \times 10 \times 10 \times 10 \times 10$
12) $12 \times 12 \times 12$
13) 8
14) 625
15) 216
16) 81
17) 512
18) 24
19) 54
20) 11

Exercise 5

1) 100   6) 10
2) 1   7) 0.01
3) 0.1   8) 0.001
4) 1000   9) 0.0001
5) 1 000 000   10) 10 000

Exercise 6

1) 2.48×10^2 6) 4.1×10^3
2) 6.8×10^3 7) 5.2×10^3
3) 7.81×10^2 8) 3.43×10^2
4) 5.63×10^2 9) 2.3×10^2
5) 7.8×10^3 10) 4.56×10^3

Exercise 7

1) 6×10^{-1} 4) 5×10^{-2}
2) 2×10^{-1} 5) 4.5×10^{-1}
3) 9×10^{-2} 6) 5.6×10^{-1}
7) 5.4×10^{-2} 10) 8.7×10^{-2}
8) 6.1×10^{-2} 11) 8×10^{-2}
9) 1×10^{-1} 12) 3×10^{-1}

Exercise 8

1) 5.8×10^4
2) 3.4×10^3
3) 1.56×10^5
4) 6.3×10^1
5) 5.97×10^2
6) 7.8×10^{-3}
7) 5.43×10^{-2}
8) 4.52×10^{-4}
9) 5.67×10^8
10) 5.9×10^{-7}
11) 4.97×10^5
12) 3.5×10^{-4}
13) 2.6×10^{-5}
14) $6.351 24 \times 10^8$

Exercise 9

1) 5300   7) 4.7
2) 340   8) 56.6
3) 690 000   9) 0.4505
4) 0.92   10) 3 200 000
5) 0.943   11) 0.014
6) 0.0311   12) 0.008

Exercise 10

1) 3.26   9) 62.8
2) 3.27   10) 62.9
3) 3.26   11) 62.9
4) 3.26   12) 62.9
5) 3.27   13) 62.8
6) 3.26   14) 62.8
7) 3.27   15) 62.9
8) 62.9   16) 62.8

Exercise 11

1) 1350   11) 5560
2) 6730   12) 4330
3) 5670   13) 6070
4) 6790   14) 4520
5) 7130   15) 3400
6) 24 600   16) 1200
7) 146 000   17) 4600
8) 3010   18) 23 400
9) 4030   19) 568 000
10) 5420   20) 4560

Exercise 12

1) 0.412	9) 0.0891
2) 0.413	10) 0.0892
3) 0.413	11) 0.0809
4) 0.412	12) 0.0810
5) 0.006 11	13) 0.005 20
6) 0.006 12	14) 0.005 19
7) 0.006 12	15) 0.006 10
8) 0.006 11	16) 0.006 09

Exercise 13

1) 5.6	7) 280
2) 3.9	8) 0.37
3) 6.2	9) 1500
4) 7.3	10) 0.51
5) 2.3	11) 64
6) 5.4	12) 5.8

Exercise 14

1) £44
2) £800
3) £6.70
4) 2 m
5) 500 g
6) 4 h
7) 25 cm
8) 8 litres
9) 6 kg
10) 4 km
11) 2000 g, 1710 g
12) 4 m, 3.9 m
13) £13, £13.02
14) 50 cm, 70 cm
15) 60, 63
16) 1200, 1071
17) 100, 90

18) (a) 100	(b) 0.1
(c) 1	(d) 10
19) (a) 3.72×10^2	(b) 4.5×10^1
(c) 6.5×10^1	(d) 9×10^{-2}
20) (a) 5.7×10^4	(b) 5×10^{-5}
21) (a) 2.56	(b) 0.659
(c) 8.08	(d) 5720
22) (a) 0.13	(b) 7300
(c) 0.037	(d) 4.5

CHAPTER 9

Exercise 1

1) 1:2	19) 5:9
2) 1:4	20) 3:4
3) 1:2	21) 4:5
4) 1:3	22) 6:7
5) 2:5	23) 5:6
6) 1:3	24) 9:10
7) 1:3	25) 2:3
8) 1:5	26) 2:3
9) 6:7	27) 2:3
10) 5:6	28) 1:2
11) 5:6	29) 7:8
12) 2:3	30) 2:3
13) 5:4	31) 9:10
14) 3:2	32) 7:8
15) 4:5	33) 5:6:7
16) 5:6	34) 5:6:7
17) 7:8	35) 4:5:6:7
18) 7:8	

Exercise 2

1) 3:1	16) 4:5
2) 1:2	17) 11:4
3) 1:25	18) 3:5
4) 3:1	19) 5:1
5) 100:1	20) 6:5
6) 4:1	21) 4:1
7) 1:5	22) 10:9
8) 1:3	23) 3:2
9) 3:1	24) 6:1
10) 3:4	25) 5:1
11) 1:10	26) 2:1
12) 5:2	27) 1:10
13) 1:2	28) 8:3
14) 1:10	29) 10:1
15) 2:1	30) 10:1

Exercise 3

1) 9:4	9) 7:3
2) 2:1	10) 1:2
3) 4:3	11) 4:1
4) 2:1	12) 2:1
5) 9:1	13) 11:6
6) 6:1	14) 13:9
7) 9:2	15) 1:10
8) 3:1	16) 16:15

17) (a) 6 oz butter
    5 oz caster sugar
    2 eggs separated
    12 oz SR flour
    2 pinches salt
    3 oz currants
    1 oz mixed peel
  (b) 18 oz butter
    15 oz caster sugar
    6 eggs separated
    2 lb 4 oz SR flour
    6 pinches salt
    9 oz currants
    3 oz mixed peel
  (c) $1\frac{1}{2}$ oz butter
    $1\frac{1}{4}$ oz caster sugar
    $\frac{1}{2}$ egg separated
    3 oz SR flour
    small pinch salt
    $\frac{3}{4}$ oz currants
    $\frac{1}{4}$ oz mixed peel

18) (a) 4 onions
    8 carrots
    8 sticks celery
    1 kg cooked beef
    four 340 g cans oxtail soup
    salt and pepper
    16 tsp curry powder
    200 g raisins
  (b) 10 onions
    20 carrots
    20 sticks celery
    2.5 kg cooked beef
    ten 340 g cans oxtail soup
    salt and pepper
    40 tsp curry powder
    500 g raisins
  (c) $\frac{1}{2}$ onion
    1 carrot
    1 stick celery
    125 g cooked beef
    half a 340 g can oxtail soup
    salt and pepper
    2 tsp curry powder
    25 g raisins

Exercise 4

1) (a) $\frac{1}{5}$	(b) 20%
2) (a) $\frac{1}{2}$	(b) 50%
3) (a) $\frac{2}{3}$	(b) $66\frac{2}{3}$%
4) (a) $\frac{7}{10}$	(b) 70%
5) (a) $\frac{4}{5}$	(b) 80%
6) (a) $\frac{5}{8}$	(b) $62\frac{1}{2}$%

M

7) (a) $\frac{3}{20}$ (b) 15%
8) (a) $\frac{1}{3}$ (b) $33\frac{1}{3}$%
9) (a) $\frac{1}{8}$ (b) $12\frac{1}{2}$%
10) (a) $\frac{2}{3}$ (b) $66\frac{2}{3}$%
11) (a) $\frac{11}{20}$ (b) 55%
12) (a) $\frac{1}{20}$ (b) 5%
13) $3:5$; $\frac{3}{5}$; 60%
14) $16:40$; $2:5$; $2:7$; $28\frac{4}{7}$%
15) 40%; £1.20; £1.80

Exercise 5

1) (a) 1.5,   (b) 3,
     ratio $1:2$
2) (a) 3,   (b) 2,
     ratio $3:2$
3) (a) 1.5,   (b) 3.5,
     ratio $3:7$
4) (a) 2,   (b) 2.5,
     ratio $4:5$
5) (a) 1,   (b) 2,
     ratio $1:2$
6) (a) 1.75,   (b) 2,
     ratio $7:8$
7) (a) 2.5,   (b) 1.75,
     ratio $10:7$
8) (a) 3,   (b) 1.75,
     ratio $12:7$
9) (a) 2.75,   (b) 1.5,
     ratio $11:6$
10) (a) 1.25   (b) 2.75,
     ratio $5:11$

Exercise 6

1) £10 : £5
2) £12 : £4
3) £25 : £100
4) £15 : £5
5) 180 g : 120 g
6) 1000 g : 2000 g
7) 250 g : 150 g
8) £20 : £15
9) 45 min : 15 min
10) 20 min : 25 min
11) 5 km : 1 km
12) 28 p : 14 p
13) 10 p : 40 p
14) 25 g : 15 g
15) £200 and £300
16) 200 g copper, 300 g tin and 200 g nickel
17) 60 cm and 15 cm

Exercise 7

1) 18 p
2) 70 p
3) 24 p
4) £1.44
5) 48 p
6) 40 p
7) £1.08
8) £750
9) £3.75
10) 99 p
11) £4.20
12) 36 p
13) £1.05
14) £3.30
15) (a) 120 miles   (b) 30 miles
16) 20 kg
17) (a) 24   (b) 48
     (c) 144
18) (a) £1.50   (b) £15
19) 4 kg
20) £1.12
21)

50 kg £1.00	8 kg £9.60
100 kg £2.00	4 kg £4.80
10 kg 20p	24 kg £28.80
20 kg 40p	1 kg £1.20

7 kg £8.40	2 kg £6.30
1 kg £1.20	1 kg £3.15
$3\frac{1}{2}$ kg £4.20	$\frac{1}{2}$ kg £1.57$\frac{1}{2}$
14 kg £16.80	$2\frac{1}{2}$ kg £7.87$\frac{1}{2}$

5 kg £5.15	3 kg £2.70
1 kg £1.03	1 kg 90p
20 kg £20.60	9 kg £8.10
40 kg £41.20	18 kg £16.20

15 kg £3.00	20 kg £1500
5 kg £1.00	10 kg £750
1 kg 20p	1 kg £75
30 kg £6.00	$\frac{1}{2}$ kg £37.50

| $3\frac{1}{2}$ kg £7.00 |
| 7 kg £14.00 |
| 1 kg £2.00 |
| 21 kg £42.00 |

Exercise 8

1) 36 days   6) 15 min
2) 3 days   7) 3 h 36 min
3) 5 sweets   8) 4 sweets
4) 20 min   9) 4 h
5) 10 min

Exercise 9

1) 50 g @ £1.00
2) 150 mℓ @ 42 p
3) 300 g @ £3.18
4) 850 g @ 51 p
5) yes
6) 10 p
7) no
8) 62 p; I save 10 p

Exercise 10

1) (a) 2 cm   (b) 150 cm
2) 2 km, 5 km, 2.5 km
3) (a) 216 cm (or 2.16 m)
     (b) 36 cm
     (c) 1440 cm (or 14.4 m)
     (d) 1800 cm (or 18 m)
4) (a) 10 km   (b) 2.5 km
     (c) 25 km   (d) 55 km
     (e) 2 cm   (f) 6 cm
     (g) 0.5 cm   (h) 1.5 cm

Exercise 11

1) 22 French francs
2) 15 German marks
3) 18 000 lire
4) 1600 pesetas
5) 60 Swiss francs
6) £5
7) 50p
8) £4
9) £2.50
10) £5
11) £8
12) £25
13) £6.25

Exercise 12

1) (a) $1:5$ (b) $5:4$
     (c) $3:4$ (d) $3:1$
2) (a) $3:5$ (b) $5:1$
     (c) $3:10$ (d) $2:1$
3) (a) $10:1$ (b) $1:5$
4) (a) $9:8$ (b) $2:3$
5) (a) 8 egg whites
     400 g caster sugar
     (b) 12 egg whites
     600 g caster sugar
     (c) 2 egg whites
     100 g caster sugar
6) $2\frac{1}{4}$ cm : $1\frac{1}{2}$ cm, $3:2$

7) £30 : £20
8) 10 : 6
9) 120 g : 30 g
10) $\frac{1}{2}$ h : 1$\frac{1}{2}$ h
11) £10 : £20 : £10
12) 24 p : 28 p
13) 42 p
14) 35 p
15) 24 p
16) 1 h 36 min
17) 35 g for 70 p
18) 10 g for 20 p
19) 100 marks
20) £12
21) 28 km
22) 4 m

CHAPTER 10

Exercise 1

1) 4
2) 6
3) 2
4) 5
5) 5
6) 3
7) 3
8) 12
9) 14
10) 3
11) 23
12) 67
13) 0.5
14) 1.6
15) 0.6
16) 1.2
17) 86
18) 2.80
19) 7.3
20) 5.8
21) 2$\frac{1}{2}$
22) 3$\frac{1}{3}$
23) 2$\frac{5}{6}$
24) 1$\frac{3}{5}$
25) $\frac{1}{4}$
26) 3$\frac{1}{4}$
27) $\frac{5}{12}$
28) 3$\frac{1}{7}$
29) 3.14
30) 1.78
31) 4.333
32) 0.106
33) 1.4
34) 6.0

Exercise 2

1) 2
2) 58 runs
3) 93 g
4) 52
5) £3.58
6) 11 years 2 months
7) 12 cm
8) (a) 1200 g   (b) 240 g
9) 12.6
10) 10

Exercise 3

1) 200 runs
2) 34 years
3) £21.70
4) 78
5) 32
6) 1012 g
7) 800 g
8) £2.50

Exercise 4

1) 34, 39
2) 55 years 10 months,
   11 years 8 months
3) £98, £104
4) 17
5) 45 g
6) 130 m
7) 13, 78, 20
8) 4
9) 90 g

Exercise 5

1) 18 p
2) 29 p
3) 28 p
4) 96 p
5) 27$\frac{1}{2}$ p
6) £1.70
7) 77 p
8) 72 p

Exercise 6

1) 3
2) 23
3) 4
4) 10.4
5) 36.1
6) 62

Exercise 7

1) (a) £700   (b) £70
2) (a) 73 g   (b) 7.3 g
3) 290 cm
4) (a) 19 goals   (b) 1.9 goals
5) 64 g
6) 24 p
7) 25.1 cm
8) 545 g
9) 6.66
10) £17 181, 200 people, £86

Exercise 8

1) 4 h
2) 3 h
3) 5 h
4) 3 h
5) 3 h
6) 3 h
7) 4 h
8) 4 h
9) 3 h
10) 2 h 30 min
11) 2 h 24 min
12) 2 h 30 min
13) 2 h 15 min
14) 8 miles
15) 10 miles
16) 24 miles
17) 60 miles
18) 75 miles
19) 150 km
20) 130 km
21) 2 mph
22) 3 mph
23) 5 mph
24) 2 mph
25) 2 mph
26) 4 mph
27) 7 mph
28) 30 mph
29) 40 mph
30) 50 mph
31) 3 km/h
32) 9 km/h
33) 50 km/h
34) 2.5 km/h
35) 12.5 km/h

Exercise 9

1) 80 miles
2) 4 h
3) 30 mph
4) 105 miles
5) 100 miles
6) 40 mph
7) 32 mph
8) $1\frac{1}{2}$ h
9) $4\frac{1}{2}$ h
10) 60 mph

Exercise 10

1) 48 mph
2) $33\frac{1}{3}$ mph
3) (a) 40 mph   (b) 60 mph
    (c) 48 mph
4) 400 km/h   (a) 5400 km
    (b) 8 h   (c) 675 km/h
5) (a) 5 h   (b) 140 miles
    (c) 28 mph
6) 2800 km, 560 km/h
7) 36 mph

Exercise 11

1) mean 3.5, median 3, mode 3
2) mean 13, median 13, mode 13
3) mean 5, median 3, mode 1
4) mean 16.8, median 17, mode 18
5) mean 36.3, median 34.5, mode 34
6) median 5, mode 5
7) mean 4.6$\dot{6}$, median 5, mode 5
8) mean 9.5, median 11
9) mean 2.4, median 2, mode 2
10) mean 91.6$\dot{6}$ g, median 92 g,
    mode 92 g

Exercise 12

1) 9
2) 9
3) 2
4) 7
5) 7
6) 6

Exercise 13

1) 3
2) 16.25
3) 28
4) 2048 g
5) 51 runs
6) (a) 140 miles   (b) 4 h
    (c) 35 mph
7) 1 h
8) $34\frac{1}{2}$ p
9) 95 p
10) (a) 45   (b) 42
     (c) 45   (d) 11
11) 7, 1
12) 175 miles, 325 miles, 6 hours, $54\frac{1}{6}$ mph
13) 0
14) 5
15) (a) 4.2   (b) 8

CHAPTER 11

Exercise 1

1) Village Fete

Income				*Expenses*		
15 Aug	Donation	£75		1 Aug	Lorry hire	£30
24 Aug	Ticket sale	124		3 Aug	Field hire	35
24 Aug	Raffle	11		3 Aug	Stall hire	15
24 Aug	Stall sales	50			Balance c/d	180
		£260				£260

2) Sports Club Gymnastic Display

Income				*Expenses*		
11 May	Ticket sale	£40		3 May	Hall hire	£50
17 May	Ticket sale	50		7 May	Ticket printing	3.75
20 May	Programme sales	14		15 May	Equipment hire	10
20 May	Ticket sale	50			Balance c/d	90.25
		£154				£154

3) Annual Works Outing

Income				*Expenses*		
5 Jul	Receipts from workers	£140		10 Jul	Coach hire	£75
				15 Jul	Teas	72
10 Jul	Subsidy	35		15 Jul	Entertainment	25
					Balance c/d	3
		£175				£175

4) School Sale of Work

Income				*Expenses*		
17 Jan	Raffle	£15		10 Jan	Stall hire	£15
17 Jan	Ticket sale	12		15 Jan	Decorations	7
17 Jan	Good-as-new stall profit	56			Balance c/d	136
17 Jan	Other stalls profit	75				
		£158				£158

254

Exercise 2

1)

Receipts	Date	Particulars	Payments	Postage	Stationery	Travel expenses	Office expenses	Cleaning
40.00	5 Jan	Cash in hand						
	6 Jan	Postage	3.10	3.10				
	6 Jan	Window cleaner	3.50					3.50
	6 Jan	String	0.65		0.65			
	7 Jan	Ballpoint pens	0.35		0.35			
	7 Jan	Rail fares	4.50			4.50		
	8 Jan	Cleaners' wage	10.00					10.00
	8 Jan	Taxi fares	4.50			4.50		
	9 Jan	Office coffee	0.95				0.95	
	9 Jan	Telegram	2.10	2.10				
	9 Jan	Envelopes	0.65		0.65			
		Totals	30.30	5.20	1.65	9.00	0.95	13.50
30.30	9 Jan	Reimbursement						
		Balance c/d	40.00					
70.30			70.30					

2)

Receipts	Date	Particulars	Payments	Postage	Stationery	Travel expenses	Office expenses	Cleaning
30.00	4 May	Cash in hand						
	4 May	Envelopes	0.60		0.60			
	4 May	Office tea	0.70				0.70	
	5 May	Pencils	0.35		0.35			
	5 May	Window cleaner	2.50					2.50
	5 May	Taxi fare	1.75			1.75		
	5 May	Postage	1.35	1.35				
	6 May	Typing ribbon	1.10		1.10			
	6 May	Cleaners' wage	15.00					15.00
	6 May	Bus fares	1.45			1.45		
	7 May	Parcel post	1.35	1.35				
	7 May	Office coffee	0.92				0.92	
	8 May	Photocopying	1.04				1.04	
	8 May	Ballpoint pens	0.55		0.55			
		Totals	28.66	2.70	2.60	3.20	2.66	17.50
28.66	8 May	Reimbursement						
		Balance c/d	30.00					
58.66			58.66					

Exercise 3

1)		2)	
	50.00		2.40
	7.50		6.00
	15.00		3.00
	10.00		1.00
	82.50		12.40

Exercise 4

1)		
		8.00
		40.00
		15.00
Total gross		63.00
Less 10%		6.30
		56.70

2)		
		105.00
		200.00
		47.50
		360.00
Total gross		712.50
Less 10%		71.25
		641.25

3)

Quantity	Description	Unit Cost	Gross
33	Jars coffee	0.50	16.50
20	Tins soup	0.15	3.00
10	Boxes biscuits	2.00	20.00
50	Tins fruit	0.20	10.00
40	Pkts sugar	0.30	12.00

R. Evans
101 Dark St
BEVINGTON   INVOICE
Tel: Bevington 3055

	Total gross	61.50
	Less 10% discount	6.15
VAT zero rated		55.35

4)

J. Saunders
45 James St
OXMINSTER   INVOICE
Tel: Oxminster 1139

Quantity	Description	Unit cost	Gross
10	Maths books	2.10	21.00
30	French books	3.00	90.00
15	English books	2.00	30.00
10	Geography books	4.35	43.50
25	History books	2.50	62.50

	Total gross	247.00
	Less 10% discount	24.70
VAT zero rated		222.30

Exercise 5

1) £13.27
2) £14.50
3) £60.55
4) £8.39
5) £8.75
6) £1260
7) £2.00$\frac{1}{2}$
8) £6219.50
9) £142.25$\frac{1}{4}$
10) £551 676
11) £1.98
12) £5.64$\frac{1}{2}$
13) £21
14) £316.08
15) £495
16) £1736.52
17) £10.50
18) £13 261.20
19) £17.01
20) £6.16
21) £6.75
22) £504.45
23) £6.24
24) £37.50
25) 34.2 cm, £2.62$\frac{1}{2}$
26) 48, £1.44
27) 1 lb coffee @ £3.04
28) 47 p
29) £206.46$\frac{1}{2}$
30) £42

Exercise 6

1) £15
2) £30
3) £75
4) £112.50
5) £144
6) £378.75
7) £80.02

8) £145.53
9) £502.56
10)

```
                555.00
               1183.00
                560.00
               ───────
               2298.00
   less 10%     229.80
               ───────
               2068.20
   plus 15%     310.23
               ───────
               2378.43
```

CHAPTER 12

Exercise 1

1) £120
2) £5
3) (a) £76   (b) £95
   (c) £114   (d) £161.50
4) (a) £3   (b) £4
   (c) £4.50   (d) £5
5) £111
6) (a) £112.50   (b) £131.25
   (c) £150   (d) £168.75

Exercise 2

1) (a) £6   (b) £10.50
   (c) £9.30   (d) £5.40
2) (a) £8   (b) £12
   (c) £4.40   (d) £5.60
3) (a) £6.40   (b) £4
4) (a) £5   (b) £10
   (c) £2.50   (d) £3.75
5) (a) £11.34   (b) £8.97
   (c) £5.68$\frac{1}{2}$ (d) £6.85$\frac{1}{2}$

Exercise 3

1) £19   4) £5.95
2) £28   5) £18.50
3) £11   6) £19

Exercise 4

1) (a) £2 (b) £4 (c) £5
   (d) £6 (e) £11.50
2) £60
3) £12
4) £20
5) £56
6) £8

Exercise 5

1) £300
2) £500
3) £750
4) £800
5) £804
6) £310
7) £340
8) £450

Exercise 6

1) £4035, £336.25
2) £350
3) £680
4) £60.25
5) £448, £496
6) £390
7) £1120
8) £71.02
9) £286.80
10) £120, £7.20

Exercise 7

1) £100
2) £4
3) (a) £9.90
   (b) £8.80
4) £92
5) £3
6) £1.10
7) £12
8) £7
9) £800
10) £62.84

CHAPTER 13
Exercise 1

1) £80
2) £280
3) 50 p
4) £100 £450 £600
   £160 £245 £375
   £240 £300 £425
   £150 £480 £600

Exercise 2

£1500	£13 500	£2088
£2000	£18 000	£2784
£2500	£22 500	£3480
£3000	£27 000	£4176
£3750	£33 750	£5220
£4250	£38 250	£5916
£5300	£47 700	£7380
£5500	£49 500	£7656

Exercise 3

1) £4.50
2) £12
3) £80
4) £96
5) (a) £2 (b) £20 (c) £8
6) (a) £1.50   (b) £10.50

Exercise 4

1) (a) £1256   (b) £1253
   (c) £1251   (d) £1246
2) (a) £11 283 (b) £11 283
   (c) £11 270 (d) £11 251
3) (a) £1255   (b) £2129
4) £1200
5) (a) £6624   (b) £11 241
6) £6000

Exercise 5

1) £600
2) £2645, £793.50
3) £3395, £4605, £1381.50
4) £1620, £3980, £1194, £4014
5) £1206, £6229

Exercise 6

1) £280
2) £70
3) £15 750
4) £3840
5) £11.25
6) £100
7) £1800
8) £1245

CHAPTER 14
Exercise 1

1) (a) £103.22   (b) 335
   (c) £95.22 + £8.00 = £103.22
2) 2000 p   £20
   2400 p   £24
   4800 p   £48
   6000 p   £60
   2480 p   £24.80
   4960 p   £49.60
   7440 p   £74.40
   8680 p   £86.80

3) (a)
  (b)
  (c)

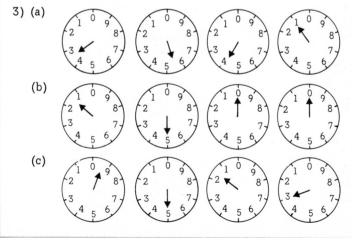

4) (a) 2502   (b) 3308
   (c) 2000
5) 1212

Exercise 2

1) £80.53
2) 1445
3) 5.17 p
4) £5.82
5) £74.71
6) £74.71 + £5.82 = £80.53
7) (a) £57.52   (b) £83.37
8) 9 December 1982

Exercise 3

1) (a) £20.45   (b) £41.95
   (c) £35.50   (d) £30.12$\frac{1}{2}$
2) 900
3) 010416
4) £163
5) £39

Exercise 4

1) £1757
2) (a) £950   (b) £360
   (c) £1585
3) £9
4) 5 p
5) £500
6) 40
7) £12.60
8) £624
9) 200 miles, 12 gallons, £21.60;
   240 miles, 10 gallons, £18;
   £3.60

Exercise 5

1) (a) £9   (b) £60
   (c) £91.80   (d) $13\frac{1}{2}$ p
2) £138
3) £3
4) £57.50
5) £5.29
6) £4.14
7) £36
8) (a) £4.50   (b) £45
   (c) £450
9) £92
10) £126.50

Exercise 6

1) £60   4) £100
2) £40   5) £80
3) £2   6) £200

Exercise 7

1) £144
2) (a) £100   (b) £10
   (c) £11   (d) £130
3) (a) £260   (b) £60
4) £10
5) £60

Exercise 8

1) £60
2) (a) £148   (b) £36
   (c) £22   (d) £78
3) (a) 2010   (b) 9500
4) £57.82
5) £13
6) £33.35
7) £1820
8) £500
9) £9.40
10) £75, £575
11) £2000
12) (a) £100   (b) £600
   (c) £60

CHAPTER 15

Exercise 1

1) A(1, 2)   B(3, 4)   C(3, 1)
   D(4, 3)   E(5, 4)   F(5, 0)

2) A(10, 5)   B(30, 10)   C(40, 25)
   D(50, 40)   E(70, 45)
   F(80, 45)   G(90, 35)
   H(100, 20)   I(110, 10)
   J(120, 5)

Exercise 2

1) (a) 108 cm   (b) 9 years old
2) (a) 38.5 miles per gallon
   (b) 15 mph, 78 mph
   (c) 50 mph
3) (a) 68 °F   (b) 37 °C
4) (a) 25.6 inches   (b) 95 cm
5) (a) 10 oz   (b) 350 g
6) (a) 50 mph   (b) $7\frac{1}{2}$ min
   (c) $12\frac{1}{2}$ min   (d) 10 min
7) (a) 20 years   (b) 200 cm
8) (a) 120 miles   (b) 1 hour
   (c) 60 mph   (d) 30 mph

Exercise 3

1) £10 per year
2) 40 metres/second per second
3) $\frac{1}{2}$
4) 20 mph

Exercise 4

1) 60 p
2) 80 p
3) 60 p
4) 64 p
5) 60 p
6) 25 p
7) 16 p

Exercise 5

1) 10 p
2) 35 p
3) 25 p
4) 35 p
5) 59 p
6) 50 p
7) standard
8) 30 p
9) 5 p
10) 12 s
11) 9 min
12) 11 units, 55 p
13) 5 p
14) 74 p

Exercise 6

1) (a) women
   (b) (i) £180 (ii) £120 (iii) £60
2) 16 p, 16 p, 8 p, 24 p

3)

4)

Exercise 7

1)

Scale: 1 cm to 20 people

2)

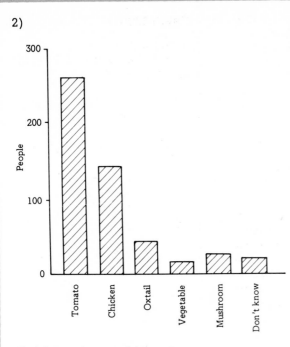

3) (a) type A   (b) type B
    (c) 11 000   (d) 8000
    (e) yes

Exercise 8

1)

Measurement	Tally Marks	Frequency
35.92	|||	3
35.93	⊥⊥⊤ ||	7
35.94	⊥⊥⊤ ⊥⊥⊤ |	11
35.95	⊥⊥⊤ |||	8
35.96	||||	4
35.97	||	2
35.98	|	1

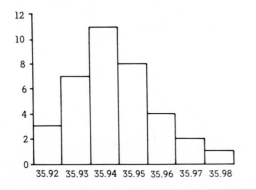

2)

Score	Tally marks	Frequency
1	|||	3
2	⊥⊥⊤ ||	7
3	⊥⊥⊤ ⊥⊥⊤ |	11
4	⊥⊥⊤ ⊥⊥⊤ |||	13
5	⊥⊥⊤ ⊥⊥⊤ ||	12
6	⊥⊥⊤ |||	8
7	⊥⊥⊤ ||	7
8	⊥⊥⊤	5
9	||||	4
10	||	2

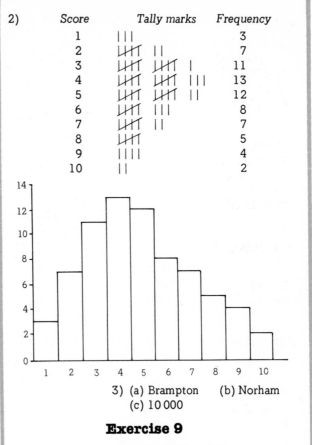

3) (a) Brampton   (b) Norham
    (c) 10 000

Exercise 9

1) 1500, 2000, 2250
2) (a) 135   (b) 120
    (c) 90
3) (a) 1978   (b) 35 000
    (c) 15 000   (d) 10 000, 25%

Exercise 10

1) (a) 5 kg   (b) 16 months
2) (a) 19 km
    (b) 19 miles; 1.6 km/mile
3) 6 km per hour
4) (a) 17 p   (b) 10 p
    (c) 17 p
5)

6)

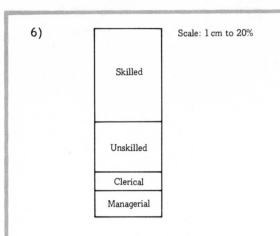

Scale: 1 cm to 20%

| Skilled |
| Unskilled |
| Clerical |
| Managerial |

7)

8)

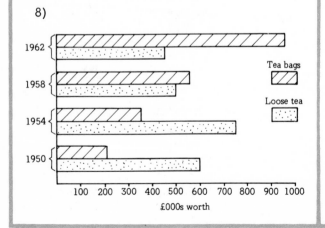

£000s worth

Tea bags

Loose tea

Mark	12	13	14	15	16	17	18	19	20
Frequency	1	4	5	7	8	11	5	3	1

9)

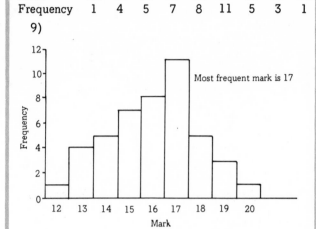

Most frequent mark is 17

Second group:

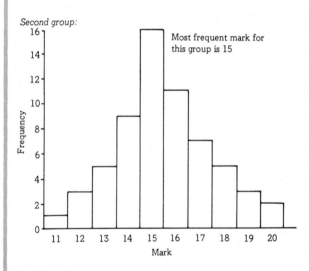

Most frequent mark for this group is 15

CHAPTER 16

Exercise 1

1) (a) A1   (b) A2
    (c) A5   (d) C4
    (e) D2

2) (a) Leeds to Huddersfield via Brighouse
    (b) Huddersfield to Halifax via Brighouse
    (c) 13 miles   (d) 12 miles
    (e) (i) 19 miles   (ii) 23 miles
       (iii) 25 miles

3) (a) 3.4 km   (b) 1.7 km
    (c) 1.8 km   (d) 4.6 km
    (e) 1.2 km   (f) 6.4 km

4) (a) 12 km   (b) 6 km
    (c) 10.8 km   (d) 13.4 km
    (e) 15 km

Exercise 2

1) 49 minutes
2) 1010
3) 10 minutes
4) 0912
5) 421
6) There is a railway connection at Stroud
7) 438, 426
8) yes
9) Sapperton, Daglingworth
10) 1217

Exercise 3

1) 9.15 a.m.
2) $1\frac{1}{2}$ h
3) 7.58 a.m., 2 min
4) 42 min
5) 1107
6) 1431 from Kemble (1317 from Worcester)
7) 0840, 4 h 2 min
8) (a) 2022   (b) 1757
   (c) 1818; 2 h 52 min, 2 h 42 min, 2 h 50 min

Exercise 4

1) 91
2) Wednesday
3) 4
4) 15 February
5) 4
6) 29 August
7) 34
8) 25
9) 6 October
10) Sunday

Exercise 5

1) 1400
2) 1900
3) 1200
4) 0630
5) 0000 or 2400
6) 1625
7) 1100
8) 1415
9) 1805
10) 0745
11) 2325
12) 0200

13) 25
14) 90
15) 40
16) 111
17) 7.15 a.m.
18) 7.35 p.m.
19) 11.14 p.m.
20) 6.48 a.m.

CHAPTER 17

Exercise 1

1) $x = 2$
2) $x = 3$
3) $x = 7$
4) $x = 7$
5) $x = 8$
6) $x = 7$
7) $x = 7$
8) $x = 3$
9) $x = 7$
10) $x = 10$
11) $x = 4$
12) $x = 3$
13) $x = 1$
14) $x = 12$
15) $x = 9$
16) $x = 14$
17) $x = 8$
18) $x = 2$
19) $x = 16$
20) $x = 13$

Exercise 2

1) $3z$
2) $2y$
3) $2t$
4) $6p$
5) $4q$
6) $3r$
7) $4n$
8) $5t$
9) $2m$
10) $3s$
11) $3p$
12) $3w$

Exercise 3

1) $x = 4$
2) $p = 3$
3) $w = 4$
4) $h = 5$
5) $y = 6$
6) $m = 4$
7) $z = 7$
8) $t = 8$
9) $z = 3$
10) $t = 12$
11) $y = 12$
12) $s = 7$

Exercise 4

1) $9x$
2) $8d$
3) $4c$
4) $16y$
5) $12h$
6) $7c$
7) $6z$
8) $6s$
9) $7t$
10) $8j$
11) will not simplify further
12) $3n$
13) $6p$
14) 0
15) $8e$
16) $5c + 6d$
17) $9m + 5n$
18) $15w + 5v$
19) $4z + 7q$
20) $5a + 3b$
21) $5a + 2b$
22) $7x + 9$
23) $5y + 9$
24) $11p + 6q$
25) $3a + 4b + 4c$
26) $8a + 3b + 1$
27) will not simplify further
28) $2c$
29) 6

Exercise 5

1) 14
2) 15
3) 14
4) 27
5) 6
6) 5
7) 29
8) 13
9) 74
10) 37
11) 5
12) 12
13) 14
14) 6
15) 13
16) 16
17) 9
18) 15
19) 136
20) 25

Exercise 6

1) b^3
2) m^4
3) n^2
4) p^3
5) s^2
6) q^6
7) r^3
8) w^5
9) z^3
10) 4
11) 16
12) 81
13) 121
14) 1000
15) 64
16) 20
17) 21
18) 202
19) 77

Exercise 7

1) pqr
2) $5st$
3) mn
4) abc
5) $8xyz$
6) $8pqr$
7) $14ab$
8) $12pqr$
9) $3pqr$
10) $11ab$
11) $3abc$
12) $2pq$

13) 15
14) 40
15) 24
16) 45
17) 200
18) 168
19) 120
20) 120
21) 120
22) 480
23) 480
24) 480
25) 26
26) 184
27) 124
28) 46
29) 288
30) 500
31) 264
32) 50
33) 49
34) 14
35) 20
36) 22
37) 7
38) 10
39) 13

Exercise 8

1) $x = 1$
2) $x = 3$
3) $x = 3$
4) $x = 3$
5) $x = 6$
6) $x = 2$
7) $x = 4$
8) $x = 8$
9) $x = 12$
10) $x = 8$
11) $x = 3$
12) $x = 7$

Exercise 9

1) $x = 2$
2) $x = 2$
3) $x = 8$
4) $x = 9$
5) $x = 5$
6) $x = 3$
7) $x = 4$
8) $x = 2$
9) $x = 3$
10) $x = 5$
11) $x = 7$
12) $x = 3$

Exercise 10

1) $x = 3$
2) $x = 6$
3) $x = 6$
4) $x = 14$
5) $x = 9$
6) $x = 4$
7) $x = 5$
8) $x = 7$
9) $x = 3$
10) $x = 25$
11) $x = 121$
12) $x = \frac{1}{4}$

Exercise 11

1) $x = 1$
2) $x = 2$
3) $x = 3$
4) $x = 1$
5) $x = 5$
6) $x = 1$
7) $x = 5$
8) $x = 4$
9) $x = 4$
10) $x = 12$
11) $x = 5$
12) $x = 5$
13) $x = 4$
14) $x = 6$
15) $x = 2$
16) $x = 3$
17) $x = 2$
18) $x = 3$
19) $x = 10$
20) $x = 1$

Exercise 12

1) $A = 63$
2) $C = 62.8$
3) $A = 314$
4) $v = 20$
5) $f = 4$
6) $s = 88$
7) $s = 3$
8) $V = 628$
9) $I = 100$
10) 242

Exercise 13

1) (a) gradient 2
   (b) y-intercept is 7
2) (a) gradient 3
   (b) $y = 5$ when $x = 0$
3) (a) gradient 2
   (b) y-intercept is 3
   (c) $y = 2x + 3$
4) (a) gradient 3
   (b) $y = -7$ when $x = 0$
5) (a) gradient 1
   (b) line cuts y-axis at $y = 6$
   (c) equation of line $y = x + 6$

CHAPTER 18

Exercise 1

1) (a) 3   (b) 6
   (c) 4   (d) 5
   (e) 4   (f) 8
   (g) 4
2) (a) 12 cm   (b) 15.8 cm
   (c) 22 mm   (d) $7\frac{1}{2}$ cm
3) (a) 6   (b) 5
   (c) 5   (d) 8
   (e) 4
4) (a) 8   (b) 12
   (c) 9   (d) 6
5) (a) 8   (b) 5
   (c) 6   (d) 16
6) Examples:
   (a)

(b)

(c)

7) (b), (f) and (g) would, the rest
   would not

Exercise 2

Acute	Obtuse	Reflex
17°	173°	190°
65°	135°	240°
54°	155°	230°
72°	169°	185°
85°	120°	270°
32°	110°	315°
88°	95°	198°
12°	103°	350°
51°	114°	210°
63°		

Exercise 3

1) 60°
2) 130°
3) 82°
4) 90°
5) 48°
6) 143°

Exercise 4

a: BÂC or CÂB   b: AB̂C or CB̂A
c: AĈB or BĈA   d: GD̂E or ED̂G
e: DÊF or FÊD   f: EF̂G or GF̂E
g: DĜF or FĜD   p: QP̂R or RP̂Q
q: PQ̂R or RQ̂P   r: PR̂Q or QR̂P

Exercise 5

1)

CÂB	60°
AB̂C	60°
BĈA	60°
Sum	180°

2)

$\widehat{CAB}$	130°
$\widehat{ABC}$	20°
$\widehat{BCA}$	30°
Sum	180°

3)

$\widehat{CAB}$	45°
$\widehat{ABC}$	90°
$\widehat{BCA}$	45°
Sum	180°

4)

$\widehat{CAB}$	70°
$\widehat{ABC}$	50°
$\widehat{BCA}$	60°
Sum	180°

5)

$\widehat{CAB}$	50°
$\widehat{ABC}$	50°
$\widehat{BCA}$	80°
Sum	180°

6)

$\widehat{CAB}$	60°
$\widehat{ABC}$	80°
$\widehat{BCA}$	40°
Sum	180°

7)

$\widehat{CAB}$	125°
$\widehat{ABC}$	30°
$\widehat{BCA}$	25°
Sum	180°

Exercise 6

1) $x = 75$ (alternate angles)
2) $a = 68$ (alternate angles)
   $b = 112$ (angles on a straight line)

---

3) $x = 110$ (corresponding angles)
   $y = 70$ (angles on a straight line)
   $z = 110$ (vertically opposite angles *or* angles on a straight line)
4) $x = 50$ (angle sum of a triangle)
5) $x = 48$ (angle sum of a triangle)
   $y = 132$ (angles on a straight line)
6) $a = 53$ (angles on a straight line)
   $b = 58$ (alternate angles)
   $c = 69$ (alternate angles *or* angle sum of a triangle)
7) $x = 122$ (angles on a straight line)
8) $x = 92$ (angles on a straight line)
   $y = 40$ (angles on a straight line)
9) $x = 28$ (angles on a straight line)
   $y = 152$ (vertically opposite angles)
10) $x = 57$ (angles on a straight line)
    $y = 57$ (alternate angles)
    $z = 57$ (vertically opposite angles)
    $w = 62$ (angles on a straight line)
    $t = 61$ (alternate angles)
11) $x = 90$ (angles on a straight line)
    $w = 36$ (angle sum of a triangle)
    $t = 126$) (angles on a straight line)
12) $y = 115$ (angles at a point add up to 360°)
13) $w = 62$ (alternate angles)
    $x = 46$ (angle sum of a triangle)
    $y = 72$ (angles on a straight line or alternate angles)
    $z = 108$ (angles on a straight line)

Exercise 7

1) 5 cm
2) 13 mm
3) (a) 8.6 cm   (b) 8.94 cm
   (c) 9 mm   (d) 8 cm
4) 26 cm
5) 7.07 cm
6) 2.24 cm

Exercise 8

1) 3 cm   5) 5.74 mm
2) 1.73 cm   6) 7.48 cm
3) 8 cm   7) 9.22 cm
4) 5.20 m   8) 6.93 cm

Exercise 9

1) 6.28 cm   6) 44 m
2) 15.7 cm   7) 62.8 mm
3) 22 mm   8) 22 cm
4) 66 cm   9) 220 cm
5) 18.8 cm   10) 12.6 m

Exercise 10

2) 5.2 cm, 20.8 cm
3) Perimeter = 40.5 cm
4) (a) and (d) will fold to make a cuboid

Exercise 11

1) (a) 225°   (b) 315°
2) (a)

(b)

(c)

(d)

3) (a) 53°   (b) 114°
   (c) 208°

4) Distance AQ = 32 km, bearing
061° from A
5) (a) 22 km   (b) 054°
   (c) 39 km   (d) 117°

CHAPTER 19

Exercise 1

1) $10 \, cm^2$
2) $18 \, cm^2$
3) $56 \, cm^2$
4) $60 \, cm^2$
5) $270 \, cm^2$
6) $165 \, cm^2$
7) $28 \, cm^2$
8) $17 \, cm^2$
9) $8 \, cm^2$
10) $7.5 \, cm^2$
11) $27.5 \, cm^2$
12) $9 \, cm^2$
13) $22.5 \, cm^2$
14) $59.5 \, cm^2$
15) $33.25 \, cm^2$
16) $80 \, mm^2$
17) $1.5 \, m^2$
18) $14 \, cm^2$
19) $10.35 \, cm^2$
20) $116.1 \, cm^2$
21) $7 \, m^2$
22) $225 \, cm^2$
23) 28 sq. ft
24) $6 \, m^2$, £13.50
25) £9
26) $1.5 \, m^2$
27) 150, £25

Exercise 2

1) $25 \, cm^2$ 7) $93 \, cm^2$
2) $103 \, cm^2$ 8) $52 \, cm^2$
3) $72 \, cm^2$ 9) $36 \, cm^2$
4) $36 \, cm^2$ 10) $39 \, cm^2$
5) $42 \, cm^2$ 11) $49 \, cm^2$
6) $64 \, cm^2$ 12) $52 \, cm^2$

Exercise 3

1) $14 \, cm^2$
2) $12 \, cm^2$

3) $18 \, cm^2$
4) $20 \, cm^2$
5) $18 \, cm^2$
6) $24 \, cm^2$
7) $66 \, cm^2$
8) (a) $108 \, cm^2$ (b) $70 \, m^2$
   (c) $38 \, m^2$ (d) 76 p
9) (a) $3 \, m^2$ (b) $1.5 \, m^2$
   (c) $1.5 \, m^2$ (d) £3

Exercise 4

1) $28.26 \, cm^2$
2) $78.5 \, cm^2$
3) $314 \, cm^2$
4) $615.4 \, cm^2$ (or $616 \, cm^2$ if $\pi = \frac{22}{7}$ is used)
5) $38.5 \, cm^2$ (or $38\frac{1}{2} \, cm^2$)
6) $9.62 \, cm^2$ (or $9\frac{5}{8} \, cm^2$)

Exercise 5

1) $113 \, cm^2$
2) $201 \, mm^2$
3) $1260 \, m^2$
4) $1.54 \, m^2$
5) $11.6 \, cm^2$
6) $11.1 \, cm^2$
7) 164 or $165 \, cm^2$
8) $26.3 \, cm^2$
9) $98.5 \, cm^2$
10) $12.3 \, cm^2$
11) (a) $100 \, cm^2$ (b) $78.5 \, cm^2$
    (c) $21.5 \, cm^2$
12) (a) $0.25 \, cm^2$ (b) $0.196 \, cm^2$
    (c) $0.054 \, cm^2$
13) (a) $16 \, cm^2$ (b) $12.6 \, cm^2$
    (c) $3.4 \, cm^2$
14) (a) $196 \, cm^2$ (b) $154 \, cm^2$
    (c) $42 \, cm^2$
15) (a) $64 \, cm^2$ (b) $12.6 \, cm^2$
    (c) $51.4 \, cm^2$
16) (a) $49 \, cm^2$ (b) $19.2 \, cm^2$
    (c) $29.8 \, cm^2$

Exercise 6

1) $30 \, cm^2$ 3) $17\frac{1}{2} \, cm^2$
2) $15 \, cm^2$ 4) $21 \, cm^2$

5) $36 \, cm^2$ 13) $56 \, mm^2$
6) $30 \, m^2$ 14) $6.4 \, m^2$
7) $21.5 \, cm^2$ 15) $104 \, mm^2$
8) $28 \, cm^2$ 16) $37.5 \, cm^2$
9) $4\frac{1}{2} \, cm^2$ 17) $60 \, m^2$
10) $66 \, cm^2$ 18) $3 \, cm^2$
11) $14 \, cm^2$ 19) $225 \, mm^2$
12) $52.8 \, cm^2$ 20) $184 \, mm^2$

Exercise 7

1) $20 \, cm^2$ 6) $62.5 \, mm^2$
2) $39 \, cm^2$ 7) $51.9 \, cm^2$
3) $59.2 \, cm^2$ 8) $48 \, cm^2$
4) $28.75 \, cm^2$ 9) $85 \, cm^2$
5) $22 \, m^2$ 10) $48 \, m^2$

Exercise 8

1) 8 cm
2) 6 m
3) (a) 6 m   (b) 8 mm
4) 4 mm
5) 2 cm
6) 14 cm
7) 5 mm
8) 6 cm
9) 24 mm
10) 14 cm

Exercise 9

1) (a) $15 \, cm^2$ (b) $16 \, cm^2$
   (c) $20 \, cm^2$ (d) $133 \, cm^2$
   (e) $9 \, cm^2$ (f) $42.5 \, cm^2$
2) $130 \, cm^2$
3) (a) $24 \, cm^2$ (b) $14 \, mm^2$
   (c) $44 \, cm^2$
4) (a) 28   (b) 60
   (c) 88
5) $7.5 \, m^2$, $14 \, m^2$, $6.5 \, m^2$, $19\frac{1}{2}$ p
6) (a) $12.56 \, cm^2$ (b) $3850 \, cm^2$
7) (a) $72 \, cm^2$ (b) $9 \, m^2$
8) (a) $32.13 \, cm^2$ (b) $48 \, cm^2$
9) (a) $12.86 \, cm^2$ (b) $67.5 \, cm^2$
10) (a) 10 cm   (b) 4 mm

CHAPTER 20

Exercise 1

1) $40\,cm^3$
2) $210\,m^3$
3) $72\,cm^3$
4) $44\,m^3$
5) $13.5\,cm^3$
6) $300\,cm^3$
7) $9\,m^3$
8) $50\,m^3$
9) $288\,mm^3$
10) $360\,cm^3$
11) $1.75\,cm^3$ (or $1750\,mm^3$)
12) $910\,cm^3$
13) $9000\,cm^3$
14) $1200\,cm^3$
15) $2800\,cm^3$

Exercise 2

1) $360\,m^3$
2) $112\,cm^3$
3) $300\,m^3$
4) $306\,cm^3$
5) $360\,cm^3$
6) $117\,cm^3$
7) (a) $900\,cm^3$ (b) $576\,cm^3$
    (c) $324\,cm^3$

Exercise 3

1) $80\,cm^3$ 4) $30\,cm^3$
2) $240\,cm^3$ 5) $260\,mm^3$
3) $9.42\,cm^3$ 6) $1125\,cm^3$

7) $2700\,m^3$ 9) $125.6\,cm^3$
8) $1540\,cm^3$ 10) $480\,cm^3$

Exercise 4

1) $4\,cm^3$ 4) $7.5\,m^3$
2) $94.2\,cm^3$ 5) $60\,cm^3$
3) $83\frac{1}{3}\,mm^3$ 6) $157\,cm^3$

Exercise 5

1) (a) $80\,cm^3$ (b) $12\,cm^3$
   (c) $80\,mm^3$ (d) $13.5\,m^3$
   (e) $512\,mm^3$ (f) $220\,m^3$
2) (a) $116\,m^3$ (b) $92\,m^3$
3) (a) $225\,cm^3$ (b) $600\,cm^3$
4) $770\,m^3$
5) $1\,500\,000\,m^3$
6) $513\frac{1}{3}\,cm^3$
7) $33.5\,cm^3$
8) $550\,cm^3$
9) $5\,cm$
10) $3\,m$

CHAPTER 21

Exercise 1

1) 8 times heavier
2) 25
3) 64
4) 45 square feet
5) (a) 36   (b) 216
6) 8 times; no, since $8 \times 52\,p$
   $= £4.16$

7) $10\,cm$
8) $10\,000\,cm^2 = 1\,m^2$
9) $100\,mm^2 = 1\,cm^2$
10) $1\,000\,000\,cm^3 = 1\,m^3$
11) The second diagram with £10 notes is 4 times larger in area, and the wad is 8 times larger in volume.

CHAPTER 22

Exercise 1

1) $\frac{1}{4}, \frac{1}{4}, \frac{1}{2}$
2) (a) $\frac{1}{150}$ (b) $\frac{1}{50}$
3) $\frac{1}{3}$
4) $\frac{1}{2}$ (b) $\frac{1}{3}$ (c) $\frac{5}{6}$
5) (a) $\frac{1}{5}$ (b) $\frac{1}{3}$ (c) $\frac{7}{15}$
6) (a) $\frac{1}{2}$ (b) $\frac{1}{4}$ (c) $\frac{1}{13}$
7) $\frac{3}{4}$
8) $\frac{17}{20}$
9) (a) $\frac{1}{9}$ (b) $\frac{5}{9}$ (c) $\frac{7}{9}$
10) $\frac{4}{7}$
11) (a) $\frac{5}{36}$ (b) $\frac{5}{18}$ (c) $\frac{7}{12}$
12) $\frac{1}{30}$
13) $\frac{1}{5}$; as tickets are taken out of the box, the proportion of winning tickets might not remain the same, especially near the end of the draw
14) (a) $\frac{2}{5}$ (b) $\frac{1}{5}$ (c) $\frac{2}{5}$
   (d) $\frac{4}{5}$
15) $\frac{5}{8}$
16) $\frac{3}{11}$

Exercise 2

1)

2)

266

5)

Exercise 3

1)

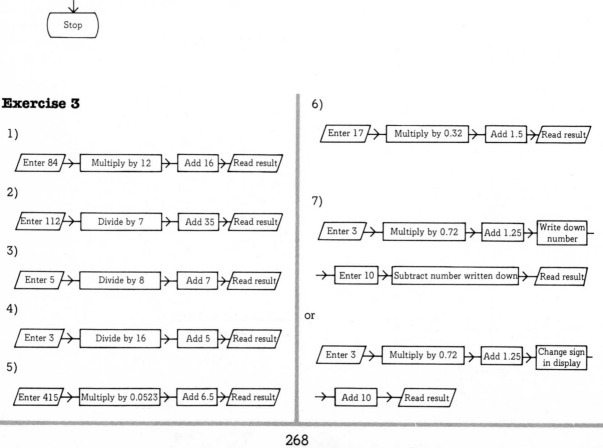

Enter 84 → Multiply by 12 → Add 16 → Read result

2)

Enter 112 → Divide by 7 → Add 35 → Read result

3)

Enter 5 → Divide by 8 → Add 7 → Read result

4)

Enter 3 → Divide by 16 → Add 5 → Read result

5)

Enter 415 → Multiply by 0.0523 → Add 6.5 → Read result

6)

Enter 17 → Multiply by 0.32 → Add 1.5 → Read result

7)

Enter 3 → Multiply by 0.72 → Add 1.25 → Write down number

→ Enter 10 → Subtract number written down → Read result

or

Enter 3 → Multiply by 0.72 → Add 1.25 → Change sign in display

→ Add 10 → Read result

8)

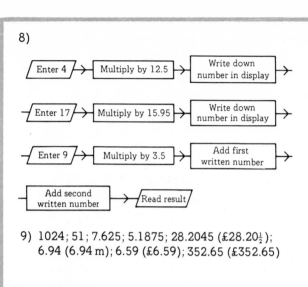

9) 1024; 51; 7.625; 5.1875; 28.2045 (£28.20$\frac{1}{2}$); 6.94 (6.94 m); 6.59 (£6.59); 352.65 (£352.65)

Exercise 4

1)

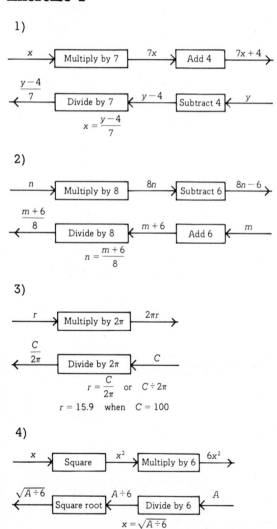

$x = \dfrac{y-4}{7}$

2)

$n = \dfrac{m+6}{8}$

3)

$r = \dfrac{C}{2\pi}$ or $C \div 2\pi$

$r = 15.9$ when $C = 100$

4)

$x = \sqrt{A \div 6}$

When $A = 714$, $x = 10.9$ (correct to 3 significant figures)

5)

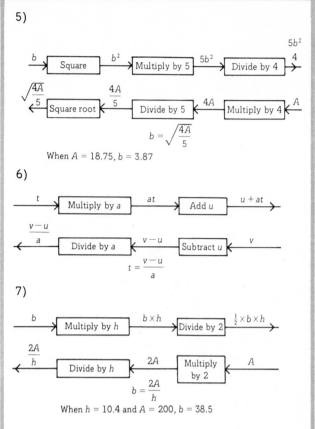

$b = \sqrt{\dfrac{4A}{5}}$

When $A = 18.75$, $b = 3.87$

6)

$t = \dfrac{v-u}{a}$

7)

$b = \dfrac{2A}{h}$

When $h = 10.4$ and $A = 200$, $b = 38.5$

MENTAL TEST

1) 110		16) 90
2) 13		17) 75%
3) 63		18) 9.13
4) £2.25		19) 4.2
5) 3.1		20) 50 p
6) 39		21) 1.5
7) 62		22) 1505
8) 0.8		23) 9 m^2
9) 760		24) 12
10) 8500		25) 64 p
11) 250		26) 10 ft
12) 11		27) 25 mph
13) 70 000		28) 0.12
14) 80%		29) 9
15) 3 cm		30) £1.55

MISCELLANEOUS QUESTIONS

1) (a) 1 229 140   (b) 1786
   (c) 31   (d) 2
2) (a) 31$\frac{1}{4}$ g or 31.25 g
   (b) 8°   (c) £15

3) (a) 29   (b) 27
    (c) 33   (d) 4
    (e) 0
4) (a) £3.79   (b) 20 g
5) (a) 81   (b) 8
    (c) 64   (d) 25
    (e) 75
6) (a) 3 units   (b) 3 tens
    (c) 3 tenths
    (d) 3 hundredths
7) (a) 1.5×10^5 (b) 1.5×10^{-4}
8) (a) 240 000   (b) 0.024
9) 16×10^3 is larger
10) (a) 0.84   (b) 0.05
    (c) 76.8   (d) 8
    (e) 8.556
11) (a) 20   (b) £3.64
12) (a) $\frac{7}{16}$ (b) $6\frac{5}{12}$
    (c) $\frac{3}{4}$ (d) 4
    (e) 16   (f) $\frac{1}{6}$
    (g) $7\frac{1}{2}$
13) (a) £2.94   (b) $\frac{1}{4}$ m
    (c) £20, £25, £15
    (d) £1.50   (e) £30
14) £57.50
15) £50
16) 56%
17) (a) 0.721   (b) 22.8
18) (a) 59°F   (b) 60°C
19) (a) 0900   (b) 1615
20) 27 min
21) (a) 30 p   (b) 17 p
    (c) 20 p
22) (a) $y = 9.5$ (b) $x = 4.5$
    (c) $y = 3x + 2$
23) (a) $\frac{3}{4}$ (b) $\frac{7}{20}$
    (c) $1\frac{3}{4}$ (d) $\frac{3}{5}$
    (e) $\frac{9}{25}$ (f) $1\frac{1}{4}$

24) (a) 0.1   (b) 0.625
    (c) 2.8   (d) 0.8
    (e) 0.125   (f) 1.75
25) (a) 20%   (b) $33\frac{1}{3}$%
    (c) $262\frac{1}{2}$%   (d) 50%
    (e) $66\frac{2}{3}$%   (f) $162\frac{1}{2}$%
26) (a) $\frac{1}{16}$ (b) $6\frac{1}{4}$%
              or 6.25%
27) $\frac{1}{3}$
28)

| 1 | . | 2 | 5 | + | 0 | . | 1 |

| 2 | 5 | + | 1 | 2 | . | 5 | = |

        13.875, £13.87$\frac{1}{2}$
29) 30
30) 3 ft 6 in
31) boy buying 4 oz
32) (a) mean 3.6, mode 2,
       median 3.5
    (b) 4
33) (a) 52   (b) 70
34) 2 h, 90 miles, 45 mph
35) 660 cm^2
36) 4190 cm^3
37) 2 cm
38) 3
39) (a) $x = 30$ (b) $y = 131$
    (c) $z = 50$
40) (a) $23^\circ 30'$ (b) 54.2°
41) (a) 40 cm^2 (b) 10 cm^2
    (c) 30 cm^2 (d) £1.50
42) 5 ft
43) 189 mm^2, 1134 mm^2
44) (a) 2.4   (b) 5693
45) (a) 3 min   (b) 40°C
46) (a) 76.2 mm   (b) 203.2 mm
    (c) 355.6 mm   (d) 1422.4 mm
    (e) 2489.2 mm

47) 518 is wrong. Correct answer
      is 520.
48) (a) $P = S - C$ (b) $s = ut$
    (c) $C = NQ + F$

MULTIPLE CHOICE REVISION EXERCISE

1) A		26) D
2) B		27) B
3) C		28) C
4) B		29) B
5) B		30) B
6) D		31) A
7) B		32) A
8) C		33) D
9) C		34) B
10) B		35) C
11) B		36) A
12) A		37) B
13) C		38) C
14) C		39) C
15) D		40) D
16) D		41) D
17) C		42) B
18) C		43) C
19) A		44) C
20) B		45) B
21) A		46) A
22) D		47) D
23) B		48) C
24) D		49) A
25) D		50) C

Index